LANDFALL

JAMES BRADLEY

HODDER & STOUGHTON

First published in Great Britain in 2025 by Hodder & Stoughton Limited
An Hachette UK company

This paperback edition published in 2025

The authorised representative in the EEA is Hachette Ireland,
8 Castlecourt Centre, Dublin 15, D15 XTP3, Ireland (email: info@hbgi.ie)

1

Copyright © James Bradley 2025

The right of James Bradley to be identified as the Author of the Work has been
asserted by him in accordance with the Copyright, Designs and Patents Act 1988.

All rights reserved. No part of this publication may be reproduced, stored
in a retrieval system, or transmitted, in any form or by any means without
the prior written permission of the publisher, nor be otherwise circulated in
any form of binding or cover other than that in which it is published and
without a similar condition being imposed on the subsequent purchaser.

All characters in this publication are fictitious and any resemblance
to real persons, living or dead, is purely coincidental.

A CIP catalogue record for this title is available from the British Library

Paperback ISBN 978 1 529 35811 7
ebook ISBN 978 1 529 35812 4

Typeset in Adobe Garamond Pro

Printed and bound in Great Britain by Clays Ltd, Elcograf S.p.A.

Hodder & Stoughton policy is to use papers that are natural, renewable
and recyclable products and made from wood grown in sustainable forests.
The logging and manufacturing processes are expected to conform
to the environmental regulations of the country of origin.

Hodder & Stoughton Limited
Carmelite House
50 Victoria Embankment
London EC4Y 0DZ

www.hodder.co.uk

'Australia's literary Nostradamus'

The Weekend Australian

'Propulsive and thought-provoking'

The Saturday Paper

'Bradley has done something very clever with *Landfall*. He entices us in with all the bells and whistles of an unputdownable crime thriller, but then demands that we pay attention and imagine what our country could look like as climate change takes hold'

The Bookshelf

'I loved *Landfall*. Of course the writing is next level: elegant and beautiful, the descriptions of decaying urban environment – and nature and its forces – just brilliant. The whole book has a very urgent, activating edge'

PAUL DALEY

James Bradley is an author and critic. His work includes the novels *Wrack*, *The Deep Field*, *The Resurrectionist*, *Clade* and *Ghost Species*; a book of poetry, *Paper Nautilus*; and a work of non-fiction, *Deep Water: The World in the Ocean*. His books have won *The Age* Fiction Book of the Year Award, the Kathleen Mitchell Award and the FAW Literary Award, and have been shortlisted for the Miles Franklin Award, The Christina Stead Prize for Fiction, the Victorian Premier's Prize for Fiction and the Queensland Literary Award for Non-Fiction amongst others. He lives in Sydney.

Also by James Bradley

Novels
Wrack
The Deep Field
The Resurrectionist
Beauty's Sister
Clade
Ghost Species

Fiction for Young Adults
The Silent Invasion
The Buried Ark
A Vastness of Stars

Non-fiction
The Element of Need
Deep Water

Poetry
Paper Nautilus

For Mardi, Annabelle and Theo

MONDAY

Sadiya was already halfway to the station when her assistant spoke softly in her ear.

Apologies, Detective Azad. You have an incoming case.

Sadiya swore under her breath. 'What is it?'

Missing child reported.

'Tell me more.'

Emma Mitchell reported her daughter, Casey, missing at 6.02 this morning. According to Ms Mitchell, Casey was last seen in the early evening yesterday.

'Is there CCTV?'

No.

'Why not?'

Casey was last seen near Bryant Street, Banksia.

Sadiya leaned back against the headrest. 'In the Floodline.'

That's correct. The officers that handled the initial report will rendezvous with you on Bay Street. Chief Inspector Nguyen has dispatched Detective Senior Constable Paul Findlay to assist you with enquiries. He will meet you at Bay Street as well.

'Who?'

Detective Senior Constable Paul Findlay. Transferred from Eastern Suburbs PAC last week. Formerly at North Shore—

'That's enough,' said Sadiya, cutting off the AI. For a moment there was silence, then she sighed. 'Tell them I'm on the way.'

Tightening her grip on the wheel she swung her car around, provoking an angry beep from the van behind her. Ignoring it she handed the navigation to the vehicle and pulled up the report in her lenses. There wasn't much in it. Uniform had attended, taken names, passed on the details: Casey Mitchell, five years old, last seen around seven o'clock the night before. She flicked the report away and stared out the window for a moment, trying to collect herself, then took control of the car again and turned onto the highway.

Although it was early the traffic was already heavy. Weaving her way through the other vehicles she passed the yellow-and-blue bulk of Ikea, its walls covered in a mass of cooling creepers, and the old Bunnings, its massive structure still topped by tarpaulins two years after its roof was torn off in a storm. Just past them the road dropped away towards the Cooks River and the half-abandoned towers of Wolli Creek. On either side of the sandbagged span of the bridge the water spread out, shimmering in the dawn light, and a greasy puddle lay across the road from the last high tide; Sadiya slowed as she reached it, the smell of salt filling the car as the water sprayed up around it.

On the far side of the bridge the buildings grew more dilapidated, the shopfronts empty and the apartment buildings run-down or under repair, but as she turned off towards Rockdale the relative order along the highway was replaced by disorder and decay, roofless buildings choked with garbage, dead trees, the rusting shells of abandoned cars and trucks. Not far from the location where she was supposed to meet the other officers she passed a small park: its narrow space was crowded with tents but the brightly coloured clothes strung on lines between them and the line of people waiting to fill water containers by the plastic tanks on the street made it clear that these shelters had stopped being temporary a long time ago.

Near the tideline she spotted two police cars parked outside the burned-out shell of some kind of commercial building and pulled up.

As she stepped out of the car the heat hit her like a wall. For days a massive cyclone had been building over the Pacific, and although the projections still suggested it would strike farther north, socials had been full of fevered speculation about whether it might bend south and strike Sydney like Brigitta the year before. Sadiya had done her best to avoid the discussion – the prospect of a storm even bigger than the last few filled her with dread – but in the glassy glare of the morning the idea seemed almost unimaginable: it was too bright, too still.

Four uniformed officers got out of the cars and walked towards her, adjusting their equipment vests and looking around warily behind their dark lenses. Although Sadiya knew the first two – a good-natured male constable called Larkin and an intense, dark-haired officer named Khoury – she didn't recognise the other two. She checked her lenses and saw their names were McEvoy and Gunasekera – the former recently transferred from St George, the latter a skinny probationary constable in a neatly pressed uniform who looked like he was barely out of high school.

'What have we got?' Sadiya asked.

'Casey Mitchell. Five years old. Apparently she went out to play last night and didn't come home. The father says he's been up most of the night looking for her.'

'Anything else? Neighbours see anything?'

'Nothing.'

'Okay. Larkin and Khoury, you come with me. McEvoy, Gunasekera, you stay here and keep an eye on the vehicles. If there's any trouble let me know.'

Larkin hesitated. 'You're not going to wait for the other detective?'

'He can catch up.' She turned to Khoury. 'Lead the way.'

None of them spoke as they set off towards the water. Khoury scanned the buildings around them, one hand resting on her vest as if ready to go for her taser or her baton; Larkin looked less like he was heading into enemy territory, but he was no less wary.

When they reached the tideline they paused. The morning air was windless, and tiny waves washed slowly back and forth on the asphalt. No matter how many times she came here she found the sight of the houses and apartments half-submerged by the invading water strangely surreal. She gestured to the right, where a floating duckboard secured to the front of an old apartment building led out to a raised walkway.

'That way?' she said, and Larkin nodded.

Although it had been constructed out of salvaged materials, the walkway was surprisingly sturdy. At first it followed the line of the road, bending here and there to avoid an obstacle or intersecting with other walkways leading to houses and buildings. While most of the single-storey structures were abandoned, the upper floors of the taller buildings were still inhabited, their peeling walls and roofs patched with bricks and tin and polymers. Some had pontoons attached to their sides, or narrow docks with boats moored beside them; others had duckboards running between them. On one, lashed to the front of a rust-stained block of flats, a woman stood watching two small children play by the water's edge. Above them the roof of the building had been torn off, and fading tarpaulins were held in place with thick cord. As they passed the older of the children, a girl of three or four wearing a grimy pink singlet looked up, and Sadiya lifted her hand and gave a small wave. The girl fell still, regarding Sadiya solemnly until the woman behind her stepped forward and pulled her back.

Just past the dead hulk of an old Moreton Bay fig tree lying on its side in the water, Larkin directed them onto a pontoon that headed off to one side. The water was deeper here, almost entirely covering the ground floor of some of the apartment buildings, and white sand and blackened leaves and rotting branches were visible scattered across the cracked asphalt a metre or two below the surface. On a patch of higher ground on the far side of the road a series of temporary structures constructed out of shipping containers rose several storeys high.

A tan-coloured dog with more than a hint of dingo about it was standing on top of one, quivering with attention at something Sadiya couldn't see; as they swung past it barked at them, then disappeared, only to emerge a few moments later on the ground level, and race along the water's edge, snarling.

After a short walk they came to a pair of old red-brick apartment blocks. Originally three-storeys, their ground floors were entirely submerged.

'This is it,' said Larkin, gesturing to the building on the left. 'Top floor. You want us to come in with you?'

'I'll be fine. Anything I need to know?'

Khoury glanced up at the building. 'Husband's a piece of work. I'd watch him if I were you.'

Sadiya nodded. 'Good to know.'

The two blocks were from the mid-twentieth century, the apartments opening off long balconies accessed by a staircase at one end. A pontoon led to the first floor landing of the first. Bags of refuse were piled against the railing, and faded clothes hung on lines. The smell of salt was strong.

As she reached the top of the stairs a man emerged from one of the apartments ahead. White, mid-thirties, reddish hair cut close to his scalp, ugly tattoos on his freckled forearms.

'Are you the detective?' he demanded.

Sadiya lifted her hand to shade her eyes against the glare. From somewhere she caught a strong waft of sewage.

'I am.'

A flicker of distaste passed across his features. 'Of course you are,' he said, then stepped back and held the door to the apartment open with his outstretched arm.

Inside it was dim, the windows shaded against the heat outside by sheets of cloth. As her eyes adjusted Sadiya saw she was in a living area, furnished with an old sofa and chairs, and behind them, a small dining table. In one corner a ratty-looking plastic dollhouse stood on a low table, flanked by two plastic tubs of toys. A woman stood beside it. She was thin and harried-looking, and beneath her lank, blond hair her face was hollow with exhaustion.

'Ms Mitchell?' Sadiya said.

'Emma,' she said, stepping forward and gesturing to one of the chairs. 'Please.'

Sadiya took a seat, and Emma sat down opposite her. The man remained by the door.

'It's just you?' he asked. His powerful frame was running to fat, but there was a threat of violence in his manner that was clearly designed to intimidate.

'I'm afraid it is.' She regarded him steadily. 'I'm sorry, I don't think I got your name.'

He closed the door. 'Jay Markley. Casey's stepfather.'

Sadiya noticed he made no move to sit down beside Emma. 'You don't mind if I record this?'

Emma glanced at Jay. He waved a hand dismissively. 'Of course not,' she said.

Sadiya activated her video. 'I understand your daughter Casey is missing?'

Emma clenched her hands and leaned forward. 'Yes. Since yesterday.'

'Maybe you can walk me through what happened? When did you last see her?'

'About seven last night. She went to play with some of the other kids once it cooled down a bit.'

'Play where?'

'She was supposed to stay near here,' said Emma. 'But they went to a place up past the tideline where they sometimes go.'

'They? She wasn't alone?'

'She was with her friend Amira, and Amira's brother, Rafi, who's a few years older, so when they didn't come back I wasn't terribly worried. But then about eight-thirty, when it was getting dark,

I messaged Amira's mother to ask if Casey was there. She said Amira and Rafi were already back, but Casey wasn't with them. I thought perhaps she'd decided to head back on her own but had got distracted or run into one of her friends.'

'What then?'

'I called Jay and he went to look for her. When he couldn't find her I started messaging people.' Her voice faltered. Sadiya leaned forward and placed a hand on her arm. Emma didn't pull away.

Emma looked around at Jay. 'And you haven't found any sign of her?'

Jay folded his arms. 'Nothing,' he said.

'She doesn't carry a tracker?'

There was a moment's silence. Emma's face was pale.

'I'm not having her monitored or tracked,' said Jay.

'Do you mind if I ask why not?'

'Too many kids have been grabbed and trafficked,' said Jay, repeating a popular conspiracy theory about the rich and powerful using trackers to kidnap children. Emma made a small, choking sound.

Sadiya waited for a moment to see whether either of them would say more, but they didn't. 'And neither of you can think of anywhere she might have gone, or any reason she might have run off? She hasn't seemed unhappy lately, or been behaving in some way that struck you as odd or unusual?'

'No, nothing like that,' said Emma, her voice cracking. 'She's a happy kid.'

'And you don't think she could be with somebody? A friend? A relative?'

'We've asked everybody,' said Emma.

Sadiya turned to Jay. 'You said you're Casey's stepfather. What about her biological father? Could he have taken her?'

Emma and Jay glanced at each other.

'No,' said Emma.

'Are you certain? Is he in contact with you? Or with Casey?'

'I haven't seen him since before she was born,' said Emma. 'He's never met Casey. I'm not even sure he knows she exists.'

Jay made a contemptuous sound.

'What is it?' said Sadiya.

'He was a dropkick. I don't know why Emma was ever with him.'

'Okay. I'll still need his name and any other details you can give me. Have you got a photo of Casey?'

Emma reached for her phone. A moment later an alert popped up in Sadiya's lenses. Casey was sitting on what looked like the landing outside. She was looking directly at the camera. She had the same eyes and mouth as Emma, but while she was smiling there was a shyness about her as well. Sadiya logged the photo with the system.

Emma leaned forward, her hands clutched together. 'Please,' she said. 'You have to understand. Something is wrong.'

'Don't worry. We're going to do our best to find her.' She stood up. 'To begin with I need to talk to Amira and her brother. And after that I need you to show me where she went missing.'

Emma stood up. 'I can take you.'

'I'm going to take another look up by the tideline,' Jay said.

'It would be better if you stayed here in case we need to speak to you again,' said Sadiya.

'I've already told you everything I know.'

'All the same, we're going to have more questions.'

'Then call me,' he said. As he spoke Sadiya noticed he had a cut on his cheek, as if somebody had hit him. She motioned towards it.

'What happened to your face?'

'Nothing,' he said, his dislike palpable.

Emma knocked on her neighbour's door and asked her to call her if Casey turned up. The neighbour, a young woman dressed in a green sari, nodded, staring warily at Sadiya. Then Emma led Sadiya, Larkin and Khoury along a series of duckboards and pontoons to a one-room apartment on the middle floor of a nearby building. Sadiya studied her as they walked, noting the way she kept smiling nervously, as if worried they might reprimand her.

A man opened the door almost as soon as they knocked. He was in his forties, squat and powerful, but with the agitated, slightly disordered manner of the fraying alcoholic. He glared at Emma. 'What are you doing here?'

'I'm sorry, Mahid, but they need to talk to Rafi and Amira,' said Emma.

Mahid snorted. 'You should have thought of that before your animal of a boyfriend came here making accusations and threatening people.'

Sadiya stepped forward. 'Please, Mr Hasan. It's important we speak to them. Casey's still missing and we need to know if they saw anything.'

Mahid looked at her with distaste. 'And who are you?'

'My name's Sadiya Azad. I'm a police officer.'

'I'm not talking to the police, and neither are Rafi and Amira.'

'Rafi and Amira were the last people who saw Casey,' said Sadiya. 'We just need to find out whether they saw anything.'

Mahid ignored her and moved closer to Emma, jabbing his finger in her face. 'Your boyfriend thinks he can come here and accuse me. He has no right!'

Sadiya was about to intervene when a woman appeared behind Mahid. She was small, her head covered with a scarf. She glanced at Emma, something passing between the two of them, and placed a hand on his arm.

'Enough, Mahid,' she said. 'This isn't the time for this. Just let her speak to them.'

Mahid turned to her. He looked as if he was about to argue with her as well, but instead he just shook himself free and waved his hand dismissively.

'You tell him that if he ever comes around here again I'll make sure he's sorry,' he said, and went back inside.

'Thank you, Hamida,' said Emma, once he was gone.

Emma and Sadiya followed Hamida through the door. The space inside was small and dark. A sheet had been pinned to the ceiling to divide off an area at the back; beside it a pair of sleeping mats lay on the floor, rumpled bedding spread across them. On one side the old galley kitchen had been stripped out, and in its place a small camp stove sat on a rusty bar fridge with an old plastic basket of food and cooking utensils beside it. A boy and a girl sat against the wall on the sleeping mats. The boy had his arm around the girl and his body angled to shield her from the intruders.

Hamida crossed to them and placed a hand on the boy's head. 'This is Rafi,' she said, and then indicated the girl. 'And this is Amira.'

Rafi was ten, perhaps eleven, Amira more like four or five. Rafi was thin, with a dark-eyed beauty quite unlike either of his parents; Amira had her mother's round face. Sadiya took a step towards the two of them and Rafi shrank away, his arm tightening around Amira. She crouched down.

'My name is Sadiya. I'm a police officer. Emma called me because Casey didn't come home last night. She says you two were the last to see her, so I'm hoping you might be able to help me find her.'

Neither of them spoke. Rafi refused to meet Sadiya's eyes, but Amira seemed unable to look away, her body tense, almost trembling.

'I promise neither of you are in any trouble,' she said, keeping her voice gentle. 'I just need you to tell me everything you know. Is that okay?'

Amira nodded solemnly. It was obvious the girl was frightened, but whether of Sadiya or something else wasn't clear.

'Emma says you went out with Casey yesterday evening. Is that right?'

Amira nodded again. Sadiya waited for Rafi to respond. Finally, he assented as well.

'And where did you go?'

There was another silence. Finally, Amira spoke. 'The lot,' she said in a small voice.

'The lot?'

'It's up past the tideline.'

'Do you go there often?'

'Most days,' said Amira.

'With Casey?'

Amira shrugged. 'Sometimes.'

She looked at Rafi. 'And you? You go along to what – keep an eye on them?'

'I suppose.'

'And is it usually just the three of you?'

'Sometimes other people come,' said Amira.

'But not last night?'

Amira shook her head.

'And there was no particular reason for that? Nothing happened? The other kids just didn't come?'

'No,' said Rafi.

'So, when you went up last night, did you notice anything unusual about Casey?'

This time they both shook their heads.

'And what happened when you got there?'

Amira glanced at Rafi. For guidance, perhaps. Or permission. Rafi gave a small nod. As he did Sadiya noticed a scar, probably a burn, on his collarbone.

'We were playing a game,' Amira said. 'Casey was supposed to be hiding, but when I went to look for her she was gone.'

'Gone?'

Amira nodded.

'You don't think she was still there and you just couldn't find her?'

Rafi shook his head.

'Could she have got stuck somewhere?'

'We thought she'd gone home,' said Rafi.

'Why would she have done that?' Did she fight with one of you?'

'No,' said Amira.

'Has she done that before? Just gone home?'

Amira and Rafi exchanged another look. Rafi shrugged. 'Once or twice.'

Sadiya looked at the girl. 'Amira?' she said, but the girl didn't reply.

'Amira and Casey argue from time to time,' Hamida said.

'But not this time?'

Amira shook her head.

Sadiya waited in case Amira said something more, then turned to Rafi. 'If we went back up to the lot, could you show me where Casey went to hide?'

She could feel Mahid behind her, staring at Rafi. But the boy didn't look at him. Instead, he turned to Sadiya and nodded.

Rafi led Sadiya and Emma through the flooded buildings towards the tideline while Larkin and Khoury followed a few steps behind. Although Rafi didn't hold Amira's hand he kept glancing back to check she was behind him. What was he guarding his sister from, Sadiya wondered. Her? His father? The world? Or perhaps whatever had happened to Casey?

Near the tideline they passed a block of apartments, its ground level protected against the rising water by huge, black polypropylene sandbags; at its rear somebody had constructed a garden on a platform above the water, plants coiling upwards from tubs, the green shocking in the bright sun; beneath it a sea of plastic and other litter floated in the shallow water, shifting and scraping on the broken asphalt as the waves moved in and out.

Back from the tideline it grew more crowded, the balconies festooned with washing lines and bikes and boxes. Many of these buildings were in better repair than the ones below the tideline, although many still showed signs of damage from the storms that moved through on a regular basis.

Finally they reached a patch of open ground, its perimeter ringed by a razor-wire fence. On the far side of the fence a few trees still stood, but for the most part the space was covered in long grass with pieces of wreckage scattered about. Rafi turned left and led them to a spot where the wire had come loose from one of the poles, the bottom metre or so half-rolled back so it was possible to crawl underneath.

'Is this the place?' Sadiya asked.

Rafi nodded.

She looked at Emma. 'Jay's looked here already?'

'I think so.'

Sadiya turned to Rafi. 'Okay. Show me where you were.'

They slithered under the wire one by one.

'Where were you?' asked Sadiya once they were all inside.

Rafi pointed towards a pair of containers in the middle of the space. 'Over there.'

Sadiya turned to Larkin and Khoury. 'Tell McEvoy and Gunasekera I want them here as soon as possible. Then check the perimeter. Look for other places somebody could get in or out.' Glancing across the street she saw people had begun to gather in the shade of the building opposite. 'And make sure nobody else comes in.'

As Larkin and Khoury headed off towards the people by the fence, she smiled at Rafi. 'Okay. Show me.'

The two children led Sadiya and Emma towards the containers. Sadiya scanned the space around them as they went, checking for signs of a struggle or places a body might be lying, but there was nothing. Rubbish was scattered everywhere – empty bottles, filthy sheets of old plastic, old shoes, broken toys – all the things the world abandons, all the garbage they were drowning in. Lines of flattened grass crisscrossed the space; presumably some of them had been made by Jay when he had searched the space earlier.

She drew level with Emma. 'Why is this area empty?'

'There were tents here until a couple of years ago but then security came and cleared it out, and I'm pretty sure it's been empty ever since.'

Sadiya waited, curious to see if she might say more. 'How long have you been living in the Floodline?' she asked, when Emma failed to elaborate.

'Since Casey was one. We came here after the floods up north.'

'Why haven't you looked for somewhere else?'

'Jay can't find a job.'

'And you?'

'I work a couple of days a week at the clinic up by the highway. Mostly reception, but I also do some cleaning.'

In front of them Rafi had stopped by the first container, Amira beside him. Its doors hung open, the tops of them covered by matted grass and the interior reeking of piss and mould.

'Is this where you were?' Sadiya asked.

Rafi pointed to the top of the container. 'Up there I can see if anybody comes in.'

She turned to Amira. 'And where were you and Casey?'

Amira pointed to the stand of trees on the far side of the space. 'Over there,' she said.

'Can you show me?' Sadiya said.

With Amira in front of them they picked their way towards the trees. Here and there old water barrels and other refuse lay amidst the long grass. Finally, they reached a sort of shelter constructed out of a couple of stakes and a piece of old plywood, the tall grass around it flattened. Amira stopped in front of it.

'You were playing here?'

Amira nodded.

Sadiya crouched down beside the girl, so their faces were level. 'Okay, I want you to think carefully and tell me everything you remember. You and Casey were together when you got here. Is that right?'

The girl gave another small nod.

'And then what? You were playing?'

The girl kept looking down. 'Yes. But Casey went off on her own.'

'And why was that?'

Amira didn't reply.

'Did you have an argument?'

Amira shrugged.

'It's okay. Do you remember where she went?' Without meeting Sadiya's eyes Amira pointed towards the back of the space, where the half-constructed shell of an apartment block rose behind a metal fence. 'Over there.'

Sadiya followed her gaze. 'And did you see her after that?'

Amira shook her head.

'Was there anybody else here?'

The girl didn't reply.

'Amira?'

'No. I don't think so.'

'And you didn't hear anything?'

'No.'

She turned to Rafi, who was standing a little way behind them. 'And you? Did you see anyone?'

'No,' he said gravely.

'Wait here,' she said to Emma, and set off in the direction Amira had indicated, scanning the tall grass as she went.

The fence was old and rusted, its panels daubed with layers of fading graffiti. Walking along it she examined it for some kind of gap or break where Casey night have crawled through, but despite the fence's general disrepair it seemed reasonably solid. At the far end of the lot it disappeared behind a small stand of she-oaks, behind which rose a brick wall. She pushed back the branches of the nearest she-oak and slid in, staying close to the fence. At some point this area had flooded, and the receding water had left scraps of swollen paper and bleached plastic in the boughs of the trees and hummocks of dead grass and garbage around their trunks and lower limbs. She turned on her side, trying to keep the needles out of her face, and pushed on, her feet sinking into the heaped mass of garbage and old leaves, until she stumbled into a narrow space just large enough for somebody to sit down.

She knelt down and touched the bed of needles. It was difficult to tell, but they appeared to have been pressed flat, as if somebody had been sitting there. Looking up she noticed a gap between the fence and the brick wall. Narrow, but wide enough for a child.

Standing up, she peered over the fence. Wild bananas and the skeletal remains of a pair of trees, presumably poisoned by saltwater during a storm surge, were submerged in a mass of coiling lantana, the abandoned shell of the apartment block looming above them. Somebody had pushed their way through the creeper very recently, leaving a path of broken branches running from the gap in the fence and the concreted area near the building.

Sadiya scrambled over the fence, landing awkwardly amidst the lantana, and picked her way through the creeper towards the building. Where the vegetation gave way to broken concrete she stopped to examine a heap of rotting bags of old building waste. Then she moved on into the shadow of the building, where a curved wall of concrete bricks led into an unfinished lobby in which sheets of plywood covered the entrances to the lifts. She pressed on one but it didn't budge. At the back of the space a mattress lay adrift in a sea of old bottles and cans and food containers. Its fabric was stained with mould and other fluids. A plastic syringe lay near the head of the mattress; pulling on a glove she bagged it and walked on to the door to the stairs. Somebody had bolted a heavy latch onto it and secured it with a padlock. She placed a finger under the padlock and lifted it slightly. It was old and flecked with rust.

She circled the space one more time, looking for anything she might have missed, then went out again and walked down the side of the building to the metal fence that separated the site from the street. The gate was locked. Turning back towards the building she looked up and checked for some sign of a camera or surveillance. Seeing nothing she turned to head back.

She had almost reached the entrance to the lobby when something caught her eye in the grass beside the fence. She turned to find a bedraggled toy monkey. Something in her chest stuttered. Careful not to disturb the area around it, she knelt down and took a photo with her lenses. Its brown synthetic fur had been rubbed bare in places, and one of its eyes was scratched and almost white, as if occluded by cataracts. Taking out an evidence bag she placed it inside and headed back to where she had left the others.

She emerged from the trees to find Larkin talking to a man she didn't recognise. White, thirtyish, dark-blond hair cut short, pale-blue shirt and dark trousers.

She ignored him and walked towards Emma, who was standing where Sadiya had left her watching Rafi and Amira. Stopping in front of her she held up the bag with the monkey in it. Emma lifted her hand to her mouth and stifled a gasp.

'It's Casey's?' asked Sadiya, although she already knew the answer.

Emma nodded. 'Where did you find it?'

'In the building on the other side of the fence. I'm guessing Casey wouldn't have left it behind by accident?'

'No, never. She takes him everywhere.' She made a choking sound. 'Oh, god. Somebody's taken her, haven't they?'

'It's too early to say. But we need to get officers down here to start looking.'

Emma was trembling. 'How could this have happened?'

'That's what we're going to find out,' said Sadiya. 'For now I need you to stay calm. I'm going to have one of the officers take you home. I'll be in touch soon, but if you think of anything – *anything* – that you think might be relevant or helpful, you let me know immediately.'

Emma stared at her, her face blank with shock. Amira appeared behind her and reached for Emma's hand. Emma took it automatically, barely seeming to notice.

'I'll also need you to find some more recent images and videos of Casey. We'll upload them to our systems immediately.'

'Yes, of course.'

Sadiya turned aside and motioned to Larkin and Khoury, who were standing nearby. 'I want you to take Ms Mitchell back to her place,' she said to Larkin when they reached her. 'Make sure she's okay and then speak to the neighbours, see whether they know anything.'

'Of course,' he replied.

She looked at Khoury. 'You take the kids, wait with them. We're going to need to talk to them again.'

As Larkin and Khoury led Emma and the two children away she turned to the blond man. 'You're Findlay?'

'That's right. I'm sorry I'm late. I got here as fast as I could. What have we got so far?'

'Casey Mitchell. Five years old. She came up here yesterday evening with the two kids who were just here. They say they last saw her heading towards the fence a bit before eight.'

'And you believe them?'

'Yes. Although I'm pretty sure they're not telling the whole truth.'

'Could they be frightened of someone?'

Sadiya shrugged. 'Their father. But I suspect that's not a new problem.'

'But they didn't see anything out of the ordinary?'

'I don't think so.'

'What about the parents?'

'The mother is upset and frightened. She seems genuine.'

'And the father?'

'Stepfather. Name is Jay Markley. We need to check him out.'

'You think he might be involved?'

'I don't know,' she said. 'But he's angry and controlling, and I think there's already been some kind of altercation with the father of the kids who were here before.'

'Where is he now?'

'Out searching.'

Findlay pointed at the bag. 'The toy? It's the child's?'

'Her name is Casey,' said Sadiya, a little too sharply. 'And yes.'

'You think she dropped it while she was being abducted?'

'That seems likely.' She looked past him. People were standing along the fence. 'Shit.' She motioned to McEvoy and Gunasekera. 'I need you to go around to the street and secure the entrance to the crime scene. Nobody goes in or out.' She turned to Findlay. 'I've already uploaded Casey's image into the system. As soon as we have more photos and videos feed them in as well, and find out whether she's been picked up on a camera somewhere. Find some photos of the parents as well and run them through the predictives. While you do that I'm going to call Nguyen at the station. We need to get some drones out over the bay, make sure there's not a body. And then we have to get whatever resources we can down here immediately. We need uniforms going door to door as soon as possible.'

Findlay considered the figures outside the fence. 'They're not going to like that.'

'I don't care,' said Sadiya. 'We've got a missing kid.'

Nguyen had been Sadiya's commanding officer for the past four years. A decade older than her, she was smart and competent, and until a couple of years previously Sadiya had seen her as, if not a friend, then at least an ally. Since then she had treated Sadiya with a distance that left Sadiya uncertain where the two of them stood. But despite that she approved Sadiya's request for support immediately.

'I'll get some more officers down there as soon as I can,' she said.

'And the four who are already here? I've sent Larkin back to the apartment with the mother. I think he'd make a good liaison.'

'Agreed. I'll assign the four of them as support. I'll also arrange a tech officer and sort out a command centre here at the station. And Sadiya?'

'What?'

'Don't fuck this up.'

Findlay was standing in the shade of the she-oaks, a screen in his hand. He looked up as she approached.

'We've got Uniform and Forensics on the way, and they're setting up a situation room back at regional,' she told him.

'I've plugged Casey and the parents' images into facial rec,' he said. 'There have been a couple of hits over the past couple of weeks, but nothing yesterday or today.'

'Okay,' said Sadiya. 'We can apply to access their phone records, but the network down here is such a mess it's not likely to tell us much. What about the predictives?'

Findlay touched his screen and sent the material to Sadiya. She opened it and scanned the contents. There was more on Jay than on Emma – he seemed to have grown up in Adelaide and Melbourne, then worked here and there until about five years ago, when he did a stint helping migrate communities in the Northern Rivers to higher ground. That seemed to be where he and Emma first crossed paths. After that he dropped off the map for a while, before finally turning up in Sydney. But it wasn't his movements that caught Sadiya's attention. Instead it was his record. There were a few minor run-ins with police – an assault charge when he was up north, a caution for disorderly conduct – but more recently he had been arrested at a protest and identified at several more, and he was a known associate of several people with links to racist and fascist groups like the Whiteliners. His socials suggested that wasn't an accident – the system had connected him to multiple posts and discussions about immigrants and vaccines and the use of adaptation and reconstruction as a form of social engineering. She flicked through them until she couldn't stomach it anymore and, feeling like she needed a bath, turned to Emma's profile.

In contrast to Jay's active online presence, Emma's socials featured surprisingly few photos or videos; instead, the little that was there was mostly random posts and memes about innocuous subjects. Perhaps interestingly there was almost no trace of Casey in her socials – a few photos of her as a baby, but after that almost nothing. Sadiya wondered whether that was Jay's influence coming into play. There were also a number of older photos and videos, taken farther north, presumably before they came south; in several a man the system identified as Casey's biological father could be seen, his arm around Emma or laughing with what were presumably friends and family. Sadiya zoomed in on him, taking in a kind expression and a slightly shy smile. Moving across she looked at Emma, the ease of her so unlike the woman Sadiya had just met. Finally she flicked to the assessment of the possibility of Jay and Emma's involvement in criminal activity. Emma's was extremely low, although the report noted it had little data. Jay's was more interesting, suggesting a reasonable chance his proximity to anti-immigration groups like the Whiteliners might be more than just accidental. Flicking back to the images of him, Sadiya considered his face again, the close-shorn head and tattoos on his arms and hands, wondering whether any of this might be relevant.

'What do you think?' asked Findlay.

'We need to talk to both of them again, get their stories nailed down. I want a clear sense of their movements before and after Casey went missing. And we need to get somebody from Child Protection here as soon as possible to talk to the kids again. If there's something they're not telling us then I want to know what that is.'

'I'll make a request to Child Protection right away.'

She turned to look at the building behind them. 'Follow me. I want to have another look around before Forensics get here.'

With Findlay behind her she shoved her way back through the trees. Careful not to catch herself on the metal, she clambered over the fence and dropped down into the undergrowth on the other side. Without looking back she pushed her way through until she reached the driveway, then stood, looking around. Findlay appeared behind her.

'Where did you find the monkey?' he asked.

She pointed to the spot.

'Any sign of a struggle?' asked Findlay.

'Not that I could see.'

'Has anybody looked inside the building yet?'

Sadiya shook her head. 'It's sealed off.'

'You don't think she could have found a way in?'

'Once we can get up there somebody can take a look.'

The two of them walked slowly towards the lobby, both scanning the area around them. Findlay pushed on the plywood blocking the lift shafts.

'I checked them,' said Sadiya. 'They seem solid.'

He pointed at the door near the mattress. 'Fire stairs?'

She nodded.

'Do you think she could be up there?'

She led him over to the door and indicated the rusted padlock. 'I'm not sure this would even open. But we should get somebody up anyway, have them take a look.'

'What about the gate?'

They walked towards the street. The gate was secured with a chain and a padlock, although this padlock was new. 'Unless they came over the fence, whoever took Casey must have come through here,' said Sadiya.

Findlay glanced back towards the vegetation where he and Sadiya had entered. 'Which means they had a key.'

'It does. We need to find out who owns the site, and who manages the security. See if they can tell us who has access to the keys.'

'On it,' said Findlay, then gestured towards a van on the other side of the road. 'Forensics are here.'

The two of them climbed back over the fence. By the time they reached the street a second van had pulled up, and eight uniformed officers had stepped out into the sun. The last, a tall, heavily muscled man, noticed Sadiya and stopped, a mocking smile on his face. Sadiya stared back until finally he turned away.

'Friend of yours?' asked Findlay.

She ignored him. 'I'm going to talk to Forensics,' she said, her voice flat and hard. 'You deal with that lot. I want them working in pairs. And tell them to watch themselves: we're here to look for the girl, and the last thing we want is some kind of incident because they were throwing their weight around.'

The Forensics team were already unloading their equipment. Sadiya was pleased to see the lead officer was Parekh.

'Azad,' she said. 'What have we got?'

Sadiya pointed towards the shell of the building. 'Casey Mitchell, five years old. Last seen going into the site behind us.' Sadiya held out the monkey in its bag. Parekh took it and turned it over in her hand. 'No sign of a struggle but she dropped this.'

'Any idea as to where a possible abductor might have entered or exited the site?'

'No. Although the gate is padlocked.'

'Okay. We'll check the lock and the gate for fingerprints and DNA, although I can't promise much. Do you know who is responsible for maintaining the site?'

'No, but we're working on it.'

'Great. Give us a moment and we'll be with you.'

Over by the other van Findlay was speaking to the uniforms, pointing to the buildings opposite and then back towards the water, his hands describing a route for each of them. Remembering that she hadn't had a chance to check him out she pulled up his file and skimmed it. Ten years in uniform, two as a detective, most recently at Waverley, before that on the North Shore, probably managing rich kids drinking or getting into fights on the weekends. No record of disciplinary action – although that didn't mean all that much, especially if he had the right friends.

Parekh's voice interrupted her. 'Are you ready?'

She swung around. 'Yes,' she said, flicking the file away. 'Let's go.'

Parekh led her to the gate and pointed at the padlock. 'This is the lock you were talking about?'

Sadiya told her it was, and Parekh signalled to one of her assistants, who stepped forward and snipped the shank with a pair of boltcutters. While Parekh bagged it, Findlay jogged across the street towards her. The uniforms were moving out in their pairs. 'They know what to do?' she said as Findlay reached them.

'They do.' He looked back. A young woman was walking behind two of the uniformed officers, videoing them as they walked away. 'Do you think there's likely to be trouble?'

Sadiya watched the woman for a second or two. 'I hope not.' One of Parekh's juniors pulled the gate open with a creak. Sadiya waited for them to go in but didn't follow.

'I'll catch up,' she said. 'You show Parekh what we've got. And get somebody to open the fire door and check the upper levels.'

She crossed the road to the block of apartments opposite. It was the kind of cheaply built building found all over the city, thrown up too fast in the years immediately before the Melt, its once-white walls faded and peeling and its windows patched with cardboard and plastic or shaded with sheets or other cloth against the heat. A group of four kids were standing in the shade of the entrance. The eldest was a girl about the same age as Rafi – young enough, Sadiya hoped, to be approachable without triggering the suspicion and fear the police usually encountered in the Floodline. As Sadiya stopped in front of them she was pleased to see the girl regarding her with a look of wary intelligence.

'Do you kids live here?' she asked.

The other three glanced at the girl Sadiya had addressed, as if waiting to see her reaction. For a long moment the girl didn't reply, and Sadiya could see her desire to show she was unafraid and in control of the situation battling with her instinct to avoid contact with officials of any sort. Finally she folded her arms.

'You're looking for the kid who's gone missing, aren't you?' she asked.

'That's right. Do any of you know her?'

They exchanged a look, then shook their heads.

'Is she dead?' one of the boys asked. He was small and thin, and held himself as if caught between the vulnerability of childhood and the wariness of adulthood.

'Why? Do you think she might be?'

When none of them answered she pointed back towards the building site. 'Do you ever play over there?'

The four of them remained silent. Finally the older girl spoke. 'No.'

'Why not?'

They shuffled uncertainly. 'There are guards sometimes.'

'You've seen them?'

The girl nodded.

'Did you see anybody there yesterday?'

The girl was about to answer when there was a shout from behind Sadiya. A woman was walking towards her.

'Why are you hassling those kids?' she demanded.

The woman wore cheap lenses with a light that showed they were recording. Sadiya lifted a hand to indicate to her to wait and turned back to the kids.

'So did you see anybody?'

'Hey! You heard me,' said the woman, louder this time. 'Why are you hassling these kids?'

Sadiya attempted to ignore her. 'Any of you? Anything?'

The kids shifted uneasily, clearly unsettled by the woman. Out of the corner of her eye Sadiya could see other people approaching. 'If you remember anything, you need to tell one of the police,' she said, trying to keep her voice calm. 'It could be somebody you saw, something you heard, anything. It might seem like nothing, but it could be the clue that helps us find the girl we're looking for.'

As she finished speaking the woman stopped beside her. 'Leave them alone!' she shouted.

Sadiya lifted her hands in surrender and stepped back. 'No problem,' she said. 'I'm going.'

'That's right,' the woman said, following her. 'You leave them alone.'

Sadiya didn't reply, knowing the encounter was being streamed. She turned and walked towards Findlay, who was standing on the footpath by the gate. The woman followed her some of the way, still shouting.

Findlay fell in beside her. 'Everything okay?'

'Just keep walking,' Sadiya said.

'Did you get anything before she interrupted?'

'One of the kids said there are guards there sometimes, so they don't tend to go in. And if they saw anybody in there last night, they aren't saying.' Finally, she allowed herself to glance back. The woman was still standing in the middle of the road. When she saw Sadiya looking, she gestured angrily and shouted again.

'If somebody took Casey they must have come out this way. We need to make sure the uniforms talk to the people in that building, find out whether anybody saw anything.'

'Already sorted,' Findlay said.

'Just make sure they take it easy,' Sadiya said. 'These people aren't the enemy. What matters is we find Casey.'

Fifteen minutes later they were back at Emma and Jay's. Larkin opened the door, Emma just behind him.

'Detective,' said Emma. 'Has something happened?'

'We have officers out looking but there's no news yet.'

Emma's face crumpled. Taking her arm, Sadiya guided her to the sofa and sat her down.

'This is Detective Senior Constable Paul Findlay. He's assisting me on the investigation.'

Findlay smiled. 'Please, call me Paul.'

Sadiya took in the empty room. Normally in a situation like this there would be relatives, friends, neighbours. Instead Emma was alone in the hot dark of the apartment. 'Jay isn't here?'

'He's still out looking. You're sure? There's nothing?'

'We have officers out doorknocking, and Forensics are at the site now. We're doing everything we can. As soon as we find anything we'll tell Constable Larkin, and he can tell you.'

Emma's mouth tightened. 'The cyclone. What if we don't find her before it hits?'

'The projections say it's going to miss us.'

'But what if they're wrong? said Emma. 'What happens then? We were here during Brigitta last year. It was like the end of the world. If Casey is somewhere out there alone ...' She stifled a sob.

'Let's cross that bridge when we come to it,' said Findlay.

Emma didn't look up.

'Paul's right,' said Sadiya. 'We can't worry about the storm now.'

Emma made a small choking sound. 'I'm just so scared.'

'I know,' said Sadiya, speaking as calmly and carefully as she could. 'But for now the best thing we can do is to focus on getting her back.'

Emma looked up at them. Although her gaze was steady her voice trembled. 'What can I do?'

'We need photos, videos, anything we can use to run through our systems,' Sadiya said. 'And we'll need DNA from you and Jay, and a sample of something of Casey's. And a list of anybody you think might have something to do with this. And Emma? When I spoke to you earlier, you said that when Casey didn't turn up last night you called Jay. So he wasn't at home when she went missing?'

A look of unease flickered across Emma's face, then she shook her head.

'Do you have any idea where he was?'

Emma didn't reply.

'Emma?'

'Before he left ... we argued.'

'What about?'

She looked stricken. 'Casey. He said she had disrespected him by ignoring him when he spoke to her. I told him she's just a little girl. Kids can be difficult.'

Sadiya regarded the other woman carefully. 'Emma? I'm going to ask you something, and I want you to tell me the truth. Do you think Jay might have had something to do with Casey going missing?'

Emma hesitated just long enough for Sadiya to know the idea had already occurred to her. Then she shook her head. 'No. Jay would never do that.'

Sadiya waited, curious to see whether Emma might say more. When she didn't she smiled as reassuringly as she could. 'Okay. Paul will take that DNA sample from you now. While he does that, I'd like to take a look at Casey's things.' She gestured towards a door on the far side of the living room. 'Is that her room through there? Do you mind if I take a look?'

'Of course. Anything.'

Sadiya went through into a tiny room. The window was covered with a sheet, and the space was hot and dark. A single bed stood in one corner, fairy lights twisted through the white metal bars of the bedhead. She went towards the window and pulled the sheet back to look out. One of the two panels of the window had been knocked out and replaced with cardboard, the other looked out on the block of flats opposite. Seen from this angle it was evident the building was in worse shape than Sadiya had realised: black plastic covered a number of the windows, and the roof had been torn off, exposing the top floor to the elements. Could somebody have been watching Casey from over there?

Lowering the sheet she looked around again. A screen lay on the neatly made bed, above which a poster of a huge-eyed anime character was stuck, and next to the bed a plastic tub held a selection of dolls and other toys. Sadiya sat down on the bed and picked up the screen. It was old, its back covered in a layer of stickers and its glass cracked across one corner. She touched it, and an animation of the anime character on the wall appeared and smiled at her. They would have to have the device examined to make sure nobody had made contact with Casey through it. Reaching down she picked up one of the dolls. It was a

Barbie, its dark hair shining and synthetic. At some point somebody – presumably Casey – had scribbled on its legs and face with a sharpie. Sadiya touched the fading mark for a moment, then put the doll aside. Noticing a hairbrush on the stool beside the bed she pulled a glove on and picked it up. A number of pale hairs were caught in it. In the next room she could hear Findlay finishing the DNA swab.

She stood up and went back through. 'Is it okay if we take these?' she asked, holding up the brush and the screen.

Emma nodded. Sadiya took out two evidence bags and slipped the brush into one and the screen into the other.

'You said you work at the clinic,' she said. 'Could you have come into contact with anybody there you think might have a grudge against you? Or who has made threats of any kind?'

Emma seemed surprised. 'No. Nobody.'

'And what about Jay?' asked Findlay. 'Is there anybody who might want to hurt him?'

Emma regarded him uneasily. 'I don't think so.'

'You're certain?' Sadiya said.

'I don't understand. Are you saying somebody might have done this to hurt Jay? That doesn't make any sense. Who would do something like that?'

'We're just trying to eliminate possibilities,' said Findlay.

'Does he work?' asked Sadiya.

Emma glanced away. 'Sometimes he picks up labouring, or work with a friend of his, but not really.'

'Does that bother you?' asked Findlay.

Emma looked at him in surprise. 'I'm sorry?'

'It's just you're working, and he's not.'

'It's not Jay's fault. His last boss fired him, and he hasn't been able to find anything since.'

'And can I ask why he was fired?'

'His boss said Jay was causing trouble.'

'And was he?'

She paused. 'Jay can be very passionate about the things he believes in.'

'What kinds of things?'

'Stuff on socials. Theories about conspiracies and things the government is planning.'

'And you? Do you believe the things he says?'

'Some of it makes sense. But there's other stuff...' She shrugged.

Sadiya thought about the scores of people she had met over the years who were caught up in the toxic webs of conspiracism and paranoid fabulation that swirled around them, their certainty they could discern truths others were too corrupt or too stupid to grasp. 'Do you think Jay would have run across somebody who took exception to his ideas?'

'If he has he hasn't told me.'

Sadiya waited for a second or two to see if she would say more. When she didn't Sadiya moved towards the door. 'Do you know where he is now?' she asked.

'He said he was going to look along the tideline. He could be anywhere.'

'Okay. I'm going to call him, but if you make contact with him before I do can you tell him I want to speak to him as soon as possible?'

Emma gave a small nod.

'And I'm sorry we don't know more yet. As soon as we do we'll be in touch.'

Sadiya stepped out onto the balcony, followed by Findlay and Larkin.

'We need to find the stepfather as soon as possible. I want all uniforms notified they should report in if they encounter him.' She turned to Larkin. 'What about the neighbours? What did they say?'

'I spoke to the woman next door and another couple. None of them remember seeing Casey yesterday, although the woman next door says she thinks she heard her playing on the balcony in the morning.'

'But?'

'They were uncomfortable talking to me. They both said they'd had disagreements with the stepfather, and that he often shouts at Emma and Casey. The couple up the way said that she thinks he locks Casey in her room, and the woman next door says that she often hears him criticising and insulting Emma.'

'Great work. Let me know if you hear anything else.'

Once they were on the stairs Sadiya called Jay. A moment later he answered.

'Mr Markley,' said Sadiya. 'Where are you? It's important we speak to you as soon as possible.'

'You're speaking to me now.'

'In person.'

'I'm out doing what you should be doing, and you want to waste my time?'

'We need to know where you were when Casey went missing. Were you at home?'

Jay was silent for a moment. 'I was with a friend.'

'You're going to have to do a bit better than that.'

'He's not the kind of person who likes talking to the police.'

'We'd still like a name.'

'You're barking up the wrong tree, Detective Sergeant,' said Jay. A beep indicated he had ended the call.

'Fuck,' said Sadiya. 'He hung up.'

'Did he tell you where he was?'

'Only that he was with a friend who wouldn't want to talk to the police.'

'You think it could have been him?' said Findlay.

'Everything Larkin just told us matches with what the predictives threw up. And even if he didn't do it, guys like him make enemies.' She stopped.

'What is it?'

'The mother's not wrong about the storm. If it hits us and Casey is still missing she's not likely to survive.' She checked the clock in her lenses – 12.57 pm. 'Nothing from Uniform?'

'Not yet.'

'Okay. Let's try the clinic, see whether we can find out anything there.'

The clinic was back towards the highway, in what had once been a cluster of shops arranged around a small car park. The parking area was now home to a collection of tubs, in which plants grew. Next door to the clinic was a legal assistance centre, a volunteer organisation that offered counselling and advice to refugees and illegals that Sadiya had dealt with many times. A group of kids were jumping skateboards on a step, the wheels spinning and clacking on the concrete. As Sadiya and Findlay turned into the car park they stopped and stared at them, their faces glistening and their t-shirts dark with sweat.

Sadiya took off her lenses as they entered the reception area. A desk stood opposite the door, and plastic chairs were arranged along the walls, the space above them decorated with posters recommending vaccinations and advertising various services. In the centre of the room a girl of about two was playing with wooden blocks with an older girl who looked like her sister. Behind them their mother sat next to an older man, watching them. Next to them were a young woman whose right forearm and hand were wrapped in a bloody cloth, a second woman in a surgical mask with her head against the wall and her eyes closed as if asleep, and a young couple pressed against each other, their thin bodies awkward in outfits that would have been more appropriate in a club.

A young man sat behind the desk. He was slim, and wore a carefully ironed shirt buttoned up to the neck in a deliberate echo of the hipster looks from the turn-of-the-millennium. From the expression on his face it was obvious he knew they were cops and he wasn't pleased to see them. Sadiya stopped in front of the desk and asked whether they could speak to whoever was in charge.

The young man waited just long enough to make it clear he didn't want them there and then told them to wait while he let somebody know. While he tapped something into his screen Sadiya looked around the room. Most of the people seated on the chairs along the walls were studiously ignoring them, but the older man returned her gaze, as if determined to show her he wasn't afraid.

'Dr Shibli will be out in a moment,' said the young man.

Sadiya thanked him. A moment later a door at the other end of the room opened and a young man emerged carrying a child of about two followed by a small woman in scrubs. 'Than, can you arrange an appointment for Omar the day after tomorrow?' she said to the man behind the desk, then turned to Sadiya and Findlay.

'I understand you want to talk to me,' she said. 'Come through.'

Shibli ushered them into a small room containing a desk and an examination table. 'Please,' she said, gesturing to them to take a seat. 'Is this about Emma's daughter?' she asked, watching them with careful composure.

'It is. We were wondering whether you could answer a few questions.'

'Of course, although I'm not sure how much help I can be.'

'Emma told us she works here three days a week.'

'That's right. She does reception and helps with the cleaning.'

'And how long has she been doing that?'

'I'm not sure exactly, but about three years.'

'And in that time have you ever met her daughter?'

'Of course. She brings Casey here often.'

'And how does she seem?' asked Findlay.

'If you're asking whether Casey has any behavioural issues, then no, there's no sign of them, and Emma is devoted to her.'

'But?' said Sadiya.

'She can sometimes be quite reserved,' said Shibli. Sadiya waited for her to elaborate, but she didn't.

'Unusually so?'

'I wouldn't want to speculate.'

'And what about everybody here? Is there any friction? Anybody Emma doesn't get along with?'

'No. She's well-liked by the other staff.'

'Any incidents with patients? People who might have made threats against her?'

'Nothing that stands out. There have been various incidents here – people getting upset and making threats – but only what you'd expect when you're dealing with a community under the sorts of pressures many people here are under.'

'What about her partner?' said Findlay. 'Have you met him?'

The doctor's face hardened. 'I have.'

'And what was your impression of him?'

She remained still. 'He's caused trouble for Emma on several occasions.'

'What sort of trouble?' asked Sadiya.

Shibli was silent for a second or two. When she spoke her tone was precise, as if she were choosing her words carefully. 'He's the kind of man who creates conflict where it isn't necessary.'

'The sort of conflict that might make somebody target Emma or her daughter?'

'The person you should speak to is my colleague John Ballard. He's had more experience with Jay than me.'

'He's here now?'

She stood up. 'I'll take you to him.'

Ballard was in the consulting room opposite. He was a lean man in his early forties, his well-cut dark hair already going grey. Like Shibli he wore scrubs, his arms tanned where they emerged from the short sleeves.

'John, this is Detective Sergeant Azad and Detective Findlay. They're looking for Emma's daughter,' said Shibli.

'We heard earlier today. Poor Emma. How can I help?' he asked.

'Dr Shibli said you might be able to talk to us about Emma's partner, Jay,' said Sadiya.

Ballard looked from Findlay to Sadiya. 'You don't think he had something to do with this, do you?'

'We're just trying to get a full picture of the situation,' said Sadiya.

He thought for a moment. 'I wouldn't claim to know him well. But I had a run-in with him a while back.'

'Here?' asked Findlay.

Ballard regarded him carefully. 'I handle the practice finances. About a year ago he decided we were paying Than more than Emma. He sent a message telling me I needed to rectify that. I told him it was inappropriate, and I wouldn't be discussing Emma's salary with anybody but her. He turned up the next day and accused me of favouring Than because he was an immigrant. It was completely out of line, and for a while I was worried he was going to get violent.'

'He threatened you?' asked Findlay.

The other man regarded Findlay coldly. 'Not explicitly. Although men like him are usually smart enough not to. But I understood what he meant.'

'Do you know whether he behaves like that often?' asked Sadiya.

The two doctors exchanged a glance. 'Emma said a few things that make me think it wasn't unusual behaviour.' He hesitated. 'We actually considered letting Emma go for a while – we can't have a situation where our staff are getting threatened by friends or family members of other employees.'

'But you didn't?' said Sadiya.

'We both like Emma,' said Ballard. 'And neither of us could see how sacking her was going to make anything better for her and Casey at home. But we banned Jay from the surgery, and instructed staff to call the police if he turned up.'

'There haven't been any more incidents since?'

'Thankfully not.'

'You said before that Casey could be quite reserved. Do you think Jay might be one of the reasons for that?'

'Absolutely,' said Ballard.

Sadiya turned to Shibli. 'And you?'

'I do.'

'Could that be because he's been abusing her in some way?'

The two of them watched her warily.

'I couldn't say,' Shibli said at last. 'But I wouldn't rule it out.'

'Did you see the way they reacted when I asked about the possibility of abuse?' Sadiya asked once they were outside.

'We should check Casey's medical records, see if there's anything there.'

'Absolutely. I don't think we can wait any longer. We need to find him immediately, work out where exactly he was last night,' said Sadiya. She was about to continue when a message flashed up. Her father's new nurse, Michelle.

'Shit.'

Findlay turned to look at her. 'Is something wrong?'

'No,' she said, not looking at him. 'It's fine.' She and Michelle had argued several times over the week prior, and she wasn't in the mood for another lecture about how Arman needed to be in a facility. But before she could decide what to do an alert appeared, followed a second later by the voice of Khoury, her voice ragged, as if she was running. 'Incident in progress. Requesting assistance.'

Opposite her Findlay had fallen still, no doubt processing the same alert.

'Fuck!' she hissed, flicking the messages from Michelle aside. 'We've got to go. Now!'

But Findlay was already sprinting away through the crumbling buildings towards the location in the feed.

A couple of minutes later they rounded a corner to find a crowd gathered outside a pair of old houses. Sweat streaming from her face, Sadiya pushed her way through the crowd. On the veranda of one of the houses a skinny, shirtless man had one arm around the neck of a female officer, while the other waved a carving knife in the air. Another man was slumped on the ground beside them, moaning and scratching at his face, presumably from the effects of the can of capsicum spray that lay by the female officer's feet. A second officer stood with his handgun out and trained on the man with the knife.

'Drop the knife, now!' he shouted as Sadiya emerged from the crowd of onlookers, Findlay beside her.

Sadiya stopped. It took her a second or two to recognise the female officer as McEvoy, but she knew the tall one with the gun immediately, although she wished she didn't.

'Fuck,' she said to herself. 'Behrens.'

'I said, drop the weapon!' shouted Behrens, his face red behind his lenses.

'No! You drop the gun,' the man replied. The onlookers jeered in agreement.

Sadiya took a step forward.

'Look out, there are more of them!' shouted somebody behind her. She turned in time to see Findlay reach for his taser. She lifted her hand to stop him. He looked at her in surprise but she was relieved to see him lower his hand, even if he remained tensed. She lifted her hands and took a step towards the three of them. 'It's okay,' she said. 'Everybody just calm down. Nobody needs to get hurt.'

'People have already been hurt!' shouted a man in the crowd.

Sadiya took a breath. Somewhere behind her a woman was screaming, 'Let him go, let him go, let him go,' over and over again, the sound like the whine of an alarm. The heat was making it difficult to think straight. Sadiya forced herself to focus. On the veranda the man tightened his grip around McEvoy's neck. Behrens took a step forward, his gun trained on the two of them.

'Drop the knife! Now!' he said again.

There was a murmur of disapproval and fear from the crowd, who pushed forward. Behrens swung around, his gun waving in front of him.

'Keep back!' he shouted. There was a crack, and Sadiya flinched, thinking it was a gun going off. But then she saw a broken bottle on the ground, liquid spilling out from it. She took a step away, frightened it might be some kind of accelerant, but then she smelt the yeasty tang of beer. Behind her two more of the uniforms were shoving their way through the crowd, their weapons drawn.

Behrens took another step forward. 'This is your last warning,' he said. 'Drop the weapon.'

'Fuck you!' yelled the man with the knife. 'Fuck all of you!'

Another bottle hit the wall behind him and exploded. A woman had begun to wail, a long, ululating sound that might be rage or weeping. The crowd kept shouting and shoving. Sadiya screamed at Behrens to calm down, but nobody seemed to hear her. She blinked, dizzy in the heat, and then something in Behrens' stance shifted, and she realised he was about to fire.

'Stop!' she shouted, racing forward. Behrens turned slightly, and so did the man with the knife. She raised her hands. 'Everybody calm down!' Seeing she had the man with the knife's attention she took a step towards him. 'Please. You don't have to do this. Put the knife down and we can work it out.'

The man stared at her, his eyes wide, his body tense with agitation. Sadiya knew that look: it meant he didn't know what to do next, and that made him dangerous. As slowly as she could, she took another step towards him. 'What's your name?'

He didn't move. His hand was trembling. 'Eli,' he said.

'Okay, Eli,' she said. 'I'm Sadiya. I'm a detective. These officers aren't here for you. We're looking for a little girl who's gone missing.'

'Then why are they at my house?'

'They just wanted to ask you whether you'd seen her.'

Eli didn't move. Sadiya recognised the look on his face, the dawning realisation of how badly he had fucked up, of the regret that was already rising, ready to drown him. She took another step towards him. Eli's hand wavered, and in that moment Sadiya lunged at him and, grabbing his arm, threw it to the side so he stumbled back. McEvoy lurched forward, her body clipping Sadiya's and knocking her off-balance so Sadiya and Eli both fell to the ground. Eli began to wrench his arm around, but before he could Findlay was there, dropping his knee onto Eli's forearm. Eli yelped and dropped the knife. Findlay knocked it aside and then wrenched Eli's arm around and behind his back. Sadiya got back to her feet in time to find Behrens standing behind her, his gun in his hand.

'Put your weapon away,' she said.

Behrens smiled. 'You've really stuffed up now,' he said. 'McEvoy could have been killed.'

Sadiya ignored him, and reached down to help McEvoy up, but the constable waved her hand away and stood up next to Behrens.

'You endangered another officer's life,' said Behrens. 'It's all on camera.'

'Really?' said Sadiya. 'And if we look at your cameras, what will we find? The two of you using excessive force or provocation?'

Behrens smiled. 'We knocked on the door to ask for information.' He inclined his head in Eli's direction. 'That one answered and began acting in a highly agitated manner. While we were trying to explain why we were here the other one approached in an aggressive manner from behind us while making verbal threats of violence. Officer McEvoy took out her spray and asked him to move back. When he didn't, she sprayed him. He fell down and I approached to restrain him, at which time the first one attacked Officer McEvoy from behind. When I realised he had a knife I drew my sidearm.'

Sadiya took in the red face, the massive arms. Out on the street people were still watching, many of them holding phones or filming with their lenses.

'You didn't provoke them?' she asked.

Behrens smiled again. 'Of course not.'

She stared at him for a second or two. 'Get the two of them out of here,' she said.

Findlay approached her while two officers led Eli and his friend towards the fence, Behrens and McEvoy behind them. 'Are you okay?' he asked.

'Fine,' she snapped.

'They're right to be angry. That was reckless. One of you could have been hurt or killed.'

She glared at him. 'We're trying to find a missing girl, and now we'll be lucky if we don't have a riot on our hands.'

Findlay didn't reply. In the street two police vans had pulled up, lights flashing. Four officers climbed out and began trying to move the crowd back. One of them was Gunasekera, the probationary constable from earlier: he looked nervous, and drew back several times as people shouted in his face. Sadiya wondered how long it would be before that nervousness was replaced by anger. Once the bystanders were far enough back, the officers who had taken Eli and the other man loaded them into the van and it slowly turned and pulled away while members of the crowd shouted and beat on the sides of it. As Behrens and McEvoy climbed into the other van Behrens turned and smiled at her. She held his gaze until the door closed between them and the second van moved off as well.

With the vans gone the crowd began to disperse.

'Come on,' said Sadiya, walking away. 'Let's get out of here.' Then she stopped. Jay was standing on the opposite side of the street. Shaking her head in fury she marched towards him.

'Good to see you have the situation under control,' Jay said when she reached him.

'Where have you been?'

'Doing what you should have been doing. Looking for Casey.'

'You said you were with a friend last night when Emma called. We need to talk to that friend.'

Jay smiled. 'And I told you he's not the kind of person who likes talking to cops. But in this case he'll make an exception. His name is Laurent Thomas.'

'And you met this Laurent when?' asked Findlay.

Jay looked at him. 'And you are?'

'Paul Findlay. I'm assisting Detective Sergeant Azad.'

Jay snorted. 'Of course you are. About eight pm.'

'And where was that?'

'The Captain Cook Tavern in Rockdale.'

'And Emma called you when?'

'A bit after eight-thirty.'

'And you came straight back to look for Casey?'

'Pretty much.'

Sadiya regarded him coldly. 'Okay. I want you to go back to the apartment. If we need to speak to you again I want to know where I can find you.'

Jay smiled unpleasantly. 'Of course.'

'You get back to the station, see whether you can track down this Laurent,' said Sadiya as they walked away. 'I'm going to go back to the site, see whether Forensics have found anything.'

'Okay,' said Findlay, then paused. Findlay caught up with her, staying close as they walked through the bystanders.

'That officer, Behrens. I saw how you reacted when he got out of the van this morning. Do you two have some kind of history I should know about?'

'Don't worry about it,' she said, her voice sharper than she had intended it to be.

Parekh was waiting at the gate when she arrived at the site.

'What have you got?' Sadiya asked.

'Not much,' said Parekh. 'The site is a mess – rubbish everywhere, lots of DNA. We're doing our best, but I'd be surprised if we find anything useful.'

'What about where I found the monkey?'

'Nothing there either.'

'And the padlock?'

'Generic, and whoever used it must have worn gloves, because it's clean.'

Sadiya's stomach twisted. 'So they came prepared?'

Parekh nodded.

Sadiya turned and looked at the Forensics officers spread out through the space. 'What about the door to the upper level? Did you get it open?'

'We did. You're welcome to take a look, but it doesn't look like anybody's been up there in a while.'

The door stood open, its lock sliced away with an angle grinder. Sadiya went in, checking the space around herself. Just inside the stairwell there was a pile of garbage, presumably washed down from above in a rain event. Stepping over it, she climbed the unfinished concrete stairs to the first level. The building had been abandoned early in its construction, so there were only a handful of internal walls. Although the space was unoccupied the presence of flattened and faded cardboard boxes and food containers and other rubbish suggested people had slept here once, some time ago. The floors above were also empty. Finally, on the top floor, Sadiya stopped and gazed out across the empty lot next door. She could see some of the uniforms standing in the shade of one of the trees on the other side of the road, and knots of people here and there. And beyond them, over the roofs, the shapes of the buildings rising from the gleaming water of the bay.

It was after five before Forensics were done and the remaining uniforms were finished canvassing residents. Sadiya waited while Forensics loaded their gear into their vans and drove away, and supervised the departure of the last few uniformed officers.

Findlay was already at the station by the time she arrived. Nguyen had assigned them one of the rooms at the back of the building, which had the advantage of being away from the front desk but was also enclosed and shut off from the outside world, save for a small window in the back wall that offered a view of the buildings behind the station. Like the rest of the station its walls were bare, their white expanse stark against the dark grey carpet.

Findlay was helping Gunasekera carry a table across the room when she walked in, while a young woman she didn't recognise but she assumed was probably the tech officer was holding a screen and looking up at an interactive display that was set up against one wall.

'Where's Khoury?' she asked.

'With Child Protection still,' said Gunasekera.

Sadiya turned to the young woman. She had black hair with a severe fringe, lenses with heavy black frames, and tattoos of serpents and ivy coiled up her arms. 'You're the tech officer?'

'That's right. Anja Novak.'

'Excellent.' She looked at the three of them. 'Okay. We all know where we are. We'll have a report from Forensics soon, but I don't think they're going to have much for us. What we do have is a potential suspect in the form of the stepfather, Jay Markley. We have witnesses who say he has a history of intimidating and threatening people, and he wasn't at home at the time Casey went missing. We need to pin down his whereabouts at the time she disappeared, and establish his movements in the hours afterwards. Novak? Can you get me location data on him?'

'I can try,' said Novak. 'Although the network is so crowded down there we may not get much that's useful.'

'Anything you can find is useful. Findlay, where are you with his alibi? Have you found this Laurent?'

'I've got a number, but he's not replying or responding to messages.'

'Of course he's not. Check what the uniforms found as well. Perhaps somebody saw him somewhere.'

'We're still working through the interviews by the uniforms but nobody's mentioned him yet. One thing, though. Somebody reported seeing a silver car outside the site about the time Casey went missing.'

'What kind?'

'They weren't sure. Just something expensive and new.'

'Can we identify it?'

'Unfortunately not. There are very few cameras down in the Floodline, and most of the traffic cameras along that section of the highway were damaged in the storm last October. I've put together a list of silver cars that might potentially have been in the vicinity at the time she went missing, but there are close to a hundred of them.'

'And none of them are connected to Emma or Jay in any way?'

'Nothing the system can pin down.'

Sadiya rubbed her forehead. 'Fuck. How about the bay? Did we get some drones out there?'

'We did, but they didn't find anything,' said Novak.

'I suppose that's something,' said Sadiya. She turned to Gunasekera. 'What about Rafi and Amira? You said Khoury was still with Child Protection. Do you know whether they've spoken to them yet?'

'I think it's happening now.'

'Great. In the meantime I want you to work with the system to review the interviews from today, see whether anybody saw anything. Look for anything to do with the stepfather or for reports of silver cars.' For the next hour or so Sadiya worked her way through the statements and other information they had managed to assemble, searching for some kind of connection or clue, but even with the system's help nothing presented itself. She was about to tell Gunasekera he should get himself something to eat when her assistant informed her Nguyen wanted to see her immediately. She paused. 'Okay. You know what to do. I'll be back soon.'

As she headed for the door Findlay followed her. 'What is it?' he asked.

'Nguyen,' she said.

'Do you want me to come?' he asked.

'No, she said. 'This is my mess.'

'Shut the door,' said Nguyen when Sadiya stepped into her office. Nguyen folded her arms and regarded her coldly. 'Perhaps you can tell me what you think happened down there today.'

Sadiya knew Nguyen well enough to know she had little patience with what she regarded as unnecessary problems. And today was clearly that.

'Behrens and McEvoy got into an altercation with some of the residents. Weapons were drawn.'

'McEvoy was assaulted. One of the residents held a knife to her throat. And she says you attempted to disarm her attacker in a way that endangered her safety.'

'I made a decision to avoid a shooting that would only have made the job of finding Casey Mitchell more difficult.'

'Behrens has made a complaint about your handling of the situation. McEvoy as well.'

Sadiya didn't reply.

Nguyen stared at her. 'Given your record I should take you off active duty while this matter is resolved, but we're already understaffed.'

'I understand.'

Nguyen sighed. 'Where are we with the girl? Any idea what might have happened?'

'We're looking into the stepfather.'

'And the girl? Any sign of her?'

'Not yet.'

'Okay. Keep me in the loop. And Sadiya? I don't like Behrens either, but if it turns out you behaved inappropriately in the situation I'll have to act on it.'

Back in the situation room Findlay was still working. He looked up as she entered, but she avoided his gaze.

'Where are we?' she said as she sat down.

'We've uploaded the materials from today into the system and the samples we took from Casey's apartment have been sent to the lab. Public Affairs have also been in touch. They want to put out an appeal for information.'

'Good idea,' she said 'We also need to pull together everything we have on the stepfather. Even if this Laurent does tell us he was with him, until we can account for his movements he has to be our prime suspect.'

'What about this silver car? Where does it fit in?'

'Could the stepfather have been using it?'

'Perhaps it belongs to a friend of his or something?' said Findlay.

Sadiya nodded. 'Okay. Let's see if we can narrow down the number of possible cars somehow.' She stopped, suddenly remembering the message from her father's nurse several hours earlier. Retrieving it she realised her muting of the original communication had resulted in her missing a string of subsequent alerts. She rang back, her heart beating fast, but the call went to voicemail. She left a message, then sent another, asking what was going on. Then she stood up.

'I have to go,' she said.

'Sorry?' said Findlay in surprise.

She knew how it must look, walking out when she was lead detective, but she didn't have any choice. 'Call me if anything comes up – anything,' she said, her voice repelling any further enquiry. 'I'll review the rest of this at home.'

Findlay regarded her carefully. 'Of course.'

She grabbed her things and half-ran to her car. As she pulled out into the street the setting sun had turned the sky to the west deep red, another legacy of the injection of particulates into the atmosphere a few years previously, but she barely noticed. Instead she kept messaging and calling Michelle, but with no success.

It was almost eight by the time she reached her apartment. Parking her car in the basement she ran for the lift, punching the button hard while she waited. On her floor she jogged down the corridor and opened the door, but when she stepped inside it was quiet, with no sign of any crisis. Hurrying through to the kitchen she found Michelle standing by the table, zipping up her bag.

'I'm sorry I'm late,' Sadiya said. 'I've been on a case. Is everything all right?'

Michelle picked up her bag and slipped it over her shoulder as if Sadiya had not spoken. Only once she was done did she turn to look at her.

'Your father shouldn't be here, at home,' she said. 'His condition is too advanced.'

Sadiya took a breath, reminding herself she couldn't afford for Michelle to quit. 'I'm sorry,' she said. 'Did something happen?'

Michelle pointed to the stove, where a blackened saucepan sat. 'While I was tidying his room he came in here and put that on. Then he forgot. When the smoke alarm went off he became extremely agitated. I was frightened he was going to attack me.'

Sadiya fought to contain her anger. Was this woman really blaming her father for becoming confused and frightened? 'I apologise for that,' she said. 'But you're all right? He didn't hurt you?'

'I'm fine. But I'm not coming back.'

'I'm sorry?' said Sadiya. Michelle had only begun the week before, and there had been two difficult handovers already. Although Sadiya had been clear when she outlined the severity of her father's condition to the agency, Michelle had consistently behaved as if having to deal with someone with such advanced dementia was an unbearable imposition.

'He's way past the point where you should be expecting people to look after him for you. He should be in supervised care.'

'He's on the list at I don't know how many facilities.'

Michelle smiled condescendingly. 'Perhaps you should have started looking sooner.'

Sadiya realised Michelle was enjoying this. 'I'd like you to leave,' she said.

Michelle stared at her, clearly taken aback. Then she smiled again, and without speaking walked towards the entrance to the apartment. As the door slammed behind her Sadiya clenched her fists, suddenly aware she was shaking. Closing her eyes she tried to calm herself, to hold back the fury that threatened to overwhelm her. When her breathing had slowed she went down the hall to her father's room and, after knocking softly, pushed it open.

Inside it was dark, the only light the glow of the screen that lay on the bed beside her father.

'Baba?' she said, but he didn't respond. She stepped into the room and said it again, louder this time, hoping he would hear her over his headphones. This time he looked up. For a moment or two he stared at her as if she were a stranger, but then his confusion was replaced by anxiety.

'It's me,' she said. 'Sadiya.'

He turned back to his screen. 'I know that,' he said, his manner childish, petulant.

'I just saw Michelle. Did something happen today?'

He continued to stare at the screen. 'No.'

'Are you sure?' she asked, although she knew it was pointless. Adrift in his failing memory he had become truculent and paranoid, so interacting with him was frequently like dealing with a difficult child.

She sat down beside him on the bed. He was watching some kind of talk show: people whose faces she didn't know seated in a studio, laughing and glittering. Watching one of them wait for a laugh, her words inaudible, Sadiya felt a sudden sadness at the thought he had probably been watching the same show all day. On bad days he would watch videos of animals, but mostly he watched comedies, old shows about people who live in apartments and sit in coffee shops, with laughing audiences and running in-jokes. For a while she had tried to find shows in Bangla, in the belief he might prefer them, but he had grown angry and agitated, so she had let him go back to his comedies and talk shows. Once she had found him watching porn; when she took the screen from him, he seemed baffled and almost frightened rather than embarrassed or defensive. After that she placed content controls on his accounts.

She took a deep breath and tried to begin again. 'How are you feeling?'

He looked up, and she realised he had already forgotten that she was there.

'Fine,' he said, curtly.

She smiled at him, uncertain whether he knew who she was. 'Are you hungry?'

He nodded vaguely but didn't reply, his attention already focused on the screen again.

Back in the kitchen she prepared a quick meal of vegetables and rice. The crop failures across Asia in the past few years meant rice was expensive and difficult to get, so she was careful not to use too much.

Sometimes cooking calmed her, but not that night. Instead, she had to fight to stop her hand shaking as she chopped and sliced. Michelle was right that her father should be in care, but she had been unable to find him a place – and even if she had, she wasn't sure it would be safe to send him: only a few weeks before ten residents in an aged-care home in Adelaide had died after the power was cut off during a heatwave. Yet neither could things go on as they were: not only was paying for care pushing her further and further into debt, but his behaviour was becoming more erratic and unpredictable. Although she didn't believe he would have tried to harm Michelle deliberately, the chances of him hurting somebody were growing.

She knew without checking that the agency wouldn't have anybody available at such short notice, but she tried anyway. After asking her assistant to leave an urgent request she decided to ask Malila. She had known her since Malila was a child, and although it had been almost a year since the two of them had spoken, the younger woman had cared for Arman before. She fired off a quick message asking whether Malila could be there early the next day. After a minute or two without a reply she sent another message. *If you can't that's okay, but if you can think of somebody else that would be great.* This time Malila messaged her back. *OK. But can't stay late.*

She sighed in relief. *Thank you*, she responded, reminding herself that whatever issues Malila might have had over the years there had always been a core of kindness to her personality. Taking out two plates she served the food and took it through to her father. Only a year earlier he would have come and sat with her, but he barely acknowledged her when she entered his room, so she left the food by his bed and went back through to the kitchen. She knew she shouldn't let him eat alone, that he often lacked the focus to finish a meal, but he preferred it this way.

Back in the kitchen she went through her notes while she ate. Replaying the interviews with Emma and Jay, she remembered the way Jay had reacted when she asked him where he had been when Casey disappeared. There was something there, in his anger, but was she falling for the obvious solution? Or was the solution obvious because it was correct? She pictured his thick arms with their tattoos, heard the contempt in his voice again. What kind of person desires control so much they bully or hurt a child? Leaning back in her seat she remembered Behrens' smile as he had climbed into the van, his certainty he had won. She knew she had behaved recklessly, but what else had she been supposed to do? Let Behrens shoot a man? Pinching the bridge of her nose she tried to clear her head, angry at herself for alienating the uniforms again, for not thinking about the implications of her decisions.

She was interrupted by a call from Findlay.

'What is it?' she said.

'I've checked out who owns the property. It's an outfit called Freycinet. They seem to be some sort of holding company that owns a number of properties in the Floodline that's owned by Horizon.'

Sadiya swore to herself.

'You know them?' said Findlay.

'I know them,' said Sadiya, her voice hard.

'Apparently they're the ones behind the redevelopment down there. It's big. A seawall, affordable housing.'

'I've read about it,' said Sadiya. 'The site where Casey went missing – it's part of that project?'

'It looks like it.'

'So who's handling security?'

'I'm still checking, but it doesn't look like it's actively monitored.'

'Somebody cleared it out at some point, though, and put that padlock on the gate. We should keep looking, try to find out who that was.'

After Findlay hung up she sat in silence for a few seconds, a heavy feeling in her gut. Then she asked her assistant for information about the project. There was an almost indiscernible pause as the AI processed her request, then her assistant replied.

The Badangi development is part of a multi-vectoral initiative intended to restore and rejuvenate the waterfront region popularly known as the Floodline that is being undertaken by Horizon on behalf of the New South Wales Government. It will result in the construction of a new seawall and more than three thousand dwellings, with a number earmarked for affordable and low-cost housing, as well as new commercial and recreation zones. Work on the first phase, incorporating around five hundred apartments, is expected to begin just over two years from now, with the first homes available twelve months after that.

'Have there been significant disputes or objections?'

There have been a number of protests, mostly focused on the question of where current residents will go if they are relocated. This has been particularly contentious because many of these residents are on temporary visas or are in Australia illegally.

'How have the developers or the government responded to those protests?'

The minister and officials have made repeated commitments to ensuring new housing will be found for anybody displaced, and reiterated that the intention of the development is to provide good-quality housing for people who do not currently have proper housing.

She stood up and took a beer from the fridge. As she closed the fridge the kitchen lights flickered. She looked up at the ceiling. The building was supposed to be self-sufficient but the batteries kept failing in the heat, and the grid couldn't keep up with the demand if too many buildings came online at once. The lights flickered again, then stabilised, but this time she heard the air conditioning wind down. With a sigh she walked to the balcony door and pushed it open, letting the hot fug of the night air wash into the room. Leaning back against the wall she ripped the top off the beer, grateful for the sharp, yeasty taste, the wash of the alcohol like breathing in after holding her breath for too long. She knew it was possible Casey could turn up unexpectedly, that they would find her hiding at a friend's house or trapped in a building somewhere, but with each passing hour that became less and less likely: children who weren't found within twenty-four hours were almost always dead; usually at the hands of family, although there were other, even grimmer scenarios she knew they had to consider.

Calling up her files again she replayed the video of Emma's interview, and her dismissal of the idea Casey's biological father might be involved. Was it significant Emma was so certain he couldn't have taken her? And why hadn't she seen him since before Casey was born? Was Jay responsible for that in some way? Something about the way they had looked at each other when she asked about him made her think he might have been. And then there was the question of Jay's political activities, whatever they were. Was any of it relevant? All of it? None of it?

Finally, she opened the videos of Casey that Emma had supplied. In one Casey was speaking to the camera, explaining what her doll was doing, speaking with childlike certainty. In another she was singing, her face painted with glitter that shimmered against her skin.

From the street outside came the pulse of music, a dog barking, the hum of passing vehicles, but Sadiya barely noticed them. Instead, all she could see was Casey, her childlike possibility, her innocence of what may have already befallen her.

*

As the woman closed the door Arman breathed a sigh of relief, reasonably confident she hadn't realised he didn't recognise her. Was she a new nurse? Or another person sent to report on him? And where was his daughter?

Looking down he noticed the screen in his lap. Had he been watching something? He picked it up and it came to life, images of people in a café somewhere long ago dancing across the screen. Did he know these people? Why would they be on the screen if he didn't? There was a burst of laughter, and he smiled worriedly, anxiety spiking in his chest. Was what he was watching funny? Who was laughing? Realising it must be he forced himself to practise smiling, the expression unnatural and uncomfortable on his face. He tried to keep smiling, the rictus making his jaw hurt, but then there was a clatter outside his door, and he froze. There was somebody there! But who? The nurse? No, she was gone. The other woman? He frowned, trying to remember. Who was she?

Confused, he set the screen down and shuffled over to the window. It was dark outside but the dirty glass was still hot to the touch. He could see buildings, lights, in the distance the curved towers of a city – but which one? Dhaka? Chattogram? No, he thought in a sudden flash: not Bangladesh, that was another life, another time. This was Sydney, this was after …

He hesitated again, suddenly aware of the gap between then and now. Occasionally he could almost make out the shape of what he had lost, of how he had been more than simply absence and confusion, but when he did it was unbearable, an ache of loss for everything he had left behind. In those moments he remembered faces, scattered images. A woman he thought was his mother, a man he was sure was his father. The village. The water. But nothing stayed.

He slumped down on the bed again. It was quiet outside, and there was no light under the door, so perhaps he was alone. With a sudden rush of anxiety he remembered something from earlier, a woman shouting at him. Hadn't she understood he was frightened of her, of how she looked at him when she washed him, the sting of her words, the rough way she pulled his clothes on and off. He knew it wasn't right, none of it was right. Shame curdled within him.

Turning to one side he lay down. The people on the screen were talking again, but he couldn't remember what they had been doing when he had stopped watching a moment before, or why he was watching it. Perhaps he used to like it? Perhaps back then, before? He didn't know.

*

Twenty-four hours earlier, Tasim stopped in front of the gate and glanced up and down the street. Satisfied he wasn't being watched he grabbed the wire and scrambled up and over the top. He landed awkwardly, stumbling forward, before recovering and darting away from the street and into the darkness beyond. The building loomed over him, its outline broken by the mass of a huge palm tree, the pale forms of roosting ibises like ghostly smudges amongst its fronds; passing the overgrown garden at the front he hurried down a driveway at the side and emerged into an open area, where broken slabs of concrete and thick bushes were outlined against the lights of the city beyond.

He stopped, trying to decide which way to go. For the past five days he had been sleeping in a park a few suburbs away, where a group of Sikhs served food from a van in the evening. But when he had arrived there a few hours earlier black-uniformed Border Force officers had been stopping people and detaining anybody without the correct identification, so he had turned and fled.

For the first hour after that he had wandered the streets, not sure where to go. Eventually he came to a highway, which he followed for a kilometre or two, before turning off onto a shopping strip lined with cheap places to eat. He hadn't eaten since the night before, and without a meal from the van he knew he was unlikely to find food any time soon, so when he reached an alley he slipped down it. The narrow space stank, the reek of the bins in the heat mingling with the smell of sewage, but at the back of one of the restaurants he found a skip, its lid open and its interior stacked with black plastic bags. He pulled one out and, tearing it open, shook its contents onto the ground and began to poke through them. Most of it was food scraps and other mess, but at the bottom he found a bag of flatbreads. Dusting it off he shoved it in his backpack. He was about to rip another bag open when the back of one of the restaurants opened and a figure emerged, a vape in their hand and smoke coiling in a nimbus around their head.

He dropped down behind the skip, his heart pounding, and sprinted away down the alley. Finding himself in a quieter street, he had followed it for a few blocks until he came to the lot with the abandoned building, its wire fence collapsing under the weight of a crowding wall of bamboo. Usually he slept in parks and other semi-public places, but the sight of the Border Force officers had left him uneasy about being anywhere exposed. As he hurried down the driveway towards the back he gazed up at the building. It was dark, and seemed to be unoccupied, but he knew enough not to take the risk of entering an empty building at night.

Near the back fence, several piles of broken concrete stood half-hidden in overgrown vegetation; clambering up the first he found a flat space and, sitting down, opened his backpack and took out the bag of bread. He opened it and took out a piece. It was slightly stale, but he didn't care: instead, he gulped it down hungrily. The first piece was gone before he was even really aware of it, so he ate a second, washing it down with a sip of warm water from the bottle in his bag. He knew he needed to make the bag last, but he allowed himself to eat a third piece before he sealed the bag up and put it away in his backpack. Picking up his bottle he took another sip, letting the warm water wash down as he took in the space around him. When he'd entered, the darkness had seemed impenetrable; now his eyes had adjusted it was possible to make out piles of rubble, clumps of grass, a mess of creeper. And somewhere nearby the glassy trill of an insect.

He lay back, the concrete warm against his skin. On either side blocks of apartments loomed above him, their windows bright, and in the distance he could hear cars, voices, a baby crying, the sounds of the city. To one side a palm tree was silhouetted against the glow of the sky, its fronds like so many fishbones. He knew he couldn't stay there, that he would have to find somewhere under cover to sleep, but for now he was happy to be safe and alone .

After a few minutes he sat up again, and took his notebook out of his bag. It was too dark to draw, so instead he held it to catch what light he could and flicked through the pages, looking at the drawings he had made, the faces and hands and other details. Reaching one of his sister he stopped. It was drawn from memory, but he knew it wasn't right, that he was losing his sense of what she looked like in life. He took out his phone and pulled up one of his photos of her, the reminder that this was all he had left of her and his mother catching in his chest.

Placing the phone back in his bag he stood up and picked his way over to a stand of oleanders by the fence. Glancing around to make sure he was alone he undid his shorts and released a hot drum of urine onto the leaves and branches. He had almost finished when something hidden in the shadow of the building caught his eye. Realising it was a van, he tensed, angry with himself for not seeing it sooner. Zipping up his shorts he darted up onto the concrete to grab his bag, then moved out across the empty space, careful to keep a safe distance between himself and the vehicle until he was confident nobody was inside it.

The van was white, its anonymous design oddly incongruous in the abandoned space. Stopping beside it he peered into the cabin and then up at the darkened structure above. Was the driver somewhere up there? Could it be the building wasn't empty? He was about to back away when he heard a car door slam and the rattle of a chain from the direction of the street. He turned. A car was coming along the driveway. Without thinking he darted around the van and dropped down behind a bush by the building.

A moment later a car pulled into the space and stopped near the van, its headlights off. Tasim sank even lower, barely breathing. The car was silver, and new. The driver's door opened and a man got out and looked around, his movements brisk and deliberate in a way Tasim knew too well not to recognise. Moving quickly the man crossed to the van and opened the back doors. Tasim tensed, ready to run, but hesitated. What if there was somebody else in the silver car? Should he risk it? He rose up slightly and peered through the window, but before he could decide what to do the man hurried back to the silver car and opened the boot. The lid of the boot stopped Tasim from seeing exactly what he was doing, but a moment later he lifted something out. At first Tasim didn't understand what he was seeing, thinking he must be holding a bag or some kind of sack, but then with a sense of mounting horror he realised it was a girl. He shrank back again, stifling a gasp, and something crunched under his feet, the sound so loud in his ears he thought the man must have heard him. But it wasn't the man who looked his way, but the girl, because that is what she was, who twisted her head and, for a split second, met his startled gaze, her eyes wide and terrified above the strip of silver tape that covered her mouth.

Tasim froze, but before he could react the man had put the girl in the back of the van and slammed the doors. He looked around again and then hurried across the space towards the building. For a second Tasim thought he was heading towards him, but then he turned aside, and disappeared into the shadow of a doorway. There was a brief flash of light, presumably from the torch on his lenses, and then he disappeared inside. Tasim stared at the door. He knew he needed to do something, but what? If he tried to open the van the man might come back and catch him. But he couldn't leave the girl there. Deciding he had to chance it he shot across the space towards the van. He grabbed the latch for the back door and pulled it, but it didn't respond. Realising the man had locked it he ran to the front and tried the driver's door. To his relief it swung open. Inside a metal grille separated the cabin from the space behind it, meaning he couldn't get the girl out that way, so he slung his bag onto the passenger seat and dropped into the driver's seat, searching desperately for the button to release the boot, but then he heard a clatter and a shout. He turned to see the man running towards him. Frantically he pushed himself out the door, almost slipping as he hit the ground. He lurched upright, propelling himself across the broken ground and away, towards the street and safety, running so fast that it wasn't until he was two blocks away that he realised his backpack was still sitting on the seat in the van.

TUESDAY

Sadiya was jolted from sleep by a machine-gun rattle of alerts, her phone pinging beside her bed. She rolled over and grabbed it.

'What is it?' she asked her assistant.

There's been an update from the Bureau, said her assistant. *Cyclone Nasreen has altered course, and is now predicted to make landfall near Sydney sometime on Friday.*

Sadiya sat up, instantly alert.

'Is there any clarity about how serious it will be?'

Category Five. Would you like information about preparing your apartment for the event?

Before she could reply her phone rang again. It was Findlay.

'Have you seen the news?' he asked.

'Just then,' she said.

'What do we do? If we don't find Casey before—'

'I know,' snapped Sadiya, then caught herself. 'The storm doesn't change anything. We have to find her as soon as possible. Where are you with the stepfather's alibi?'

'That's why I was calling. He's still not answering my messages, but I've got an address. He runs a business out of a yard in Rockdale.'

'Fantastic work. Let's get over there and talk to him.'

She ended the call and took a deep breath, trying to relieve the sudden grip of anxiety in her chest. If the cyclone hit it would be the third in four years, each worse than the last. And while in one sense its approach altered nothing – it was still vital they find Casey as quickly as possible – she also knew it would make doing that even more difficult. The department would want to direct all its resources towards preparation, and the city itself was likely to be in a state of upheaval as it readied itself for the latest emergency.

Taking another breath she directed her assistant to override the younger woman's do not disturb settings and contact Malila, then she went through to the bathroom and gulped down two glasses of water and ran a third, grateful for the way it eased the pressure of dehydration behind her eyes. She was brushing her teeth when Malila messaged her back to say she'd be there as soon as she could. Sadiya closed her eyes, suddenly aware of how worried she had been, then asked her assistant to say thank you, uncomfortably aware Malila hadn't even arrived for her first day and she was already overstepping.

While she pulled on her clothes she opened the balcony door. Somewhere nearby a cicada trilled in the early-morning light, the sound shimmering, metallic. She paused, listening. Once, the cicadas had appeared every summer, their songs cutting through the heavy heat like a wave, but in recent years they had been less reliable, whole seasons passing where they were so few in number they were almost unnoticeable. Yet despite the wave of extinction that had rolled across the globe in recent decades some still endured, perhaps protected by the length of their life cycle, the years spent in the earthy dark underground.

She first came across the insects not long after she and Arman arrived in Australia. They were in one of the camps for the displaced that had been constructed outside Sydney in the aftermath of the Melt when she found one of the casings left by the nymphs clinging to the underside of a branch. To her child's mind there was something remarkable about the idea an animal should leave such a perfect copy of itself, an echo of Egyptian death masks or the casts of the dead in the ruins of Pompeii. Throughout that first summer in the camp she spent hours gathering them from the limbs of scrubby plants near the overflowing toilet area, carrying them back to the tent she shared with her father and crawling beneath her sheet to stare at them in the dark. By Christmas her collection had begun to stink; for the best part of a week she did her best to ignore the reek of death that filled the hot air of the tent, until finally Arman arose from his bed, and as she screamed and cried took her precious hoard of rustling skins and cast it out into the night. She had wept, the destruction of the shells just one more loss on top of too many, but Arman didn't attempt to comfort her: instead he just went back to his bed, leaving her to sob herself to sleep on the thin foam of the bedroll.

The memory of that time, of the grief and desperate loneliness, followed her into the kitchen as she made coffee and waited for Malila to arrive. It was only as the kettle boiled that she realised why the name of the cyclone was nagging at her, suddenly recalling that there had been a Nasreen in the camp with her and Arman: she remembered the day the other girl had left, walking away through the gates with her parents and her brother. She shook her head, the converging reminders of the past making her feel like the walls were closing in.

She was reading through Jay's file again when the buzzer sounded. Picking up her lenses, she activated the video feed from the building entrance and saw Malila waiting there. She told her to come up and went through to open the front door for her.

Sadiya had been a probationary constable when she met Malila. Malila's mother, Charlie, had moved into the apartment next door to Sadiya's. Even then Sadiya tended to keep her distance from people – or perhaps they had already learned to keep their distance from her – but Charlie bypassed all that.

The first time she and Charlie spoke was at seven on a Sunday morning. Charlie knocked on her door to ask for some milk. Sadiya was asleep – she'd been on duty the night before – and she emerged blinking and disoriented.

Charlie apologised for waking her. 'I'd go to the shop,' she said. 'But my younger daughter is sick, and the older two are starving, and the only food I've got that they'll eat is cereal.'

Sadiya told her it was fine, regarding her neighbour carefully. Charlie had a kind of high-cheekboned and clear-eyed Nordic beauty Sadiya had always admired, but exhaustion and stress had drained all the light out of it, leaving her skin blotchy and her unwashed hair lank and flat. And although she gave the impression of height and athleticism, as she turned away Sadiya realised she wasn't much taller than she was, and painfully thin.

'I'll bring some to replace this tomorrow,' Charlie said as Sadiya handed her the milk. 'And I'm sorry to come so early.'

'Please don't apologise,' Sadiya said. 'It's totally fine. And no need to return it.' But as she closed the door she saw it was 7.02 am, and realised that Charlie must have been waiting until seven before knocking, and found herself wondering how long the other woman had been awake.

In the months afterwards Sadiya found herself spending more and more time with Charlie and her daughters. At first she did her best to keep her distance, but the children had other ideas. On hot days Charlie would let the three girls play in the cool space of the hall, keeping the door propped open as they ran up and down, bursting out of their skins despite the heat; often Sadiya would come home to find their toys scattered from one end of the corridor to the other. If Charlie was within earshot she would tell them to leave Sadiya alone, or apologise for their behaviour, her manner distracted, exhausted.

Gaia, the oldest of the three, was eight, Aurora was five and Malila had just turned four. Although close in age, the three girls looked little like sisters. Gaia – the product of a one-night stand when Charlie was twenty – had her mother's almost Scandinavian beauty, while Aurora and Malila had their Islander father's looks. Nor did they share much in the way of temperament: Gaia was suspicious, aloof, oddly angry, while Aurora was dreamy and sweet, and Malila was a ball of uncontrollable energy and affection.

Despite her constant exhaustion, Charlie was a devoted and generous mother. Over time, Sadiya discovered her parents were members of a fundamentalist Christian sect who had thrown Charlie out when she was fifteen for taking drugs and refusing to follow their rules. For a time she had lived on the streets, bouncing from boyfriend to boyfriend, until Gaia arrived, and she became determined to raise her with the love that Charlie felt she had been denied. On the rare occasions that Charlie spoke about the past Sadiya knew there was a lot the other woman wasn't telling her.

Eventually Sadiya moved out of the apartment, taking another place a suburb away, but she and Charlie stayed in touch. And then, one evening, Charlie called. Sadiya knew at once that something was wrong from the tremor in Charlie's voice

'It's Aurora,' she said. 'She's in the hospital.'

By the time Sadiya arrived she had the whole story. Charlie had been out with Aurora and Malila when Aurora had wandered away. Somehow, she had slipped and fallen into a drain. By the time Charlie worked out where she was the girl was still, unresponsive, her body limp.

Aurora never woke up, and twelve hours later, when the ventilator was turned off, it was Sadiya who took Charlie and Malila home. Their apartment, once so familiar, felt like a stranger's house when they arrived, its air silent in a way Sadiya found so unbearably familiar it made her want to turn and run. But she forced herself to stay, sitting with Malila and Gaia while their mother slept and only going home late in the evening, once the two girls were in bed and Charlie was asleep again.

Over the next few weeks she was in and out of their apartment, helping where she could and just being there where she couldn't.

After that first day, when she was catatonic with grief, Charlie seemed to withdraw into herself, rigidly performing the business of being a parent with a mute efficiency that frightened Sadiya.

But if Charlie had changed, Gaia was altered almost beyond recognition by the loss of her sister. Always the least malleable of the three girls, she became sullen, cruel, prone to outbursts of anger and long periods of chilly hostility. Most of this behaviour was directed at Charlie, but a lot ended up being visited on Malila as well. A few weeks later Charlie discovered Gaia hadn't been going to school, and a few weeks after that she found out her daughter had somehow made contact with her father, and announced she was moving in with him.

Amidst all this Sadiya had done her best to stay in contact with Malila, spending time with her and Charlie on weekends and sending her messages when she could. But as time passed the contact diminished, and eventually stopped altogether. Malila was skipping classes, drinking and getting into trouble and by the time she was fifteen she was out of school altogether. On those rare occasions that Sadiya saw Charlie she was almost unrecognisable: so fragile she seemed barely functional, and one day she just stopped returning Sadiya's calls.

That would have been the end of it, until one Friday night a couple of years earlier. Sadiya had been on her way to meet a friend for dinner when she ran into Malila on Redfern Street. Malila was walking with a pair of women her own age. The two of them caught each other's eye, and for a moment Sadiya wasn't sure Malila was going to acknowledge her, but then she stopped and smiled as if it had only been a few days since they saw each other. While Malila's friends hovered nearby Sadiya asked her how she was, and Malila told her she was living with her boyfriend. When Sadiya asked her whether she knew where her mother was Malila looked pained, and said she had moved somewhere down south, and as she spoke Sadiya saw the child she had known so many years before was still there at the core of the young woman in front of her. Arman had just been diagnosed, and on an impulse Sadiya asked Malila whether she would be interested in checking in on him for her from time to time, perhaps making him lunch or dinner on the nights Sadiya was working, and to her surprise Malila agreed. Over the next few months Malila visited Arman a couple of times a week, dropping off shopping and tidying and reporting back to Sadiya on his condition and state of mind. Arman was often difficult for her, but she managed his abruptness and ill temper with surprising poise for a seventeen-year-old. But despite Malila's friendly manner Sadiya found herself aware of the way Malila carefully controlled what she told Sadiya about her life – in particular her relationship with her considerably older boyfriend, Zac. Part of that was simply the caution one would expect from somebody Malila's age. But Sadiya suspected it was also because there were aspects of Malila's life she didn't want Sadiya to know about. When Arman had started needing full-time care, about eighteen months ago, she started relying on Malila less, but she still called on her occasionally.

Malila emerged from the lift and walked briskly towards Sadiya. She was dressed in high-cut shorts and a singlet that showed off the lean muscles of her shoulders, but she was thinner than the last time Sadiya had seen her, and there were dark shadows beneath her eyes. Seeing Sadiya she smiled, although there was something fragile about the look.

'Thank you for doing this,' Sadiya said.

'Of course,' said Malila, smiling again.

'You know where everything is, right?' Sadiya said as she picked up her jacket. 'And you can call if there's a problem?'

As she spoke Findlay called again. Sadiya accepted the call, waving to Malila and heading for the door.

'What's up?'

'I heard back from Sex Crimes. Their system has flagged a sex offender whose movements have thrown up an alert. It looks like he's been in the area a few times, and was nearby on Sunday night.'

Sadiya took a breath, her stomach falling away. 'What do we have on him?'

'His name is David Morrison. He was a teacher. He groomed a student back in the late thirties, and did two years for it. No offences since.'

'Do we have an address for him?'

'I'm working on it. And that's not all. When I saw Jay had been arrested at that protest it made me wonder whether there was more there. I called a friend in Anti-Terror. He said he's been on their radar for a while.'

'Did they say why?'

'Their systems think it's possible his involvement isn't just casual.'

'So he's in one of the right-wing groups? Do you think that's relevant to this?'

'It would explain why he's been so difficult to deal with. And it makes it more likely Casey's disappearance might have something to do with his connections. But either way we should keep it in mind.'

She closed the door behind herself. 'Okay. Let's talk to this Laurent first. Find out what he says about Jay. Then we can look for Morrison.'

Findlay was standing on the footpath when she arrived. He looked tired, his eyes bruised and puffy. She pointed to a wire fence a little way down the street.

'Is that the place?' she said as she got out of her car.

Findlay nodded.

The fence was high, and topped with rusting barbed wire, but the gate was open. A pair of large tip trucks were parked to one side, while at the rear a black ute was parked beside an old prefab office. As they approached the office the door opened and a man stepped out. He was in his early forties, with close-cropped dark hair and the shadow of a black beard.

'Can I help you?'

'We're looking for Laurent Thomas.'

He regarded them carefully, clearly sizing them up. 'And you are?'

Sadiya pulled out her ID and showed it to him. 'I'm Detective Sergeant Sadiya Azad, and this is Detective Senior Constable Paul Findlay. We wanted to talk to you about what you were doing on Sunday night.'

'This is about Jay's kid?'

'That's right. Has he been in touch with you?'

'He has.'

'Would you mind telling me what he said?'

'He told me his kid was missing and the cops wanted to talk to me to confirm he was with me on Sunday night.'

'And was he?'

'He was. I met him at the Captain Cook a bit before eight. He got a call from his missus about forty-five minutes later and left.'

'Jay didn't ask you to tell us that?'

Laurent's lip curled as if he had just tasted something unpleasant. 'Let's just be clear. Even if this didn't involve a missing kid, I wouldn't lie to help Jay.'

'You don't like him?'

Laurent laughed. 'When I saw him on Sunday he was trying to get me to give him work again. I told him that wasn't going to happen.'

'Why not?'

'Because he's caused trouble every time I've used him.'

'Can you tell me what kind of trouble?' said Sadiya.

'Turning up late, arguing with the other guys – bullshit like that.'

'What kind of work is it you do here?' asked Findlay.

'Demolition, clean-up, waste disposal.'

'Where do you get most of your work?'

'All over. Now if you'll excuse me, I have things to do.'

'One more thing, Mr Thomas,' said Sadiya. 'You said Jay called you. When was that?'

Laurent took out his phone and glanced at it. 'One-fifteen pm,' he said, then held the phone out to them. 'Would you like to check that?'

Sadiya glanced at Findlay, who stepped forward and looked at the screen.

'He's telling the truth,' he said.

'Are we done?' asked Laurent. Sadiya stared at him for a moment and then nodded.

'What do you think?' said Findlay once they were back in the street.

'If I had to guess I'd say he's telling the truth. But it's interesting Jay called him before he told us who he was with. Perhaps he wasn't certain Laurent would back up his story?'

'Or perhaps he was making sure they had their story straight. Or telling Laurent what to say.'

'Exactly,' said Sadiya. 'I think we need to talk to Jay and Emma again. And we need to find this Morrison.'

The Floodline was still quiet as they made their way out along the duckboards towards Emma and Jay's. Ordinarily she would message a family instead of turning up on their doorstep unannounced, but she wanted Jay off-balance when they asked him about his political associations.

Larkin answered the door, Emma behind him. 'Has something happened?' she said, but Sadiya cut her off.

'There's no news,' she said.

Emma's face crumpled. Then she gasped. 'Have you heard about the storm? What are you going to do? What if you don't find her in time?'

'Please,' Sadiya said. 'Let's talk inside.'

The interior of the apartment was dim, the windows blocked against the morning heat. Jay was standing in the kitchen area, shirtless above a pair of shorts, a bottle of water in his hand. Emma sat down on the old sofa and clutched her hands together on her knees.

'They say it's going to strike on Friday.'

'I know,' said Sadiya. 'And that just makes it more important we keep looking.' She looked up to find Jay staring at her. He still hadn't spoken.

'Has something happened?' she asked.

Emma glanced at Jay, but he avoided meeting her eyes. 'There are people on socials saying Jay and I had something to do with Casey disappearing,' said Emma. 'And other people are saying the police are going to use this as an excuse to clear the Floodline, and that we're somehow involved with that.'

Sadiya took a breath. 'I know how difficult it must be not to look, but you should stay away from socials. Our systems are searching for anything that might be useful. If there's anything there they'll find it.'

'You don't think it was us, do you?' said Emma.

Sadiya kept her eyes on Emma. 'We've got a few more questions for Jay.'

Jay folded his arms. 'This should be good.'

She turned to face him. 'We have information to suggest you've been involved in protests and online activities associated with right-wing groups like the Whiteliners.'

'So?'

'So we'd like to know how far that involvement goes, and whether it might have anything to do with Casey going missing.'

'And how is that any of your business?' said Jay.

'We need to be sure those connections have nothing to do with whatever happened to Casey,' said Sadiya, holding his gaze.

Jay smiled coldly. 'You know Amira's mother helped organise one of the protests about the evictions last month, right? Have you talked to her about that?'

'If we need to ask Hamida or anybody else questions, we will. For now we're asking you,' said Sadiya.

Emma turned and looked at Jay wordlessly, her expression taut, tense.

Jay ignored her, instead fixing a contemptuous stare on Sadiya. 'Don't think I can't see what you're trying to do.'

'All we're trying to do is find Casey,' said Sadiya.

'The people I know have nothing to do with this. And you suggesting they might is just proof you're not doing your jobs.'

'Are you sure about that?' Sadiya asked. For an instant she thought she saw a flicker of doubt behind his eyes. She pressed on. 'We're not interested in your political views or your activities. We just need to be sure we're not missing something, or wasting time we could be using to find Casey.'

'In the same way your officers weren't wasting time yesterday?'

'Please, Mr Markley,' said Sadiya, 'we're not the enemy here.'

Emma cut Jay off before he could reply, her voice clear and angry. 'Jesus, Jay, stop it. Just tell them.'

Jay glanced at her, his face cold with anger. Then he seemed to reach some kind of decision and smiled. 'I have some friends who are involved in some of the groups you're talking about. And I've been to a few of the marches and rallies. But I'm not a member of any of them.'

Emma looked down, as if already regretting her tone. Sadiya waited for a moment before speaking again.

'And can you think of any reason somebody connected with one of those groups might have taken Casey? Have you come into conflict with any of them? Could they be trying to pressure you in some way?'

Jay shook his head.

'You're certain?' asked Sadiya.

'How many times do I have to tell you the same thing?' said Jay. 'Nobody I know has anything to do with this.'

Outside they stopped in the shade of the building. A young woman was standing on the staircase of the block opposite, a phone trained on the two of them. Sadiya ignored her.

'Well, that was interesting,' Findlay said. 'Do you believe him?'

'Guys like him, they think everything's a game. You can't trust a word they say.' She paused. 'Even if he was telling us the truth when he said he didn't think it had anything to do with his political connections, he's not telling us everything.'

Findlay was about to reply, but then he tensed, his attention shifting to his lenses. 'We've got an address for Morrison.'

'The sex offender? Let's go find him.'

Morrison's apartment was in Waterloo, so they swung past the station along the way so Findlay could drop off his car. The building was an unlovely turn-of-the-century tower with splashes of orange and green on the façade. Beside it was a narrow park, part of which was cordoned off with orange tape because of the huge tree that listed to one side in its corner, the ground around its base broken and swollen where the roots had emerged from the earth.

In the entrance area Sadiya pressed the button for security. After a moment a man answered.

Sadiya held up her ID. 'We're looking for David Morrison. Apartment 715.'

'Does he know you're coming?'

'No. And we'd like to keep it that way.'

The lock whirred and clicked. 'Seventh floor,' said the guard. 'I'll clear the lift.'

Sadiya slipped her ID back into her pocket. 'Thank you,' she said. 'You have a good day.'

'You too,' said the guard.

In the lift Findlay smiled.

'What?' she asked.

'Who knew you could be so charming.'

She surprised herself by smiling back. 'It's a gift.'

'Clearly.'

'Don't push your luck.'

The doors opened on a dimly lit corridor in which the smell of mildewed carpet and blocked drains hung in the air. 'This way,' said Sadiya, pointing to the left.

They stopped in front of apartment 715 and Sadiya knocked. A moment later the door swung open on a man she recognised as Morrison. He was wearing loose shorts and a faded green t-shirt, its neck stretched and frayed. According to his file he was in his mid-forties but he looked older, the boyish, slightly preppy good looks of the photo in the file replaced by a receding hairline and the puffiness of a heavy drinker. He regarded the two of them with surprise.

'Can I help you?'

Sadiya held her ID up again. 'My name is Sadiya Azad. I'm a detective. My colleague and I would like to ask you a few questions.'

Morrison's eyes widened, and for a moment Sadiya thought he was going to faint. He put a hand on the doorframe and steadied himself.

'What about?'

'Perhaps we could come in?'

Morrison glanced over his shoulder nervously. 'Okay,' he said. 'As long as you're quick.'

The apartment was small: a truncated entry area that led into a kitchen and a narrow living area dominated by an L-shaped sofa that was too big for the space. At the far end blinds shrouded glass doors, holding back the heat; through the gap between them a narrow balcony was visible. Although it smelt better than out in the corridor the smell of mildew was still present.

Morrison closed the door behind them, and circled around the back of the room, visibly uncomfortable with their presence.

'What do you want?' he asked.

'We're wondering whether you can account for your whereabouts between six and nine the night before last,' Sadiya said.

'Why?'

'It would help us if we could eliminate you from an enquiry.'

'I went to visit somebody.'

'And this somebody. Are they a friend?' Findlay asked. 'What's their name?'

Morrison looked uneasy. 'Please. I don't want any trouble.'

'We understand that,' said Sadiya. 'But it would be very helpful if we knew where you were.'

'What's this about?'

'Just answer the question, Mr Morrison,' said Findlay, his voice calm but firm.

Morrison shifted nervously. Then he seemed to reach some kind of decision. 'Rockdale. Down near the Floodline.'

'Thank you,' said Sadiya. 'And who was it you were visiting?'

Morrison blanched. 'I don't have to tell you that.'

'No,' Sadiya said. 'You don't. But if you don't, we won't be able to confirm your whereabouts.'

'This person you were visiting. Are they someone who shares your ... interests?' asked Findlay.

'You don't have the right to harass me like this. I haven't done anything.'

'Nobody's saying you have.'

Morrison was sweating.

'Perhaps you could walk us through your memory of what happened?'

'I ... I caught the train down at about seven. I got off at Rockdale station. Then I walked to my friend's house. I left a bit after nine and got the train back again.'

'So, you were with him for about two hours?'

He looked uncomfortable. 'No.'

'What do you mean?'

'I ... he wasn't there when I got there, so I waited until about eight forty-five.'

'And then you stayed, what? Fifteen minutes?'

He kept looking at Findlay, as if he couldn't bear to look at Sadiya. 'I suppose.'

'And what did you do while you waited?'

'Walked around.'

'Did you go into the Floodline while you were walking around?'

'What? No.'

'You're sure about that?' asked Sadiya.

'Yes.'

'If we check your phone records we won't find you went on a detour?'

'I didn't have my phone on.'

'Why not?'

'I don't like being tracked.'

'Is your phone on now?' asked Findlay.

Morrison looked confused. 'Yes.'

'So you don't like being tracked except when you're at home?' asked Findlay. 'Or is it just when you're outside?'

Morrison didn't reply.

'Please, Mr Morrison,' said Sadiya. 'You must be able to see how this looks. We ask you where you were and you tell us you happened to have your phone off.'

'Please,' said Morrison. 'I didn't do anything.'

Sadiya and Findlay glanced at each other. 'This person you went to visit. What was their name?'

Morrison looked like he was going to throw up. 'Please,' he said. 'It was nothing.'

'Then tell us.'

'I went to buy a new controller for one of the sims I play.'

'And do you have some proof of that? Did you exchange messages or something?'

'I arranged it online.'

'Do you remember the address?'

'I wrote it down. I'm not sure what I did with the piece of paper.'

'So you were visiting somebody whose name you can't remember at a location you can't recall?'

Morrison didn't reply, his face pale and sweaty.

Sadiya held up her screen and showed Morrison a picture of Casey. 'Have you ever seen this child before, Mr Morrison?' she asked.

His eyes focused on the screen for a second or two. Then he shook his head. 'No. Never.'

'And you're sure about that?'

'Yes, I promise.'

Sadiya stepped back and looked through the half-closed door to the bedroom. A woman's dress lay on the bed. Morrison watched her nervously.

'Do you live alone, Mr Morrison?'

He glanced past her to the bedroom.

'Mr Morrison?' Sadiya said, her voice hard.

'No.'

'Who else lives here?'

'My partner. It's her apartment.'

Findlay hadn't moved. He stood, facing Morrison. 'And where is she now?' he asked.

'Out. At work. Please, I need you to leave.'

Findlay ignored him. 'Your partner. What's her name?'

'Sienna. Sienna Moore.'

'And would I be right in thinking she doesn't know where you were the night before last?'

Morrison's eyes widened.

'Or about your history?' Findlay asked.

'Please,' Morrison said. 'She doesn't need to know. You can't tell her.'

'Does she have a child?' Findlay asked, his voice cold.

'What?'

'You heard me,' said Findlay.

'Yes, but she lives with her father. I don't have anything to do with her.' When neither of them replied he continued, his voice pleading now. 'Please. It was a long time ago. I'm not like that. Not anymore. I've changed.'

Sadiya regarded him coldly. 'We're going to check your movements,' she said. 'If we find out you've been lying to us, I can promise you, your life won't be worth living.'

Outside in the corridor Findlay didn't speak until they got into the lift. 'I need a bath,' he said.

Sadiya turned, startled by the anger in his voice. Findlay was staring directly ahead, his face set. Yet while he was clearly upset, there was no suggestion of physical threat.

'What did you think?' she asked him.

'His story is bullshit,' Findlay said, 'but I don't think he was pretending when he said he didn't recognise Casey.'

'Except?'

'Except he was nearby, and he can't account for his movements at the time she disappeared. And why turn his phone off if he wasn't up to something?'

'Agreed. At least if he took the train we should be able to confirm whether he left when he says he did.'

'We also need to find whoever it was he was supposed to have been visiting.'

As she spoke, she noticed a string of messages from Malila. She took a breath.

'What is it?'

'Nothing,' she said, already hurrying towards the car. 'I just need to make a quick detour.'

Back in the car she pulled out into the traffic and directed her assistant to call Malila back, but there was no response. She tried again with the same result. Keeping her eyes on the road she gripped the steering wheel tighter. She could feel Findlay looking at her but she ignored him. She pulled up on the street outside her building. Findlay reached for his seatbelt buckle but she shook her head.

'No. You wait here.'

For a moment she thought Findlay was going to argue with her, but something in her expression warned him off, and instead he lowered his hand and nodded.

She slammed the door and ran inside. Malila was standing in the living area when she opened her front door. Pillows and papers were strewn about, and a pot plant lay on the floor near the door, dirt spilling out of it across the floor.

'Where is he?' Sadiya demanded, but before Malila could answer there was a crash from Arman's bedroom. Sadiya bolted down the hall towards it, but the door was closed. Grabbing the handle, she tried to open it, but it collided with something heavy. She leaned against it and pushed, but it would not open any further.

She pressed her face to the door. 'Baba?' she said. 'It's me, Sadiya. Are you all right?'

There was another crash.

She turned to Malila, who was standing behind her in the hall. 'What happened?'

'He attacked me.'

Sadiya didn't reply, momentarily unable to process the younger woman's words. Behind the door there was a thump, followed by a low moan. Sadiya turned back to the door.

'Baba!' she shouted. Placing her shoulder against the door she shoved it, hard. The door bumped forward slightly. On the other side something toppled to the floor with a clatter. Sadiya shoved the door again; this time it jerked forward several centimetres. Turning, she pressed her back against it and pushed again. It slid forward a few more centimetres. She gave it one more shove and then pushed herself through the gap, trying not to catch her buttons on the frame.

On the other side of the door Arman's room was in chaos, his bed flipped over and clothes strewn around on the floor. Arman was huddled in the far corner, cowering behind an overturned chair.

'Baba!' she said, clambering over the mattress towards him.

Arman shrank back, whimpering. 'No. Stay away.'

She paused. 'It's all right, Baba. It's me, Sadiya.'

'No, you're not Sadiya,' he said, his dark eyes terrified and uncomprehending.

She took another step towards him and knelt down, but he flinched and pulled away, moaning. Catching the stink of shit, she lifted her arm to her face.

'Yes I am, Baba. You know that.'

'No. Go away. I want Lina.'

Sadiya slumped back on her heels. 'Lina's dead, Baba,' she said. 'You know that. There's only me. Only me.'

Arman stared at her. Then his face crumpled, and he began to sob. Ignoring the stink, Sadiya moved in and sat beside him. Reaching across she took his hand and enclosed it in hers. Arman didn't look up, but nor did he resist.

Once he was calm, she placed his hand back in his lap and stood up. Malila was waiting in the hall. She took one more look at Arman to make sure he was sitting calmly and pulled the door closed behind herself.

'Tell me what happened,' she said.

'I'm not sure. I was in the kitchen and I heard him clattering about in the living room. When I came through to see what he was doing he was pulling things over, like he was looking for something. I tried to stop him but he ran into his room and locked the door.'

Sadiya felt the moment stretch out as she considered what came next. 'Did he hurt you?' she asked carefully.

Malila pursed her lips, then shook her head. 'No. He just frightened me.'

Sadiya nodded, grateful for Malila's calm response to the situation. 'I'm sorry. I should have warned you. He's been getting worse.'

'It's okay.'

Sadiya sighed. 'It's not, and I'm sorry.' She leaned back on the door and took a breath, trying to calm herself. 'I promise I will find somebody else as soon as I can, but is there any way you can stay, even just for today? This case ... I can't be here, and I can't leave him alone.'

Malila opened her mouth but didn't speak. Then she seemed to reach some sort of decision. 'Sure,' she said.

Sadiya relaxed back against the door. 'Thank you.' She paused. 'He needs to be cleaned up. I can do that. But do you think you could change his sheets?'

Malila's reply was cut off by a knock on the front door. Hurrying, Sadiya went through to the living room and found Findlay standing in the doorway staring at the disarray.

'I'm sorry,' he said, his voice faltering. 'The door was open.'

'I thought I told you to stay downstairs,' Sadiya snapped.

'We have a possible ID on the car that was seen near the site. And an address.'

'I'll be there as soon as I can.' Sadiya turned to Malila. 'Can you get me some clean clothes?' she said, forcing herself to keep her voice level.

In the bathroom she lowered Arman's tracksuit pants and helped him step out of them, holding her breath against the stink. Her father had never been a big man, but his legs were thin and wasted, his skin papery and covered in bruises and contusions, patches of broken skin that weep and flower. Even the dark hair that once grew on his thighs had largely disappeared, buffed away by age. She pushed the crumpled heap of his pants to one side, then lifted his t-shirt over his head and helped him into the shower recess. Once he was in, she unclipped the showerhead and twisted the tap. Water dripped out, brown and feeble. She turned it further. For a moment it seemed it wouldn't help, but then the water gurgled and spurted out in a strengthening stream. She held it up to her hand, testing the temperature as for a child. For a moment Casey's face from the video appeared to her, and she tightened her mouth. She closed her eyes, pushing it away. Who would have children in a world like this?

She held it over Arman's hand. 'How's this?'

He yanked his hand away, fear and confusion on his face, then tentatively extended his hand again, and allowed the water to play across his skin before giving a small nod of assent.

Sadiya lifted the showerhead so the water sluiced down his legs and buttocks, sending the filthy liquid spilling across the tiles into the drain. When the worst of the mess was finally gone, she squirted some soap into her free hand and began to wash, working quickly, carefully up his legs and buttocks and rinsing them clean again. When she was done she placed some more soap in his hand and motioned towards his groin.

'Now you,' she said.

For a moment Arman seemed not to have understood. Then, moving slowly, he began to wash his crotch, soaping around his testicles as if they were new to him, his expression childlike, confused. Something about his confusion reminded Sadiya of their first days in the camp, his silent retreat into himself. She pushed the memory away and lifted the showerhead, letting the water rinse the soap away.

When the last of the suds had vanished she turned the water off. With one hand on his arm she guided him out of the shower and wrapped him in a towel. Gently she dried him and then helped him change into clean shorts and a t-shirt before leading him back to his room. But when she reached the door she was startled to find Findlay standing in front of the wardrobe, an armful of clothes held to his chest, and Malila leaning over the now-upright and freshly made bed.

Findlay smiled at her. 'Nothing seems to be broken.'

'That's good,' she said, then caught herself. 'Thank you.'

Next to her Arman let go of her arm and stepped past Findlay and Malila to his bedside table and picked up his screen. Sitting down on the side of his bed he flicked it on and leaned over it, already absorbed. Findlay placed the last things in the cupboard.

'I'll wait outside,' he said.

Sadiya nodded, not meeting his eye. Once he was gone, she took Malila's arm and drew her towards herself. 'Are you sure you're going to be okay with him?'

Malila smiled. 'It'll be all right.'

'I'm sorry I missed your messages. I won't let it happen again.'

'It's all right,' she said. 'I understand.'

Findlay was waiting in the car when she got back downstairs.

'An officer has reported seeing a late-model silver Polestar entering the Floodline just after seven-thirty on Sunday night,' he said as she climbed in. 'The system cross-referenced that with the cars it had already identified and determined it was a vehicle registered to a woman called Nina Lukic.'

'Do we have any idea when it left again?'

'No. Either whoever drove it out again managed to avoid passing through a camera – or it's still there somewhere.'

Sadiya sighed. 'Okay. We need to get some officers down there, see if they can find it. What about Lukic? Do we have anything on her?'

'She has a place in Bellevue Hill. But the car is registered at a business address in the city.'

'She's more likely to be there this time of day. Where is it?'

Findlay smiled. 'That's the interesting bit. She works at Horizon.'

Sadiya hesitated. Findlay looked over.

'What is it?'

Sadiya shook her head. 'Nothing. Shall we try her office?'

'Sure.'

Findlay brought up the address and they headed off. For a while neither of them spoke. But as they turned onto Victoria Road, Findlay broke the silence.

'How long has he been like that?' he asked, his voice gentle.

'A couple of years. But these past few months...' Her voice trailed off.

'Have you got other people who help? Family?'

Sadiya shook her head. She could feel Findlay watching her, but she didn't look up.

'And the girl? Malila?'

'She's ... a friend. She helps out when I can't get anybody else.'

'You don't have a nurse or somebody professional?'

'He's driven them all away.'

Findlay was quiet for a few seconds. 'I'm sorry. That can't be easy.'

Sadiya looked away. 'Thank you.'

Horizon's offices were in the Eora complex on Pitt Street. The temperature dropped twenty degrees as they stepped into the foyer, the heat and glare outside replaced by filtered light and cool air. An atrium rose half-a-dozen floors above them, its inner wall lined with plants, giving the space the feel of a gallery or a greenhouse. Aware the building's systems were already scanning them and trying to match their faces to its records, Sadiya walked quickly towards the human guard who sat behind a desk near the liftwell. Holding up her ID for the camera, she told the guard they were looking for Nina Lukic. The guard lifted a finger to indicate they should wait, no doubt consulting with the building's systems, then leaned forward and pointed towards the lifts, telling them to take number three to the thirty-fifth floor.

The lift opened onto a glass-walled reception area containing a pair of sofas. Sadiya approached the screen that stood by the door to the offices beyond, and a face appeared, their discreetly non-binary, ethnically ambiguous features a giveaway they were AI, presumably housed in a server farm somewhere thousands of kilometres away and handling dozens of similar requests simultaneously.

'We're here to see Nina Lukic,' she said.

The face on the screen smiled, the AI's simulation of human emotion seamless. 'Of course. Can I say who's calling?'

Sadiya held up her ID. A few seconds later a woman opened the door. She was in her early twenties, well-groomed and professionally dressed – but there was something uncertain in her manner, as if she feared being reprimanded.

'You're here for Nina?' she asked.

'That's right. Is she here?' asked Sadiya.

'I'm afraid she's not in today.'

Sadiya and Findlay exchanged a glance. 'Do you know when she'll be back?' Sadiya asked.

'I'm afraid not.'

'Was she here yesterday?' Findlay asked, but before the woman could answer, the glass door swung open again and a man stepped out. He was about forty, with thick, sandy-blond hair and a face that hovered on the brink of handsomeness. The way his suit hung on his lean frame suggested it had been expensive.

'I can take this from here, Ariana,' he said, and stepped towards them. 'I'm Oliver Manning. The guard downstairs tells me you're looking for Nina Lukic?'

Sadiya smiled and tucked her ID away. 'That's right,' she said. 'I'm Detective Sergeant Sadiya Azad, and this is Detective Senior Constable Paul Findlay. Is there somewhere we can talk?'

'Of course,' he said, opening the door and gesturing them to step through.

His office was on the corner of the building, its smart-glass walls looking out through the towers to the north-west. Between two the harbour was visible, the half-submerged waterfronts of Pyrmont and Balmain rising above the water.

'Please,' he said, closing the door behind them and gesturing towards a small conference table in one corner. As she sat down Sadiya noticed three digital frames on Manning's desk. The first displayed a portrait of Manning seated with a blond woman and two little girls, the four of them laughing in a staged way; the other two displayed more recent images of the same girls, the older standing alone in a school uniform – SCEGGS? MLC? – the younger posing with her arms around Manning.

'Can I ask why you're looking for Nina?' he asked.

'We need to speak to her in relation to an investigation we're conducting.'

Manning looked confused. 'You think she's committed a crime?'

'We're not at liberty to disclose that,' said Findlay.

'Of course,' Manning said. 'It's just we're all a bit worried about her here. She didn't turn up for work yesterday or today, and we haven't been able to contact her.'

'I assume that kind of behaviour is out of character for her?'

'Very much so. She's one of our most trusted team members.'

Sadiya leaned forward. 'Would you mind telling us what position she holds here?'

'She's part of our audit team.'

'So, she has access to financial records and financial transactions?'

'That's right.' He paused. 'Why? What are you suggesting?'

'We're not suggesting anything, Mr Manning,' said Sadiya. 'But have there been any irregularities? Reasons she might want to disappear?'

'No. Of course not.'

'What about personal matters? Has she had relationship problems? Family issues?'

'Not that I know of, although I wouldn't expect to. She's a very private person.'

'Could she be unwell?' Findlay asked.

'I don't think so.'

'Do you have an emergency contact on file? Or her next of kin?'

Manning's eyes narrowed as he accessed something in his lenses. 'That's odd,' he said.

'What?'

'She doesn't seem to have anybody listed.'

'Nobody at all?' asked Sadiya.

'No. It looks like she never supplied us with a contact.'

'I assume that's unusual?'

'Definitely. Although it's also possible it's a glitch in our systems. I'll flag it and get HR to follow up.'

'What about her home address? Our records show she lives in Bellevue Hill.'

Manning hesitated, checking. 'That's right,' he said. 'Birriga Road.'

'Thank you,' she said. 'Before we go, we were wondering about her car. It's registered here. Do you know whether it belongs to her or whether it's owned by the company?'

Manning thought for a moment or two. 'I'm pretty sure the car is part of her package. I can find out if you like. Why do you ask?'

'She doesn't share it with other employees?'

'If it's part of her remuneration then it will be for personal use.'

'Can you think of any reason she might have been down at the Floodline on Friday night?' asked Findlay.

'No. But as I say, I don't really know her outside of work.'

As they stood up Sadiya noticed an image on one of the screens on the wall, lines of modular houses spread across a hillside.

'What's that?'

Manning glanced at it. 'A new refugee processing centre we're constructing out west.'

'Is that the kind of project you normally handle?'

Manning smiled a little condescendingly. 'Mostly I work on housing projects, but I've done a few like this.'

Sadiya didn't take her eyes off him. 'Are you aware of a property Horizon owns down in the Floodline?' she asked.

Manning smiled. 'You'll have to be more specific. We own a number of properties down there,' he said.

'This is a property on Adam Street.'

'I don't think I know that one in particular, but it would be part of the Badangi development.'

'And does your security do inspections on the properties that are part of the redevelopment?'

'SecurCorp handle all our security,' said Manning. 'Is there any particular reason you need to know?'

Sadiya regarded him carefully. 'We're investigating the disappearance of a five-year-old girl. She was last seen at the Adam Street property.'

Manning looked dismayed. 'I'm sorry. That's terrible. And you think Nina going missing might have something to do with whatever happened to this little girl? I don't see how that could be.'

'Why not?' asked Findlay.

'Nina would never do something like that.'

Sadiya waited to see if he would say anything else, then she stood up. 'Thank you, Mr Manning. You've been very helpful. If we have more questions we'll be in touch. And if Ms Lukic makes contact with you or anybody here, could you please let her know we're looking for her and she should contact us as soon as possible? It's extremely important we speak to her.'

'Of course,' he said, ushering them out again. As they reached the lifts he paused and glanced over his shoulder as if making sure nobody else was listening. 'I'm sorry to do this, but I have to ask. Should we be worried about Nina? Is there some reason to think something may have happened to her?'

Sadiya smiled blandly. 'I'm sure everything is okay.'

Manning exhaled. 'That's a relief,' he said.

In the lift Sadiya faced away from the camera. 'Her home address is in Bellevue Hill. What say we go there now?'

'Definitely,' Findlay said. 'What do you think?'

'I don't like the fact she's not here.'

'And what about the lack of a contact?'

'It could mean nothing, but it feels like something isn't right.'

Despite the street cooling, the heat enveloped them as they left the building. By the time they reached the car Sadiya's shirt was soaked with sweat and she felt dizzy. Noticing her steady herself as she opened the door, Findlay asked if she was okay.

'Fine,' she said. 'Just hot.'

Inside Findlay turned the air conditioning up to maximum, the sound of the fans filling the cabin as they pulled out into the traffic. Sadiya closed her eyes and let the cool air wash over her.

Nina's apartment was in a 1920s block perched on a crest above the street, its dark-red brick and tiled roof elegant against the glare of the sky. Sadiya's assistant interrupted her as they stepped out of the car.

Inspector Nguyen is calling you.

'Shit,' she said, and motioned to Findlay to stop.

'What the fuck is this I hear about you turning up at Horizon's offices?' demanded Nguyen.

'We've identified a car that was in the vicinity when Casey went missing,' said Sadiya. 'It's registered to a Horizon employee. We went to try to find her.'

'You're sure this car has something to do with Casey's disappearance?'

'It seems likely. The owner hasn't been at work for the past two days and isn't answering calls or emails. We're at her place now.'

There was a brief silence. 'Okay. See what you can find out. And Sadiya? Stay away from Horizon unless you have no choice.'

'What was that?' asked Findlay when she hung up.

'Just Nguyen. Don't worry about it,' she said, already walking away from him.

By the time Findlay caught up with her she was at the front door. She didn't look around as she located Nina's apartment on the old-fashioned intercom panel and pressed the buzzer. After a few seconds she tried again. When there was no response, she pressed the buzzer below it. A moment later a woman's voice answered.

'Yes?'

Sadiya leaned in. 'Hello. My name's Sadiya Azad, I'm a police officer. We're trying to contact Nina Lukic, who lives in apartment four, but she's not answering. You don't happen to know whether she's in, do you?'

There was a brief silence. 'You're police?' Her voice was young, slightly vague, as if she were half-asleep or on drugs.

'That's right. Do you know Nina, Ms ...'

'Not really. I haven't seen her for weeks.'

'I see. And you've no idea where she is now?'

'No.'

'Would you mind letting us in so we can take a look around?'

There was a long silence. 'Who did you say you are?' the young woman asked again.

'I'm a police officer,' said Sadiya. 'We're looking for Nina Lukic.'

There was a long silence, and then the lock clicked open. Sadiya raised an eyebrow at Findlay and pushed the door open.

Nina's apartment was on the first floor. Sadiya knocked on the door, and almost instantaneously a dog began to bark behind the door. Sadiya took a step back, then tried again. The dog's bark grew higher, more urgent. She was just lifting her hand to knock again when the door on the far side of the stairwell opened, and a young woman appeared. She had long, dark hair, and wore a loose singlet that exposed her pale, almost luminous, white skin.

Sadiya turned towards her and realised she was even younger than she had sounded. Eighteen, tops. No more than a child, really. She smiled reassuringly. 'Hi. I think we spoke on the intercom a moment ago.'

'She isn't home.'

'How do you know?'

'The dog. He whimpers when she's not around.'

'You can hear it from your apartment?'

'All the time. Simon hates it.'

'Who's Simon? Your boyfriend?'

She nods again.

'Is he there with you?'

'He's at work.'

'How long has the dog been whining?' Findlay asked, his voice gentle, non-confrontational.

The girl looked uncertain. 'Two days?'

Findlay shot Sadiya a look.

'We need to look inside,' Sadiya said.

'Do you want me to get Uniform out here?'

The dog howled and scratched at the door. 'No time,' Sadiya said. 'If something's happened to her and she's in there we need to know.'

She turned back to the girl. 'I don't suppose Nina left a spare key with you?'

'She and Simon don't get along.' A thought crossed her face. 'I think she keeps a spare key above the window.'

Findlay turned towards the window that lit the landing. 'This one?' he asked. Reaching up, he ran his hand along the top of the frame until it connected with something. He lowered his arm to reveal a key in his hand.

Sadiya motioned to the girl to step back. 'Can you wait inside?' she said.

Once the girl had closed the door, Findlay slipped the key in the lock and turned it.

There was a yelp of fear as the door swung open, and a bundle of gold-furred fury darted away down the hall, its claws scrabbling on the polished timber before it skidded to a halt and started barking again.

'Police!' called Sadiya. 'Coming in!' She took a step forward and the dog leapt backwards in terror before releasing another fusillade of barks. Behind her Findlay laughed.

'Pomeranian?'

'Expensive breed,' said Sadiya. She knelt down and extended a hand. Almost immediately the dog stopped barking and stared at her.

'Come on,' she said, trying to sound unthreatening. 'It's okay.'

The dog waited for a moment or two more, then, ears back, retreated a few steps and stopped again, just out of reach. Keeping her hand extended in front of her Sadiya inched after it and clicked her fingers gently.

The dog yipped and backed away once more, its dark eyes regarding her intently.

'Hungry?' said Findlay behind her.

'Probably.' Sadiya stood up. The dog trotted away down the hall. Sadiya followed it, emerging into a living area containing a table and a sofa and chairs. The walls were clean and white against the black stained floors. Music was playing softly; something classical that Sadiya half-recognised. Bach? Handel? Ahead of her the dog walked into a small kitchen, its claws clacking. Following it, Sadiya found it standing beside a pair of bowls, regarding her expectantly. It barked again, but less angrily this time.

'You check the bedrooms,' she said to Findlay. 'I'll deal with the dog.'

She started with the cupboards above the bench, opening them one by one in search of some food. The kitchen was spotless, except for a wine glass beside the sink. Finally she found a bag of dog food under the sink and shook some into one of the bowls. While the dog bolted the biscuits down she filled its water bowl at the sink and then went back into the living area, where Findlay had just reappeared.

'Any sign of her?' she asked.

'Nothing.'

She indicated the speaker from which the music was emanating. 'Do you think that's for the dog?'

'Possibly,' Findlay said. 'Anything in the kitchen?'

Sadiya pointed at the glass on the sink. 'Looks like she wasn't planning to be away for long.'

'So what now?'

'Hopefully Traffic will get some kind of hit on her car or it will turn up somewhere down in the Floodline. In the meantime we need to put a request in, see if we can locate her phone. And work out her movements around the time Casey went missing.'

'And then?'

Sadiya gazed around at the empty apartment. None of this made any sense. 'We need to talk to Casey's parents again. See if they've ever heard of Nina. And we need to work out where Morrison was.'

'You think there might be some connection between him and Nina?'

Sadiya shrugged. 'It doesn't seem likely, but we need to be sure.'

Findlay nodded, his expression grim. Sadiya knew he was thinking the same thing she was, that with every passing minute their chances of finding Casey alive were receding.

'Come on,' she said. 'Let's get out of here.'

Findlay looked down. 'What about the dog?'

Sadiya knelt down and carefully slipped an arm under its body. To her surprise the dog didn't resist. Standing up she held it to herself, its trembling body surprisingly slight beneath the flowing fur.

'Let's ask the neighbour.'

Out in the hall the girl was hovering by the door.

'Nina wasn't there?' she asked.

'I'm afraid not. You're sure you haven't seen her?'

The girl seemed less vacant, but Sadiya couldn't shake the feeling there was something wrong.

'I didn't get your name,' said Sadiya.

'Jess.'

Sadiya smiled. 'Okay, Jess. We're going to keep looking for Nina, but until we work out where she is somebody needs to look after the dog.'

'I can't. Simon hates dogs.'

'It'll only be for a day or two,' Findlay said. 'Somebody needs to feed him.'

Realising it was being observed the dog tilted its head and fixed the girl with the same look of bright intelligence Sadiya had noticed earlier. Jess held out a hand. For a second or two the dog regarded her warily, then it leaned forward and licked her fingers, its small tongue startlingly pink.

The girl laughed delightedly, her manner suddenly, carelessly childlike.

'I think he likes you,' Findlay said.

Jess let the dog lick her fingers again, then stroked its tiny head. Sadiya placed the dog in her arms. The dog yipped happily.

'You don't mind?' Findlay said.

The girl smiled at the dog, which was gazing up at her as if expecting her to perform some marvel at any moment. 'It's okay,' she said. 'I'll tell Simon we have to mind him.'

'How old do you think she was?' asked Findlay as they went down the stairs towards the car.

'Don't,' said Sadiya.

'I've made a request for the location data on Nina,' Findlay said. 'Hopefully we'll have something soon.'

'And the car?'

'Still nothing. After it was seen heading into the Floodline it wasn't seen again.'

Sadiya leaned back in her seat and sighed. 'So we don't know where either Nina or the car went. What happened? Why didn't she come home? People who have dogs don't usually leave them alone like that. So is she hiding? Or …'

'Or has somebody done something to her?'

Before Sadiya could reply an alert pinged for both of them simultaneously. Findlay opened it first. 'Something's happening down in the Floodline,' he said.

Twenty minutes later they pulled up outside a block of apartments a few streets from the site where Casey was last seen. A crowd of thirty or forty people were shouting and jostling, held back by a group of black-uniformed Border Force officers, their faces blank behind their visors. Two riot vans were parked on the footpath alongside a transport wagon. Sadiya and Findlay shoved their way through the crowd and flashed their ID at one of the officers.

'Who's in charge here?' she demanded.

For a moment Sadiya thought the woman was going to ignore her, but she stepped aside and let them through.

'Over there,' she said, nodding towards one of the vans.

Three more Border Force guards stood alongside the van, looking up at the building.

'What's going on?' Sadiya demanded.

The officers looked around. One of them – a smallish woman, thickset in her body armour – gave Sadiya a dismissive glance. 'I'm afraid that's operational.'

Sadiya clenched her fists, restraining herself. 'We're working on a case in the area. It would be useful to know whether this affects that.'

'It's a standard sweep. We'll let you know if anything comes up.'

On the other side of the cordon a woman was shouting at one of the officers, her finger jabbing angrily as she remonstrated with him.

'You're not here in response to specific information?'

'Can't help you,' the woman said. 'File a request if you need information.'

Findlay intervened. 'We're looking for a missing child,' he said. 'A confrontation here will make it even harder to get help from the local community.'

The officer shrugged. 'Like I said, can't help you.'

Sadiya stepped towards the officer, but Findlay shot her a look. A pair of Border Force officers emerged from the apartment building, escorting two women, one in her twenties or thirties, the other older. Behind them a third officer carried a boy of about three, and led another, slightly older girl by the hand. The women's arms were tied behind their backs, and their heads were down. The officers led the women towards the wagon, and, opening the back, pushed the older of them in. But as the second officer pushed the younger woman in, she twisted around and said something to the officer, her voice low and urgent, her face wild with fear. Sadiya couldn't hear exactly what she was saying or the officer's response over the shouts of the crowd, but a second or two later the woman cried out and lunged towards the officer with the two children.

The officer holding her stumbled forward but recovered quickly, pulling himself upright and yanking the woman back, towards the waiting wagon. But the woman resisted, struggling and shouting, her face red with distress in the heat. The officer attempted to drag her back again, but she lunged forward once more, screaming and crying.

In the third officer's arms the smaller child had started crying as well, his face screwed up in distress. Only the girl was silent, standing staring, her face pale.

Over by the cordon the people in the crowd were shouting furiously at the officers, many of them holding devices aloft or recording: Sadiya knew the scene was already being shared on socials, could imagine the proliferating threads and spreading condemnation. By the cordon there was a shout, and one of the officers recoiled, as if they had been shoved. Overhead a drone descended, collecting video so the protesters could be identified; seeing it, people in the crowd began to point and shout. Over by the van the woman gave one last shout as both officers grabbed her arms and manhandled her into the back of the wagon and slammed the door. A crash came from inside the van, the sound of somebody pummelling the walls, the noise making the younger of the children cry louder. There was a loud crack and glass shattered behind Sadiya. She spun around in time to see a broken bottle lying on the ground behind her and a tall man in loose trousers and shirt launching another at the drone overhead. The machine darted sideways, its motion unsettlingly insectile, and the bottle smashed to the ground and exploded, scattering dark brown glass across the asphalt. The drone dove downwards and then stopped, hovering above the crowd. A moment later two of the officers holding the crowd back lunged forward, nightsticks raised; the system had identified whoever had thrown the bottle, and was now tracking them. At first the crowd parted before them, perhaps wary of being struck, but then a woman stepped in front of one of them, her hand upraised and pointing angrily at the officers, her face contorted as she shouted something Sadiya couldn't make out. The officer lifted an arm and swept it sideways, catching the woman in the neck and sending her crashing to the ground.

There was a shout, and several people surged forward, but the officer who struck the woman raised his stick and lunged towards them, and they backed away. Two more officers dove in behind them and rolled the fallen woman onto her front, one of them kneeling on her back as they cuffed her hands behind her back. The second officer lunged forward and grabbed a slight man in a loose t-shirt and threw him to the ground. He landed hard, and another cry went up, but the officer was already on top of him, his knee on his back, while the first officer advanced on the rest of the crowd, his stick swinging in front of him.

'Let's get out of here,' Sadiya said, her voice shaking with anger, and stalked back towards the car.

'Fuck!' she said once they were back in the car. 'Why weren't we warned about this? Between yesterday and this nobody down here is going to trust us.'

'We could talk to Nguyen,' said Findlay.

'It's too late for that,' said Sadiya. 'The damage is done. Let's just get over to Jay and Emma's and talk to them about Nina.'

Jay was waiting at the door when they arrived, his face flushed in the heat.

'What's going on over in Bay Street?' he demanded. 'Have you found something?'

'It's a Border Force operation,' said Sadiya. 'It's got nothing to do with us.'

'Shouldn't you be working with them? What if somebody there has something to do with Casey going missing?'

'Is there somewhere you think we should be looking?' asked Findlay sharply.

Jay glared at him with barely concealed contempt. 'All I know is that you seem to be able to muster two trucks of officers to arrest some women and a couple of kids, but when it comes to looking for Casey you've done jack shit.'

'Please, Jay,' said Emma.

Jay shot her a look, the muscles in his forearm tensing.

'I'm sorry you think that,' said Sadiya before he could say anything. 'I promise you we're doing our best.'

'And what does that mean?' demanded Jay, turning his back to her 'Are you even investigating displaced people or illegals? Or are they out of bounds?'

'We'll look at anybody,' said Sadiya. 'All we care about is finding Casey.'

'It certainly doesn't look that way.'

'I promise we're doing everything we can,' said Sadiya.

Emma stepped up behind him and placed a hand on his arm. Jay flinched, and for a split second Sadiya was afraid the violence she had seen in him might suddenly be released. But then he seemed to falter. Lifting a hand, he ran it across his close-cropped scalp and exhaled, his breath coming raggedly. Sadiya watched him carefully. He was the kind of man who couldn't set aside his sense of entitlement, or recognise shared suffering. But she also knew how often people used anger to keep going, the way its release left them at the mercy of whatever it was that frightened them the most.

'You said you wanted to talk to us,' Emma said. 'Have you found something?'

'We've identified a vehicle we believe was in the area when Casey went missing. We wondered whether you know the woman who owns it, Nina Lukic?'

'No,' said Emma. 'Who is she? Do you think she had something to do with Casey going missing?'

Sadiya kept her eyes on Jay. 'We're just eliminating possibilities. Mr Markley, do you know her?'

'No.'

'Are you sure?'

'Of course. Why would I lie to you?'

'I don't know. That's what worries me.'

She waited to see if he would fill the silence. He didn't. 'Just find her,' he said.

Back at the car Sadiya climbed in and slammed her door.

'That went about as well as I thought it would.'

'He's not an easy guy to like.'

'No argument there.' She sat up. 'He's right, though.'

'About what?'

'We've got nothing. It makes no sense. Nina has no connection to them, no connection to people they know. Why would she have taken Casey?'

'People take kids for all kinds of reasons. Perhaps she knows the ex?'

'I ran the ex through the predictives. He's still up north, and there's no sign he's been in contact with Emma for years.'

'What about Nina? Is there any connection between him and her?'

'Not that I've seen.'

Findlay stared out through the windshield. 'But she's involved somehow. She has to be. Why else would she be missing?'

'Somebody could have done something to her and taken her car.'

'But who?'

'I don't know. And if something happened to her, was it before or after Casey went missing?'

They were both silent for a moment.

'If Jay is so worried why isn't he helping?' Findlay said. 'Why make us fight for everything?'

'Because he's got something going on the side that he doesn't want us to know about? Because it makes him feel powerful. Because he's a right-wing arsehole who thinks cops go easy on illegals. Especially cops who look like me. Maybe all of the above.' She shook her head disgustedly. 'Who the fuck knows.'

Findlay sighed. 'So, what do we do?'

'What can we do? Keep trying to find Nina. Keep searching for other possibilities. And we need to look at Morrison again.'

'Could he be connected to Nina somehow?'

'It's possible.'

'We need to find this person he says he was visiting.'

'If they exist.'

'Until we find them, we should assume he's lying. Have we put in a request to see whether he was on the train when he says he was?'

'Novak is on it. But even if he was on the train as claimed, that doesn't mean he didn't do something to her. He would have had time. He could have hidden the body and got to the station.'

'Do you really think that?'

Sadiya looked out the window. 'I don't know what to think.'

Back at the station Sadiya stopped just inside the entrance. 'You go ahead,' she said. 'I have to talk to Nguyen.'

Nguyen was in her office. She looked up when Sadiya knocked and motioned her in. Sadiya closed the door behind her.

'Who authorised the Border Force operation today?' she said, trying to keep her voice from shaking with anger.

'I'm sorry,' said Nguyen. 'I've only just found out about it myself. We informed them about our inquiry but they seem to have ignored that.'

Sadiya stared at her. She couldn't think of any reason for Nguyen to lie. Finally she nodded. Nguyen pointed to one of her chairs. Sadiya sat down.

'You should have told me about the Horizon connection. As it was, I got a call from the assistant commissioner demanding to know what you thought you were doing. Apparently Horizon's security system flagged you as soon as you turned up at the building.'

Sadiya didn't reply.

'Explain again why you were there.'

'We've identified a car that was parked outside the premises where Casey went missing. The owner is a woman called Nina Lukic who works for Horizon. She's been missing since Sunday as well.'

'Do you think she might have Casey?'

Sadiya paused. 'I suppose it's possible. But we don't have any evidence of a connection between her and Casey or Casey's parents, and no indication of a motive.'

'Any priors? Or history of mental illness?' asked Nguyen.

'Not that we know of.'

'What about this sex offender? Morrison?'

'He's hiding something, but we haven't managed to place him at the scene.'

'And the stepfather?'

'We're not getting the full story there, either.'

'How are things between him and the mother? Is there any sign of tension, or that she suspects him?'

'I think she's frightened of him, but she says he wouldn't hurt Casey.'

'And you believe her?'

'I believe she doesn't suspect him. But that doesn't mean he had nothing to do with it.'

Nguyen took a breath. 'Okay. I don't have to tell you how important it is you keep pushing. We have to find her.'

'We need more resources. I've got a couple of uniforms looking for the car down in the Floodline but it's not enough.'

'I appreciate you want more people but we haven't got anyone to spare. Everybody we have has already been assigned to get things ready for the storm.'

'We've got a missing kid.'

'I know that. But we have a whole city to protect.'

Sadiya stood to leave, but Nguyen motioned to her to stay.

'I've watched the footage from yesterday. I can't see any grounds for Behrens' complaint.'

Sadiya let out a breath. 'Thank you.'

'But that doesn't mean it's over. You can't keep giving them ammunition they can use against you.'

Sadiya stared back at her impassively. 'Yes, ma'am,' she said.

People watched her pass without speaking as she left Nguyen's office. Sadiya ignored them and walked quickly towards the stairwell. Closing the door behind her she leaned back against the wall, pressing her head and shoulders into the cool concrete. Then with quick, savage motion she slammed the back of her arm into the wall and cursed, first once, and then again and then again.

Back in the situation room Khoury and Gunasekera were at work on their screens, while Findlay was standing with Novak. They looked up as she entered. Perhaps Findlay saw something in her expression because he left Novak and walked towards her.

'Okay,' she said, trying to keep her voice level. 'Where are we?'

Khoury cleared her throat. 'We've still got two uniforms down in the Floodline looking for Nina's car. And there are drones up as well.'

'And the stepfather? Did anything turn up in Casey's medical records?'

'Nothing out of the ordinary.'

'What about the interview with Child Protection? Anything there?'

Khoury shook her head. 'I watched the entire interview. Amira eventually told us that the two of them had an argument and that's why Casey went off on her own. Child Protection didn't think there was anything there to be suspicious about.'

'And you? You believed her?'

'I did,' said Khoury.

Sadiya nodded. 'How about Morrison and Lukic? Do we have anything on them?'

'I've requested location data for Lukic,' said Novak. 'We also have a positive hit on Morrison at Redfern at 9.35 on Sunday night.'

'Alone?'

'As far as I could tell.'

Sadiya and Findlay exchanged a glance. 'So we know he left the area when he says he did,' said Sadiya. 'But not what he was doing before that.'

'I've also examined the logs for the screen you recovered from Casey's bedroom,' said Novak. 'There doesn't seem to be any sign she's been communicating with anybody online.'

'I suppose that's something. While we wait for more location data I want to go back to basics and look at what we have again. Casey went missing at about eight pm on Sunday night. Her parents both have alibis, and nobody seems to have seen anybody going into or leaving the site where she went missing. What we do have is a report that places a silver car outside the crime scene at the time she disappeared, which we've identified as belonging to Nina Lukic. Lukic is an employee of Horizon, which owns the site, but she's also missing. There doesn't seem to be any connection between Nina and Casey or Casey's parents. Meanwhile we have David Morrison, a convicted paedophile, who was nearby at the time in question, and can't account for his movements. What is it we're missing?'

'It sounds like Lukic is the key,' said Gunasekera, then caught himself, as if suddenly uncertain of his right to speak. He glanced around, then added, more tentatively, 'We should concentrate on finding her.'

'Agreed,' said Sadiya. 'She hasn't been at work for the past two days, but she must have relatives, friends, workmates. One of them may know something. Get the system to work through her socials and any online accounts we can access, see whether we can track down anybody who knows her.'

'What about Morrison?' said Khoury, her voice flat and hard.

'We need to liaise with Sex Crimes, see whether they have anything on him,' said Sadiya. 'And again, we need to pin down his movements.

Once we've done that we can apply pressure to his story, find out what he was doing down there.'

'And Jay? Is there any way we can confirm his alibi?'

'I've spoken to the hotel. They don't have CCTV so we still only have his mate Laurent's say-so that they were there at the time she went missing.'

'All right. We need to get somebody over there, see whether any of the staff remember him.' She stopped, aware Gunasekera was staring at her.

'What is it?'

'Do you think it was Morrison?'

Sadiya looked at him. 'Let's hope not,' she said.

It was almost nine before Sadiya got home. Along Victoria Road traffic was being redirected, although whether due to preparations for the storm or for some other reason wasn't clear, which meant she had to find her way down back streets. Malila was on a call when she opened the door; Sadiya had time to hear the younger woman hiss something, her voice low and tense before she hung up and turned towards her.

'Everything okay?' Sadiya asked.

'Fine,' Malila said, although she seemed agitated.

Sadiya waited for her to volunteer something more. When she didn't, she said, 'I'm sorry I'm so late. How is he?'

'Okay. Watching his screen.'

'You didn't have any more problems?'

'No. He's been good. Quiet.'

'Has he eaten?'

Malila shrugged. 'Not really. I offered him some dinner earlier but he didn't seem to want it.'

'That's not unusual.' She paused. 'Tomorrow is okay?'

For a moment Sadiya thought Malila was going to say she couldn't come. But then she smiled, and for a brief moment Sadiya saw the girl she used to know. Where do those other versions of ourselves go, she wondered, especially when we reject them or ignore them. We cannot go back yet they linger, a reminder of who we might have been.

'I'm sorry about today,' she said. 'It shouldn't have happened, but it meant a lot that you didn't freak out.' She hesitated. 'This case, it's ...' She shook her head.

Malila checked her phone. 'I have to go. It's late.'

Sadiya watched her thoughtfully. 'You know you can talk to me?' she said. 'If you're ever in trouble or you need help?'

Malila smiled unconvincingly. 'Thanks,' she said. At the door she paused. For a moment Sadiya thought she was about to say something, but then she seemed to think better of it.

'See you tomorrow,' she said.

Sadiya waited for the sound of the lift in the hall outside, then she went through to Arman's room and knocked on the door. He looked up as she entered, then back at his screen. She noted the smell from earlier still lingered, a reminder she needed to wash his clothes.

She sat down on the bed facing him. 'Are you hungry?'

He regarded her over his screen, his face angry, suspicious.

'Baba? It's just me, Sadiya.'

'You were here before,' he said.

She leaned back, trying to ignore the sense of hopelessness. 'That's right. I was.' When he didn't reply she forced herself to smile. 'I'll grab some food,' she said.

By the door she stopped and looked back. He was looking at his screen again. Perhaps feeling her eyes on him he glanced up, and she saw a look of confusion pass over his face before he returned to whatever he was watching.

She cooked quickly, throwing together dhal and rice that she took through to him in his room, and then ate hers alone in the kitchen. When she was done she took his clothes out of the washing machine and hung them on the rack to dry, before going back through to the kitchen and packing the dishwasher. Although the air in the apartment was cool she could feel the heat pressing on the glass of the window, its weight a reminder of the fragility of the barriers that kept the world's violence at bay. Finally she sat down at the table and opened her files, intending to review the day's progress. She began by reading through the forensics report again, looking for anything she might have missed, then moved on to the other documents. None of it made sense. There was no sign of a body, either on the land or in the water; Casey hadn't been picked up on facial rec, they had no real suspects, and the one person who seemed to have been nearby appeared to have no connection to Casey but had disappeared all the same. In frustration Sadiya closed the files and opened her socials. They were full of chatter about Nasreen, the heat, the protests overseas, but there was no sign of anything that might point to Casey or her whereabouts.

She took a beer from the fridge and, opening the door to the balcony, stepped out into the heat. The air smelt swampy, estuarine, salt mingling with the stink of mangroves: in the wetlands on the far side of the highway the tide must have been high. Almost without thinking she called up the temperature in her lenses and saw it was still more than 35 degrees. Beneath the temperature she saw the forecast for the next few days, the unbroken line of temperatures in the mid to high forties. She closed her eyes, trying not to think about what that meant if Casey was alive somewhere without air conditioning. In her first year as a constable she had attended a welfare check in one of the tent cities out west. It was December, the heat already extreme. After asking for directions they found their way to a container, its front locked tight. They had pounded on the front without response, then cut the lock. Even as the door swung open the smell told her what they were going to find, but it turned out to be even worse than she had imagined. Inside it was impossibly hot, and by the door lay three bodies, the largest a girl, perhaps eight or nine, hair cropped close to her skull, the next a boy, half that. And between them the naked form of a baby.

Her partner at that welfare check was an older woman with a few years' experience. She had turned away, unable to look; Sadiya still remembered the noise she made, not a cry, more a sort of choking sigh. Only that morning she had been showing Sadiya pictures of her sister's children. Sadiya didn't look away. Instead she knelt down, trying to take in their thin forms. She had an idea she needed to catalogue this, to remember them so they wouldn't be forgotten. Turning the girl's hands over she saw they were bruised and torn, as if they had been beating and scratching on the door. She looked at the door. Somebody must have heard them. How had they not stopped, tried to help?

When she stood up she was shaking with fury. She wanted to grab one of the people standing outside, push their face down so they had to look at what had happened. Perhaps they understood, because when she emerged nobody would meet her eyes. Later they would learn the mother was an illegal who had been picked up in a raid. It was her habit to leave the kids locked in while she was at work at night. She had been screaming and pounding on the door in one of the detention facilities, but nobody had bothered to turn on a translator to work out what was wrong. Sadiya never found out what happened to her. No doubt she was transferred away to one of the camps. But for weeks after, Sadiya had wondered about her. How could anybody survive loss like that? Especially knowing they could have been saved?

Not long afterwards the officer she had been with that day quit. At the time Sadiya wondered whether it was at least partly about what they had found, but a few months later she heard she had joined Border Force and was working to detain illegals. Sadiya had been shocked. What did she tell herself she was doing? Did she ever remember those children? Did she think she was helping?

She took another sip of her beer and gazed out at the balconies of the building opposite, the purple sky above. The heat and the smell of the salt were a reminder that she had once had another life, a different life, one that was both far away and right there. She knew that if she closed her eyes she would be back there, back in that small space where she slept after they left the camp.

The day they were released Arman told her they were going to talk to a man from home who would help them find a place to live. In the street outside the facility they had found a bus, bargained their way on; as it passed through the streets she had stared through the glass at the unfamiliar city. After a year in detention she had thought she should be happy to be free, but now they were out she found she was afraid of the strangeness of it all.

The address Arman had turned out to be a block of flats a street or two back from the tideline. At some point the water had come through, staining the walls and killing the grass. Beside the road ruined cars sat on bricks, their bodies stripped or converted into sleeping quarters; along the footpath dead trees stood like ghosts, their limbs twisted and pale. Three men were sitting on the doorstep, squatting on their heels as if on a Dhaka street. Sadiya thought at first that her father might speak to them but instead he ignored them, drawing her after him towards the intercom. While he pressed the button she turned. One of them was looking at her. He was small, skinny, his black hair loose above a sharp-boned face and improbable moustache, and he wore a loose shirt and pants. He didn't smile, just sat, watching her. He had a toothpick in one corner of his mouth; with a practised motion of his lips he shifted it to the other side. Behind her she heard a click, and her father pulled her after him, into the building.

The man from home found them a place nearby, in a house that had been converted into a dozen tiny rooms. Twenty people, sometimes more, all sharing one kitchen and two toilets. At night the sounds of voices, music, other, lower sounds came through the walls; sometimes she would meet Arman's eyes but he would only look away.

The room cost $300 a week, but Arman's visa meant he couldn't work. And so he took illegal jobs with the man who had found the room for them, working to convert more houses. Arman knew how to use tools – his father had made sure of that – but this wasn't skilled work. Most days he worked with a Gujarati called Pandit. Even as a child Sadiya had understood that Pandit hated her father, perhaps because he saw something weak in him, perhaps for some other reason she had been too young to understand, and so went out of his way to torment the older man, insulting him in front of the others, giving him jobs he knew were beneath Arman.

On the days Arman worked Sadiya was left with Rumeen, a woman who rented two rooms in the same building, another Bangladeshi with three children of her own. Like the place Arman and Sadiya rented, Rumeen's rooms were small and dark. One was given over to sleeping, an old mattress on the floor for the three children, another for Rumeen and her absent husband beside it. On the nights the husband was away the youngest of the children slept with their mother.

Although there was a yard behind the house Rumeen didn't allow Sadiya or her children outside. Instead she kept the door closed and the windows covered with pieces of old fabric. Trapped in the claustrophobic space the three children and Sadiya lay on their mattress or sat slumped at the small table and stared at a screen, or chased each other around the room. The oldest boy was ten, a wiry, angry boy with a high forehead and very dark, almost black eyes. When he grew bored he would torment his younger brother until the other boy threw himself at him: Sadiya learned to stay out of his way.

What Arman thought of Rumeen wasn't clear to Sadiya. When he collected her in the evening his exchanges with her were usually limited to a few polite words and a handover of cash. Back in their room afterwards Arman would be exhausted while Sadiya would be wired, agitated from being cooped up and hours staring at games and videos. Oftentimes she would lie in the cave-like space with her feet on the walls, staring at the blue light of the screen while he slept, his snores soft and intimate. In those moments she thought about her mother and Lina, their absence, the ache of it. Part of her knew Arman wouldn't talk about them because he didn't know how, but lying in that room she hated him for it.

It wasn't long before she realised this was worse than the camp. At least there she had freedom to walk around and go outside; now she spent her days locked up indoors. But then, one morning, Arman knocked on Rumeen's door, and there was no answer. Sadiya stood watching as he hammered, shouting, until finally a door opened a little way down the corridor and a man leaned out.

'They're gone,' he said.

'What do you mean? I saw her yesterday,' said Arman.

The man shrugged. 'All I know is they left last night.'

For a long time Arman didn't move. Often when she was with him Sadiya could almost feel the weight that sat on him. Up the hall the man grunted. Arman continued to stare at where he had been standing. Finally, he turned the handle on Rumeen's door, and it swung open. The table and chairs and the mattresses remained, but everything else was gone, the only sign the rooms had been inhabited just the day before a pile of empty cartons and bottles on the sink, a few pieces of paper scattered on the floor.

'Where are they?' she asked.

Arman just shook his head. 'Does it matter?'

In the hall a door opened, and a moment later the man who had spoken to them appeared in the doorway behind them. He was overweight, his belly straining against his stained white singlet.

'What do you want her for?'

'My daughter. Rumeen minds her while I work.'

The man kept his eyes fixed on Arman. 'If you leave her here I can keep an eye on her.'

There was a long silence. Sadiya moved closer to Arman, and he took her hand. 'No need,' he said, his voice loud in the small space. 'She can come with me.'

When the van pulled up Arman took her hand and opened the door. The other men stared at the two of them.

'We do childcare now, do we?' said the driver.

The others laughed, but Arman ignored them. 'She can stay in the car,' he said, lifting her in.

'Pandit won't like it,' said the driver as Arman closed the door, but Arman didn't reply.

Next to her the smaller of the men smiled at her. Sadiya smiled back.

It was almost midday before Pandit turned up. They were working in the Floodline, stripping an apartment block. Sadiya was playing in a corridor, a game that involved skipping several times and then stopping dead without falling over, and she turned around to find a man with a beard standing behind her. She didn't know how long he'd been there, and although he was smiling, she didn't think it was a smile for her.

'Who's this?' he asked.

Sadiya didn't reply, just stood, staring back. Pandit glanced past her, and although the smile didn't leave his face she saw something cruel in him. Turning, she saw her father had appeared in one of the doors behind her.

'Is this lovely little lady yours, Arman? Who'd have thought you would have produced such a beauty.'

Sensing Arman's concern Sadiya backed away and pressed herself against the wall. Pandit gave a soft snort, and stepped past her, his false bonhomie still in place.

Sadiya didn't follow, just stood silently as Pandit followed her father into the apartment he had been working in.

'Is this all you've done?' Pandit demanded. 'You seem to work slower every day. Who knows why I pay you at all. And now you bring children with you? What do you think this is? A kindergarten? Perhaps I should get her to do your job – she'd probably do it faster.'

Sadiya's face burned listening to him, and her father's mumbled response. Why did he let this man speak to him in this way? Closing her eyes she wished she was somewhere else. When Pandit emerged he was still smiling.

'What do you think, little girl?' he asked, standing in front of her, his powerful body heavy with some kind of cologne. 'You could do your *pitā*'s job for him?'

She clenched her fists. Pandit laughed and, turning away, disappeared down the corridor.

When Arman emerged again he didn't look at her, just told her to go into one of the rooms and sit down, out of the way. As she went, she caught one of the other men watching her, his face hard. Arman didn't take her back to work after that. Instead he left her in their room, with instructions not to leave.

A week later, he told her she was starting school. There was already resistance to the idea the displaced should have access to public services, but the notion children should be refused education hadn't yet taken root. The school was a kilometre or so from their home, and on the first day Arman walked her through the empty streets to drop her off. Outside the gate parents were kissing their children goodbye and talking and laughing amongst themselves. Arman led her through the knot of people to the entrance; Sadiya remembered the way he moved, his thin body rigid, his chin held high, as if to repel all contact. By the gate he touched the back of her head and motioned her in, but he didn't bend to speak to her or embrace her. Once she was inside Sadiya looked back; he was still standing, his arms at his side. Catching her eye he didn't smile, but motioned with his head for her to keep going. When she looked again, he was gone.

The first weeks at school were confusing and difficult. Although her English was good, her time in the camp meant her reading and writing were well behind where they should be, and she struggled to adjust to the school environment. And while there were others who were worse off than her, it was difficult not to feel isolated. One recess, in the covered area that served as the playground, she found herself facing off against three boys for some slight – the three of them had been calling her names and whispering insults for days – and as they went spilling to the ground, Sadiya spitting and biting and tearing at their hair, she felt a sort of satisfaction, not just at hurting them, but at them feeling her hurt them. She had just got her arm around the neck of the biggest when she was grabbed by the shirt and pulled up by one of the teachers.

In the office afterwards she sat in silence, while the principal spoke to Arman. He had come when called, arriving just after lunch. Sadiya knew without asking he had lost the day's pay. The principal was blond, and dressed in a black blouse and skirt. Sadiya listened while she explained that she understood Sadiya had experienced difficulties, but violence in the schoolyard wasn't acceptable under any circumstances. When she was done, she asked Arman if he had any questions. There was a long silence, and then Arman said, in his careful, thickly accented English. 'There were three of them. All boys?'

The principal nodded.

'And how does this happen, in your school? Three boys attacking a girl?'

'As I've just explained, Mr Azad, they didn't attack her. All of them agree it was Sadiya who started the fight.'

'Did you ask her why?'

Sadiya looked at her father in surprise, startled to hear the anger in his voice.

The principal leaned back in her chair, her practised businesslike manner replaced by a bland dislike. 'We don't tolerate violence in this school,' she said.

But if Sadiya had thought her father's words in the principal's office were an indication he would be understanding or sympathetic afterwards, she was wrong. When she got home that evening he was coldly furious with her, barely speaking to her.

The three boys she had fought with still whispered amongst themselves when she was nearby, but they steered clear of Sadiya after that. And, although she still felt awkward, out of place, somehow in the weeks after the fight she found school less difficult. No doubt at the principal's suggestion she was moved to a different table, where she sat with some other girls, several of whom were also displaced. With her skinny, angry body and hard stare, Sadiya wasn't really one of them, but they allowed her to sit with them, and in time she became one of their group. She also began to work at her lessons, finding refuge in the clarity of the tasks.

After school she walked home, navigating the streets alone. The anger that would coalesce in the years that were to come was already brewing, expressing itself in running battles between the police and environmentalists and the anti-immigrationists. Several times she saw people dragged out of cars or onto the streets by police; many more times she saw acts of violence against immigrants and the displaced. But for the most part she enjoyed that time alone, the freedom it gave her, so different to the long evenings in the room with Arman, the joyless meals cooked on their single-ring burner.

Yet as much as she resented her father, he didn't completely abandon her. In the evenings he sat with her while she did her homework, drilling her on her maths, insisting she always be better than her peers in tests. And while these sessions didn't bring them closer together, as the months passed she found herself moving through her sums and schoolwork with increasing ease. Yet if he was proud of her, he never showed it, never let her feel it.

Lifting the bottle to her lips she drained the last of her beer. Would she have been different if he had been a different father? Would that have made a difference to everything that came afterwards? In the distance there was a shout, the staccato blare of a siren. She listened for a moment, then stood up and went back inside, sealing the door again against the evening heat.

*

Arman woke to the sound of a door somewhere nearby. Darkness, the distant hum of air conditioning, a room he didn't know but should. Outside a helicopter could be heard, the heavy thrum of its rotors like some malevolent insect. He remembered the same sound waking him once, long ago, the oppressive heat and a child crying. Somewhere he needed to be, something to do with the helicopters, but what?

When he was a boy, he loved watching planes. Not just the passenger jets as they soared high overhead, their great fuselages pale against the blue sky, the idea of all those bodies so far away, up there, incredible to him, but also the fighter jets that occasionally broke the morning silence to slice the sky in ones and twos. Much later he would fly in one himself; as it took off, he closed his eyes, felt the tiny lurch as the wheels lifted free of the tarmac, and knew he was in the air. Next to him Sadiya gripped his hand, her small body damp-smelling, salt. Or was that another flight, another year?

He closed his eyes, tried to steady himself. The problem wasn't the forgetting, it was the remembering. All the things once buried that came flooding back, more vivid than the experience itself; the inability to tell what was real, what was imagined. The smell of salt a reminder as well, but of what? In the hot dark the room seemed to float, suspended. When he was a boy the salt smell was everywhere, filling the air, a soft weight. In the grey warm of the mornings, when the line dividing the sky and water was almost invisible, he would walk along the beach, his feet sinking into the fine, grey sand, the smell of sulphur at the back of the throat. People sometimes talked about the dawn being silent, but it was never that. If you listened you could hear the world waking up, the cries of the birds mingling with the soft lap of the waves, the heavy plop of a fish as it flung itself from the water, even the soft skitter of the crabs on the boundary of the forest, each a reminder of the way all of this connected, the degree to which it was bound together, one vast, living whole. Behind him in the village someone was singing, farther off the call to prayer echoed over the water. Out on the grey sea a boat creased the surface, its engine puttering.

All of it gone.

If he had had his way he would never have left, would never have moved away. But his father insisted he had to go to school.

'I was a fisherman's son,' he said. 'I won't see my son be a fisherman.'

How was it his father's voice was so clear, but his face had faded?

And so that time by the water wasn't to last. Instead, he was sent to the school in the town, walking the half a kilometre to the main road to catch the bus. He loved the clarity of the work, the way it felt like he was turning a key in a lock to reveal something. While the other children struggled and dreamed the day away, Arman found himself able to see the shape of what they were doing, like light.

His teachers saw it as well, focusing their attention on him, pushing him to succeed. When the time came for him to go to secondary school, they arranged for him to attend the better school in the next town along. The boys there knew he was a village child, tormenting him with jokes about the smell of mud, the stink of fish. In the evenings, as he walked home, he wished he didn't have to go back, that he could stay in the village, by the water, but it wasn't to be. And so he gave himself over to the work, the precision of the mathematics, the elegance of pi and sines and cosines, the intricate puzzles of partial differential equations and working in the evenings at his family's table, the smell of the lamp hissing beside him, the soft lapping of the water just outside, in the dark.

The work left little time for other things, and certainly not for fishing or playing with the other boys. And so just as his origins made him an outsider at school, his new life at the school isolated him in the village.

When he was seventeen, he sat the exams, working his way through the questions with the brutal efficiency that had become his trademark. And once the results came, he won a place at Khulna, where he had applied to study engineering.

The years at Khulna were long and lonely, at least at first. The other students weren't like him; they came from good homes and wanted to work in industrial design or build computers. But Arman knew what he wanted to do. The millennium had just passed, and although the world was convulsed with the Americans' plans to invade Iraq, Arman had read enough of the science to know the water was coming, so he wanted to build levees and bridges, to find ways of managing the rising sea. And although he might not have admitted it to his friends, he wanted to go back to the shore, to be there, where he had grown up.

His first assignment was with a firm in Chattogram. His boss was a man called Rajib. As they worked to develop systems to move the water, Rajib rarely smiled, but he wasn't cruel or unpleasant either. Quite the reverse, in fact: although he could be startlingly direct, he was careful and thoughtful, and often took time to praise Arman's designs.

'This is excellent work,' he would say, before offering some improvement or correction. Only after they had been working together for a few months did Arman finally understand the source of his dourness, which lay in a belief that what they were doing was largely pointless, that what was here would be swept away, regardless.

'There is so much talk. But none of it means anything. Water flows downhill, it fills from the bottom, and we are the lowest, both in sea level and in regard. The Americans, the British, the French, they will not care until the water is lapping at their own doorstep, and by then we will be underwater.'

Arman harboured similar thoughts. But still, he argued. 'You do not think they will realise? Surely they will not let us drown?'

Rajib looked at him, a bitter smile on his face. 'Let me tell you a rule for this life, Arman. Never bet against water; it will always win.'

Arman met Leah a year later. He was out in the field, directing some of the labourers, when one of the team leaders appeared, a young woman in tow. She was slim, her dark hair tied back modestly, but when the team leader stopped in front of him and introduced her, she met his eye with a directness he found discomfiting and liberating in equal parts.

'She's joining us as an intern,' the team leader said.

Arman looked down. 'I hope that will be rewarding,' he said.

'I do as well,' said Leah. But when Arman looked up, she was smiling.

Why did he remember her smile, but not the last time they spoke, or the names of her parents? They were married, he knew that, but whatever was there was gone, washed away.

Over the next few weeks he found himself showing her around, offering her advice and directing her. She wasn't what he had expected – although in truth what he had expected had been simplistic and unfair. Most of the tourists he encountered were loud and careless, their faces and bodies communicating their discomfort with the world they were moving through – his world – their tendency to recoil from beggars or children. By contrast Leah was attentive, observant, her manner relaxed but not careless or disrespectful. Whether with Arman or the women she paid attention to what was being said, to the person who was speaking. Yet despite her manner there was also a reserve to her, a sense she was holding something back.

Then one evening, as he walked her back to her apartment, she had explained. As he already knew, she had spent time in Indonesia and Bangladesh as a child, courtesy of her father's work with the World Bank. They had been happy years, she said, and she had been sorry when her parents had returned to Sydney for her final years of school. She did well, winning a scholarship to university in Canberra, access to a coveted college. But at the end of her first term her parents decided to visit. The plan was they would drive down after work on Friday night. At ten they hadn't arrived, and she had called them, listened to her mother's phone ring out.

'I knew then,' she said. 'It makes no sense, but it was like I'd always known.' When the police called, a few hours later, she listened and then put the phone down without speaking.

Because she was in a new city, with few friends and no family, she chose not to tell anybody, not even the people she knew in her college. Instead she went to Sydney for the holidays, did what she could to pack up their lives, and then returned to Canberra, where she withdrew into herself, sitting at the back in lectures, barely speaking in classes, studying late in the library and her room. By year's end she had made a cocoon capable of protecting herself.

When she finished her story she looked at him and smiled, the sadness behind her gentle exterior now plain.

'I'm sorry,' she said. 'It seemed only fair you know.'

Later, once they were married, he would return to this conversation, wondering whether it held a clue to her detachment. It wasn't that he didn't believe that she loved him, rather that despite her openness he often felt there was something buffed away in her, as if her equilibrium came at the cost of some larger emotional amplitude.

There were other problems as well. His parents in particular didn't understand his decision. Although Leah did her best to ease relations with them, their visits were always prickly, guarded affairs, often marred by his father's stiff silence and disapproval of what he saw as the moral failings of their life together.

It was easier with people their own age. Leah was always friendly with their neighbours, and they with her, but the relationships rarely ran deep. And while the few friends Arman had liked Leah, there was always a sense their relationship separated him from them in some way, a barrier across which they seemed unable to communicate.

As a result the two of them spent most of their time together alone, and when they did socialise it was mostly with other members of the international community. Arman never enjoyed these events, the constant discussion of local manners and society, the assumption of superiority contained in the judgements and observations. And while the men would often make a point of speaking to him, addressing him directly and asking him his opinions, as the evenings progressed they always drifted away from him, falling into clubby groups, and leaving him alone, an outsider.

Did Leah see any of this? If she did, she never said. And because he was ashamed and angry, Arman never told her. And so they lived quietly, spending most of their time working or together.

When Leah became pregnant with Lina, Arman thought it might be a turning point, that a child would change their lives together. And for a time she did. When Lina was born he was startled by the suddenness of his love for her, the way she brought the three of them together. Although he couldn't have explained why, Lina seemed to change something in Leah, making her more open, more complete. And while whatever it was that had begun to reform within her was focused on Lina, it also affected her relationship with him, making her seem more present, more alive.

Two years later, when Leah fell pregnant again, he was frightened at first, worried the new child would disturb this new equilibrium. But she was so happy, so certain that a second child was the right choice that he did his best to put his concerns aside. The first birth had been relatively easy, but when Leah went into labour for the second time the baby would not turn, and when it finally arrived, Leah began to bleed and had to be taken into surgery.

Arman waited for her in the delivery suite, his newborn child in his arms, with no idea where Leah was or whether she was going to be all right. When she was finally wheeled back in and he handed her the baby he started shaking when he saw how pale she was and he realised how close he had come to losing her.

But if he had thought it was over he was mistaken. Once they returned home, Leah was different. Not just physically weaker but drained somehow, diminished, as if she had shrunk. At first Arman thought it would get better in a week or two, but it didn't; indeed, if anything, it got worse. Some days he would return home and find she hadn't left the house all day, hadn't even dressed, and as the weeks passed he became worried about leaving her alone, cutting his days short to return home as soon as possible.

In the evenings he would take Lina out, watch her play in the small garden outside their building, delighting in her beauty and alertness. But it wasn't the same with the baby, who they had named Sadiya, the name chosen by Leah despite his misgivings. In his mind she was always crying and fretting, her wakefulness hollowing Leah out even further. Sometimes he would catch Leah holding her as if this angry, blotchy scrap of a child was the only thing keeping her here, her eyes watching Arman as if he were a stranger – or worse, a threat. And when he looked inside himself he could find no love for the child, only blankness.

*

Tasim could still see the girl's face in his mind when he stumbled into the dark space beside an apartment building two blocks away. He slumped against the wall, his breath coming hot and ragged, and listened for sounds of pursuit. He heard music and a siren in the distance, but otherwise the street was quiet. Still panting, he cursed himself for fleeing without his bag. It had everything in it: his few documents, his clothes, his pens, his drawings – he started frantically checking his pockets back and front first once and then again – his phone. He subsided against the wall. He had lost everything. How could he have been so stupid? In the street a car swung past, and he shrank back, pressing himself further into the darkness, but it didn't stop. Who was that man? Why did he have the girl? Had he seen Tasim's face? At this he gasped. The man had his ID! What if he used it to come after him?

Standing up, he lurched back towards the street. He knew he had to get away, to lose himself. In the distance he could see the neon towers of the city centre rising in the lilac-bruised sky; not knowing where else to head he went towards them. After perhaps half an hour he stopped in a small park and sat down. He felt naked without his bag, keenly aware he had no money, no food, not even the blanket he had picked up all those months ago. But it wasn't them he missed most. It was the phone, the photos. Without them his mother and his sister Dewi were truly gone, as was everybody from his old life. It was sometimes difficult to convince himself that world – his school, his neighbours, his friends – had ever existed. Closing his eyes, he tried to remember the shop on the corner, the huge tree above it, the monkeys who lived there until the heat killed them all. He could see the colours – the grey of the concrete and the hazy air, the green of the tree – but the rest was elusive.

A sound interrupted him. Opening his eyes, he saw a pair of men in the darkness nearby. He stood up and began to walk again. Somewhere in the distance sirens were audible.

Dawn was already approaching when he finally stopped. It was hot, the sweat running down the back of his neck. He followed a lane into a back street, hemmed in on both sides by buildings. Keeping to the shadows he made his way past the bins and rubbish piled against the wall until he came to a driveway. The gate was locked, so he crouched down behind one of the bins.

An hour passed, maybe more. At one point he dozed, jolting awake at what sounded like a shot. He leaned back and stared upwards. He was hungry and desperately thirsty. He was just about to stand up when a scooter came up the lane and turned in. He sat, unmoving, willing the rider not to notice him. The door jerked upwards, rattling as it rose, and the rider accelerated in.

Tasim waited for a few moments, then leapt up and, keeping close to the wall, ran after him. At the bottom of the ramp he stopped and peered around the corner. Behind him the door rattled closed again. The rider had already disappeared. On the far side of the space another ramp descended, the concrete floor scuffed and marked beneath the overhead light. In an alcove in the opposite corner a heavy red door was daubed with graffiti: testing it, he discovered it was locked. For a few seconds he stood staring at the keypad, then gave up and headed down the ramp. There were three more levels below, each lined with storage spaces and car parks hidden behind heavy grilles. At the far end of one he found a door that led into a corridor, and off it a pair of rooms lined with pipes and wires. Choosing the smaller he lay down in the corner and tried to sleep.

At first he thought it an impossible feat – he was too agitated – but finally he slipped down into dreamless darkness, awaking hours later with a start. He could hear voices – a woman talking in English, the one-sided conversation making it clear she was on a call. Getting to his feet he crept back out the way he had come, waiting for a scooter to enter before darting out into the street.

Outside it was still brutally hot, but the sun was low and the sky was turning orange. Realising he had been asleep all day he began to walk. He needed to find water and food. Eventually he found his way to a main road, and begged a glass of water from a man in a noodle shop. His eyes aching he walked on. The sun had set, and the street was ablaze with lights. A tram of some sort went by, sweeping down the road with a soft whirr. He watched it pass, suddenly reminded that somebody had told him there were trucks that handed out food near Central. He looked left towards the towers of the city, then right. Another tram was approaching. Stepping out he began to hurry towards the stop, waiting for the tram to stop before he stepped through the doors.

He took a place near the door, ready to run if an inspector boarded at the next stop. Even with the air conditioning the air in the tram was hot, heavy with the smell of bodies. Opposite him a pair of older men with elaborate, teddy boy haircuts sat close to each other, unspeaking, beside them a woman and two children. The older was a girl, her black hair pulled into tight pigtails. All at once he was reminded of Dewi, the reminder of her absence so painful he closed his eyes. But then the memory of Dewi's face was replaced by that of the girl he'd seen the night before, the way she had struggled as the man pushed her into the boot. He tried to blot the image out, to erase it, but he couldn't. What had happened to her? Was she dead? Why hadn't he tried to help? Opening his eyes, he found the girl with the pigtails was smiling at him. He looked away.

When the tram reached Central he disembarked and wandered with the crowd until he reached a long park bounded on one side by a raised sandstone wall. A line of vans was parked at one end, serving food from bain maries. Tasim joined the queue for the nearest, keeping his eyes down; when he reached the front, he took a plate and walked away quickly, before stopping beside a fallen tree to eat. Some of the men around him stood in small groups, talking as they ate, but most ate alone like him, watching the people around them warily. When he was done, he put his rubbish in the plastic bag provided and walked through the trees until he came to a water fountain. He bent down to drink, sucking on the weak stream of warm water thirstily, then lifted a hand to rub it onto his face, grateful for the wetness. He stood up to find a man standing directly behind him. Startled, he took a step back, but the man lifted his hands and opened them in front of himself.

'Whoa, it's okay. Jesus, man.'

He was skinny, his hair cropped close to his head on the sides and across the front and long down the back, emphasising his protuberant cheekbones and blotchy skin.

'What do you want?' Tasim asked.

The man grinned, revealing a jumble of teeth. 'You look thirsty.'

'It is permitted to drink here?'

'Of course.' He took a step closer and Tasim stiffened.

'It's okay. I'm not going to hurt you. Are you on your own?'

Tasim hesitated and then nodded again.

'You're new here?'

Tasim shrugged.

'You got a name?'

'Tasim.'

'I'm Axel.'

'You live here?'

Axel laughed and glanced around. Tasim noticed a tattoo of a cross on the side of his neck, its blue ink blurry.

'I suppose.' He pointed to a pile of plastic bags near the fence beside the park.

'That's me there.'

Tasim shifted uneasily. Axel was watching him like he wanted something, but he didn't understand what.

A little way off a security guard was watching them.

'Come on,' Axel said. 'Let's get out of here.'

Tasim followed him, glancing around uncomfortably as they moved back towards the fence. Refuse lay on the ground, a mess of discarded food containers and syringes and broken toys. Farther along the wall sat other men and a few women, hollow-eyed, twitchy. Axel sat down in his little shelter and motioned to Tasim to do the same.

'You gotta watch the guards,' Axel said. 'They think they own the fucking place.'

Tasim didn't reply. He was watching a man on the far side of the park, the way he walked reminding him of the man the night before.

'You got any money?' Axel asked.

Tasim leaned back, uncomfortably aware of Axel's closeness, the smell of him. He shook his head.

'So what? You have nothing? How's that work?'

Tasim shrugged. He knew better than to tell anybody too much.

Next to him Axel brought out a battered phone. Tasim looked at it for a moment, a thought stirring in his mind.

'Can I use that?' he asked.

Axel tensed. 'Why? Don't you have your own? Did you lose it?'

Tasim shrugged.

'Somebody stole it?'

Tasim nodded, not looking up.

Axel stared at him. Finally he placed the phone in Tasim's hand. Tasim called up the browser and entered the address for the device locator, aware of Axel sitting too close, ready to snatch the device back.

The page appeared. He shifted his body slightly, trying to angle the screen away from Axel and entered the password. He knew there was almost no chance it would work: even if his phone was still intact the battery could be flat, or the phone out of range. For a space of seconds, the spinner turned, and then, just as he was about to give up, the page opened, and a map flashed into view. Tasim's stomach lurched, and his hand tightened on the phone. The map pulsed, once, twice, three times, then it zoomed inward, first once, and then again, until it came to rest on an address.

'Is that it?' Axel asked. Tasim could barely move.

'Do you know where this is?' he asked Axel.

Axel twisted the phone towards himself and examined the screen. 'Sure. You think this is where they took your stuff?'

Tasim inclined his head in assent and Axel told the phone to remember the location. 'We'll go find it tomorrow.'

Tasim wanted to ask why they couldn't go now, but something in Axel's manner held him back. Instead he lay back. He needed to sleep, but the heat made him anxious, and when he closed his eyes he could feel the past drawing him down, like a whirlpool, into the darkness.

It had been hot like this the night before he lost Dewi and his mother, the heavy blanket of air close in the darkness of his room. Tasim had been able to hear the whine of the scooters on the road outside, the distorted ululation of the call to prayer; in the room next door Dewi slept, her breathing coming regular and slow, like the whisper of the waves. All that week it had been growing hotter, the heat relentless, and when he closed his eyes he could still see the glare of the sun behind them, a black orb etched on his eyelids, the snaking lines of red around it.

Taking out his screen he had flicked it on and checked the weather forecast one more time. There had been heatwaves before, but not like this one: a week of temperatures over 50 degrees, with the conditions tomorrow expected to reach 53 or 54. For days socials had been full of images of overflowing hospitals and shrouded bodies piled in refrigerated trucks. Earlier, over the evening meal, his mother had waved her hand at him when he tried to talk to her about it, telling him it wouldn't happen, that it would be okay, and when Tasim tried to argue, to tell her they needed to have a plan of some sort, she grew angry with him, telling him she had to work.

'Who do you think pays for the food you eat?' she had demanded.

'We can go to the mosque,' he had said. 'Or the mall.' But his mother just lifted her hands and made the chittering sound she used to block out things she didn't want to hear.

Later he had gone into Dewi's room and sat with her while she stared at her phone in the dark. He wanted to talk about what was coming but as he looked at her, sprawled on her bed, her face illuminated by the flickering light of the videos she was watching, he knew there was no point, that it would only agitate her. And so he went back to his room and tried to sleep.

The next morning he woke in the darkness before dawn. Outside the heat was already gathering, the air hotter than blood. School had been cancelled the day before so Tasim and his sister were at home, but his mother was still determined to go to work. Once again he pleaded with her to stay but she told him she had no choice, then paused, and pointed through the door at the hose in the concrete yard at the back of the building.

'Use that,' she said. 'And look after your sister.' After she left Tasim went back to his room. He knew he and Dewi should go to one of the cooling stations but he was worried about what would happen if it got too crowded and they ended up back in the street. And so instead he sat in his room and tried to cool off with the fan.

By nine it was already over 40 degrees. Hugging the shade he went outside to the hose and filled a plastic tub. Bending down he tried to lift it but his head began to spin, and he had to lean back against the wall, panting. The air felt hot in his throat and lungs. When he felt steady, he leaned down again and dragged the tub back towards the house. Inside he banged on Dewi's door until she came out, her face flushed and sweaty and angry. He pointed at the tub and told her to climb in and try to cool herself.

Going back to his room he opened the blind and looked out into the street. The light was searing, the road quiet. On the opposite side a man was sitting in a car, the windows up and air conditioning on. Closing the blind again he lay down on the bed by the fan.

By eleven the temperature was 48 degrees outside and the air in the apartment was so hot and thick he could hardly move. He was light-headed, and felt ill and dozy, but he knew he couldn't fall asleep. In the kitchen the water in the tub was now hot, and when he and Dewi splashed it on themselves it didn't seem to make them any cooler. Tasim could see it wasn't making any difference, yet he kept encouraging his sister to pour the water on herself in the hope that with the fan angled towards the two of them it might somehow help.

They had just reached the end of the water in the tub when the lights went off and the fan on the ceiling wound down. Tasim got to his feet and, crossing to the wall, flicked the switch up and down, but there was nothing. Dewi stared at him dazedly.

'What is it?' she asked.

'Nothing,' said Tasim. Her gaze drifted to one side, unfocused. Tasim went back and picked up the tub. 'Let me fill this,' he said. She nodded, although he wasn't sure she'd really understood.

Out in the yard the sun was blinding, the heat against his skin almost unbearable. He stumbled towards the hose and turned it on: the water that poured out was scalding; with a cry he dropped the hose and backed away. In the shade of the tree behind the house a black and brown cat lay on its side, its flank rising and falling rapidly. Tasim realised he was finding it difficult to focus, then there was the sound of something hitting the ground, and then another. He looked around: a pair of birds lay on the ground; one was still moving, half-furled wings poking up and twitching, but the others were still, already gone. He reached down and managed to lift the tub, but when he was halfway back to the door he heard a crash from inside. Dropping the tub he staggered forward to find his sister sprawled on the ground next to the chair she had been sitting on. He dropped to his knees beside her and turned her face towards him. Her eyes were half-closed, and she seemed to be murmuring something. He said her name, shaking her in the hope of waking her, but she just twisted weakly away, moaning slightly. He touched her face and shoulder: her skin was clammy, and her face was grey.

'Dewi!' he said, but she didn't reply. Grabbing her wrist, he tried to take her pulse, but he couldn't find it. Standing up he groped for his phone and pressed his mother's name, but the network was down. Kneeling down again he lifted Dewi's head up and cradled it in his lap, stroking her cheek. Her skin was damp and cool, as if she had been in the water too long, and for a moment he wondered whether he had done this to her, whether his attempts to bring her temperature down had somehow made her sick, but he couldn't make the idea make sense.

'Wake up,' he said. 'Please. Please.'

She was breathing faster now, panting shallowly like the cat outside. Tasim knew in some distant way that he had to get her somewhere cool, but he didn't know how to do that. He stroked her cheek again, willing her to wake up, to talk to him, but instead she just lay, panting.

He said her name once more, then lowered her head to the floor and got to his feet. He had to get help, find a doctor or somebody who could help him get her somewhere cool, so he staggered towards the front door and stepped out into the glare of the sun once more. Outside it was strangely quiet, the distant hum of the traffic and horns absent. He staggered towards the street and out onto the road. There were cars and vans here and there along the side, but as he stumbled past them he saw they were empty. By the third he stopped, and turning, saw a woman lying on the ground outside the shop that sold phones, lenses and internet credit. He took a step towards her, trying to work out what the stain on the asphalt around her was, only realising when he saw her pale, staring face that it was a spreading pool of urine. He took a step back and noticed a man leaning against the wall of the next building, vomit staining his shirt, his eyes closed. Pushing on the shop door he tried to open it, but it was locked, so he pressed his face on the glass. Inside it was dark, the space empty, save for the dark shape of a body on the floor. He stepped back again. Over the road, outside the mini-mart, another man sat slumped against the wall. Tasim stared at him, trying to comprehend what he was seeing, until all at once he had an idea, and he stumbled across the road towards the store.

Inside it was dark, the power gone, but at the back of the store the owner's daughter, Setia, who was a year ahead of Tasim at school, lay on the ground beside her parents in front of the fridge doors. He staggered towards them, feeling the shiver of cooler air. Setia turned to look at him, her expression dazed, confused.

'Dewi,' Tasim managed to say. 'She's sick.'

Setia didn't reply. Tasim let his eyes move towards her parents. Her father was still breathing, but her mother was still. Slowly he began to back away. It was no good: he had to get back.

Outside the heat was unbearable. Dazedly, he weaved his way along the middle of the road, ignoring the threat of traffic. In the distance he could hear sirens, sobbing, somebody crying out for help over and over again, but it all seemed impossible, incomprehensibly far away.

Back inside he knelt down beside Dewi, but even before he did, he knew something was different, that some vital quality had departed. He said her name, once and then again, touching her cheek and turning her head towards him, but she was still and empty. Sitting cross-legged beside her he drew her head to him and held it in his lap, as if she were asleep and might wake, although he knew that would never happen. He waited for tears to come, but they didn't. None of it seemed real.

After what might have been a few minutes or an hour he stood up and staggered outside again. He didn't know where he was going, just that he had to find somewhere cool. Keeping to the shade as much as possible he followed the streets towards the river, hoping it might be cooler there. The fact of Dewi's death filling his mind yet somehow unapproachable, like something he kept glancing off. It was as if he had left the world and drifted away from shore without noticing, and now he couldn't find his way back.

Under the trees and in the shops people sat slumped or lay motionless. He could smell smoke and hear sirens. Sweat made his eyes sting, and liquid dripped from his nose, while his lips were cracked and crusted. Finally, he reached a lane that led down towards the river and turned onto it, grateful for the shade of the trees. When he reached the broken concrete path that ran along the bank he stumbled, almost falling forward. Below him, the muddy water gleamed dully in the sunlight, its surface broken here and there by the bodies of men and women and children. Some sat, or lay back, crowding into the shade of the trees that extended out over the water – a mother cradling a baby, dripping water onto its head; an elderly man in a stained white skullcap staring dazedly around – but as Tasim descended to the water he realised others lay unmoving in the shallows or floated face-down farther out in the stream. At the water's edge he pushed past the people clustered there and waded out; the slow-moving water was hot, but still cooler than the air, and Tasim fell forward into it, ignoring the foul, sulphurous smell as he slid beneath the surface.

He lifted his head. A few metres away a young man sat, staring at him. He had a round, moon-like face and a thin moustache, and his shirt clung wetly to his pudgy frame. He was lifting handfuls of the filthy water to his mouth and trying to drink them, but the water wouldn't stay in, and with each handful more ran down his cheeks to stain his neck and shirt; he turned and looked at Tasim for a moment, his eyes wide with fear. Tasim backed away, but the young man didn't attempt to follow him, instead he scooped faster and faster, sobbing as he did.

Looking around, Tasim noticed the white shape of the bridge a couple of hundred metres away, and began to stumble towards it, hoping to shelter in the darkness beneath its arches. As he splashed through the shallows, he passed people sprawled in the mud and huddled in what shade they could find. In the river more bodies drifted, some catching on the bottom, or gathering around obstructions, like the fish that filled the rivers the year before when the last of them finally died. Tasim stared at them, both understanding and not understanding what he was seeing. Near the bridge he pushed out into the water, shoving his way through the bodies as he headed for shade and deeper water, until finally he clambered up onto a ledge along the edge of one of the arches, and spreading himself out on the concrete, slipped down into darkness.

WEDNESDAY

Sadiya woke in the pre-dawn light, her bladder full and her brain already buzzing. Knowing she wouldn't sleep again she went to the bathroom, then picked up her screen and sat on the side of the bed in the half-light. The news was full of information about Nasreen. Overnight the storm had passed to the south of New Caledonia, its outer edge still powerful enough to wreak havoc. For a few seconds she flicked through the images of the damaged buildings and uprooted trees in Nouméa, the footage of the wind smashing through the streets, sending sheets of metal and other refuse flying, the old feelings of dread percolating up her spine. Although Nasreen was bigger than anything they had seen before it was only two months since the last major storm, a year since Brigitta, two years since fire consumed the east coast once again, but every time disaster struck all the other times returned, as if they had never ended, and were instead still there, just below the surface of the present. Realising her fists were clenched she forced herself to breathe, and flicked the news about Nasreen away, instead pulling up the reports that had come in overnight. She read through them quickly, looking for signs of unrest in the Floodline or anything that might be relevant to the case before directing the system to search the information for possible connections. She was still working when Findlay called. She answered immediately.

'What is it?'

'They found Nina's car.'

Sadiya sat up straighter. 'What? Where?'

'It's in Rosebery. But it's been torched.'

'Shit. How do you know this?'

'I know the uniform who was the first to arrive. He saw I'd authorised a trace on it yesterday so, rather than leave it to the system to send me an alert, he called me.'

'Tell him thanks.'

'Don't worry, I did. But that's not all.'

'What do you mean?'

'There's a body in the boot.'

Sadiya fell still, the room around her suddenly remote. 'Is it . . . ?'

'Apparently it's an adult, so it's not Casey.'

She closed her eyes, exhaled. 'Nina?'

'I'd guess yes, wouldn't you?'

Outside the sky was slowly lightening. 'Where are you?'

'On the way to the scene.'

'All right. I'll be there as soon as I can.'

'It's okay. Do what you need to do.'

Sadiya bit back on a retort, realising he meant it. 'It's fine. I won't be long.'

Out in the living area she checked Arman's door, saw it was still closed. She told her assistant to call Malila, and asked if she could get there right away.

'Again?' Malila said, her voice sleepy.

'I wouldn't ask if it wasn't important.'

There was a long silence. 'Is he awake?'

'I don't think so. You can eat here if you want.'

Malila said something to somebody else, her voice muffled, as if she was holding her phone against her chest. A man's voice said something, and Malila replied, her tone strained. 'Okay,' she said. 'I'll be there in half an hour.'

'Thank you,' Sadiya said. 'I'm going to leave him alone, so please don't be any longer.'

She dressed quickly, pulling on a shirt and tying her hair back. Out in the kitchen she checked the locks on the knife drawer and cupboards, pulling on each of them one at a time. Then, opening the cupboard in the hall, she opened the safe and took out her gun and clipped it onto her belt. She paused by Arman's room one more time and listened, then headed for the door.

The streets were already busy, a steady stream of vehicles heading for the main roads out of the city, so it took almost twenty minutes to reach the address Findlay had sent her. It was only as she pulled up that she realised she had been there before. Five years before? Six? A murder-suicide in a block of flats a few doors further down, a mother who had dosed herself and her children with sleeping pills. The children were young – four and seven – and Sadiya remembered staring down at the woman's body curled around the two of them as if in sleep, anger and disbelief filling her until she had to fight back tears. How could any parent make that decision, she had wanted to ask the woman, how could they choose to harm the people they were entrusted to protect? Afterwards she tried to ask herself whether she had the question wrong, whether it might not be fairer to ask what parent wouldn't, given what they knew about the future. Yet something told her that question was a dishonest one, a way of making it about the asker, not the asked, that nobody had the right to make that choice for another.

The block was still there, its dilapidated shape rising on the far side of the street. As she climbed out of the car she wondered who lived in the apartment now, whether they had any idea of what had happened there. People forget so quickly, preferring to erase the past, hide it away. They were even better at not thinking about the future, or only ever letting themselves think about bits of it. How would any of us survive if we didn't?

A handful of locals were already gathered in the street, standing in the shade of the trees or sitting on the low wall of the flats; Sadiya snapped images of them in her lenses as she passed. A uniformed officer Sadiya didn't recognise had been stationed by the gate; he greeted her with a quick nod and opened the gate to let her through.

The building was a long-since-abandoned turn-of-the-century business park now missing its roof courtesy of a storm. The charred shell of the car was in a parking area at the rear, hidden from the street by the building. Findlay was standing to one side watching a blue-suited Forensics officer take scans. He looked around as Sadiya approached.

'Sorry I took so long,' said Sadiya, trying to ignore the reek of burned plastic. 'What do we have?'

Findlay led her around to the back of the wreck and stopped beside the Forensics officer. 'Parekh,' said Sadiya. 'Good to see you again.'

'Detective,' said Parekh.

Sadiya stepped towards the car. 'Walk me through it,' she said.

'Late model Polestar, full security package, fire lit using some kind of accelerant,' said Parekh. She straightened and pointed to a can lying on its side a short distance away. 'There's biodiesel in that, so I think we can assume that's where it came from.'

'And the body?'

Parekh took a step forward and slipped a hand under the lid of the boot. With a small grunt she pushed it up to expose a body, its skin blackened and seared. A cloud of flies and the stink of ashes and decaying flesh spilled out. Findlay turned his face away and stepped back. Lifting her hand to her face Sadiya forced herself to focus on the details. Her head was turned inwards, leaving only the blackened scalp with its tendrils of hair exposed, but the scorched limbs were twisted, the hands curled in as if in some dreadful palsy. Here and there scraps of burned clothing were melted into the charred skin.

'Was she dead before the car was set on fire?'

Parekh glanced down at the body. 'I don't know yet. There isn't any sign she was restrained, though.'

'I suppose that's something.' Sadiya took a step forward. 'Do we have a positive ID?'

'Not yet,' Findlay said. 'But I think we can assume it's Nina.'

'What about a time of death? Did anybody see the fire?'

'I spoke to a guy who lives in the flats next door. He says the car was set on fire on Sunday night.'

'Did he say when?'

'About eleven.'

'Why wasn't somebody dispatched to see what was going on?'

'That's not really clear. One of the neighbours streamed the fire, and the system logged that footage, but it seems to have decided it was low-priority, so it wasn't actioned. I think the real answer is it fell between the cracks until early this morning, when Uniform stopped by to check it out.'

Sadiya sighed. 'We need to get that stream. Did anybody see who lit the fire? Or see anybody hanging around?'

'Somebody told one of the uniforms they saw a kid running away shortly before the fire.'

Sadiya turned. 'Did they recognise them? Or get a photo?'

'Afraid not. On either count.'

'We should talk to them again, try to get a description.'

'Absolutely.'

She turned to Parekh. 'How long will it be before we have some definite answers about who she is and how she died?'

'Later today.'

'Great.' She turned to face the building. The doors were boarded up, the windows above broken or blank and filthy. 'What do we know about this place?'

'Not much,' Findlay said. 'It's been empty for a while by the sound of it.'

'Any idea who owns it?'

'No, but I can find out.'

'Good. Does anybody live here?'

'I had a look around earlier. People have been here, but there's nobody in there at the moment.'

'You think they cleared out when they saw the uniforms arrive?'

'Possibly, although it's locked up, so my guess is nobody's been here in a while.'

'Interesting. Let's have another talk to this neighbour who saw the kid.'

The neighbour was sitting on the wall outside the block of flats on the far side of the road. He stood up as they approached. He was in his mid-twenties, with glasses and the sort of large, rangy frame that usually went with private schooling and years of rugby. He looked relaxed but also pleased to be the centre of attention. Although judging by his carefully tousled hair he was probably usually pretty pleased with himself, thought Sadiya.

'Apparently you saw what happened on Sunday night,' Sadiya said once she'd introduced herself.

The neighbour pointed to a window on the second floor. 'I live up there,' he said, 'I'd just got home when I saw the fire.'

'And you came out to see what was happening?'

'Yes, although there wasn't much to see, so I didn't hang around.'

'And did you see anybody?'

He shifted uneasily. 'Not then. But a few minutes earlier, when I was coming home, I saw a kid come over the fence.'

'Male, female?'

'Male.'

'What did he look like?'

The neighbour shrugged. 'Thin, dark skin. Fifteen or sixteen, perhaps. I think he was wearing a yellow t-shirt.'

'And how did he seem to you?'

'What do you mean?'

'How would you describe his demeanour?'

'That's the funny thing. He looked frightened.'

'Can you recall anything else about him?' asked Findlay.

The man shook his head. 'Sorry. But he went that way,' he said, pointing down the street. He was enjoying this, thought Sadiya: their questions feeding his sense of importance.

'And you didn't see where he went after that?'

'I'm afraid not.'

'Thank you,' said Sadiya.

'Is that it?' the man asked, clearly surprised they weren't more interested.

'For now. If we need more, we'll be in touch.'

'What do you think?' Findlay asked as they crossed back to the other side of the street.

'I think we should get the system to look for surveillance footage of kids in yellow t-shirts. And we need to access the car's security system, find out whether it recorded anything that's helpful. If this kid was near it, we might be able to identify him from that.'

'You think the kid might have been involved?'

'I think he might have seen something. Funny what he said about him looking frightened.'

'I know.'

'Does that sound like somebody who had just set a car with a body in it on fire?'

'No.'

Sadiya turned to look back through the gate at the building. 'The real question now is whether there's some connection between this and whatever happened to Casey.'

'There has to be, surely?'

She shrugged, thinking. 'So, what are we thinking? Nina had some connection to Casey? Or saw something?'

'Perhaps she could identify whoever was responsible for Casey's disappearance?'

'Then why bring her here? Why burn the car?'

'Perhaps there was evidence they needed to destroy?'

'It seems a lot of trouble to go to over a kid from the Floodline.'

Findlay thought for a few seconds. 'Or maybe there's something about this place. Some reason whoever it was brought her here?'

'Or perhaps it has nothing to do with Casey at all? It's just a coincidence?'

'Do you really think that?'

Sadiya shook her head. 'No.'

'So what now?'

'Let's get somebody over here to search the building, see if they can find anything. If whoever burned the car used an accelerant to light the fire, perhaps they've left something behind we can use to identify them. Meanwhile we'll go back to Horizon and see whether we can find out anything else or track down her next of kin.'

*

It wasn't quite dawn when Tasim drifted upwards into consciousness once more, his mouth thick and his eyes aching from the heat. In the grey light the space of the park was covered with the huddled shapes of sleeping bodies. A metre or so away on his right, Axel was stretched out on his side on the strip of blue sleeping foam he had produced the night before, his back to Tasim. For a few moments he wished he was still asleep – the night had been restless and unsettled, the heat and the whine of the mosquitoes and the movement of people through the park jolting him awake many times – but now he was awake he wanted to get moving, to find his bag and his phone. Getting to his feet he made his way towards the water fountain and filled the water bottle Axel had given him the night before. Holding it under the bubbler he filled it and drank greedily, barely noticing the rusty flavour, then filled it again and screwed the lid back on. He followed the path a little way and then began to pick his way back through the sleeping bodies.

Axel was sitting up on his foam strip when Tasim reached him. Tasim regarded him warily, uncomfortably aware of the threat of violence contained in Axel's slightly too-loose movements, his oddly restless stare. Could he trust him? Did he have a choice?

'My phone,' Tasim said. 'I need to find it.'

'Chill, little man,' Axel said. 'What's your rush?'

'When will we go, then?' he asked.

Axel swung around to stare at him. 'You should learn to appreciate your friends better,' he said. For a moment Tasim thought Axel might be about to attack him, but then he smiled. 'I get it,' he said. 'You just want your stuff.'

Tasim began to reply but then stopped, staring at the man beside him. He and his dog had arrived late the night before, the man moving unsteadily and swaying from side to side as if disoriented or drunk. Eager not to attract his attention Tasim had pretended to be asleep. Later, though, he had woken to hear him moan softly in the dark, his breathing shallow and quick.

He was lying on his back, his dog beside him, but his mouth was open and his eyes were staring sightlessly upwards. Noticing the shift in Tasim's manner Axel turned to see what he was looking at. Next to the man's immobile form the dog growled, the sound low and menacing.

Axel reached into his backpack and pulled out a plastic bag. Reaching into it he withdrew a bread roll. The roll clutched in one hand he stood up slowly, unfolding himself with a peculiar, loose-limbed motion.

'Don't move,' he said, and holding the roll in front of him took a step towards the dog. It was orange and white, with a big, blunt head and a powerful chest, but Axel didn't hesitate, even when it lowered its head and growled again. Instead, he moved slowly out and around it, drawing close without approaching it directly. The dog's eyes followed him, its growl giving way to a quick, warning bark. Axel held the bread out, but instead of attacking, the dog's attention shifted towards the bread. Its mouth opened, its growl becoming a low pant. Axel held the roll out for a second or two longer and then tossed it sideways so it landed a couple of metres away. The dog waited for a moment and then trotted after it, suddenly docile. Axel knelt down beside the man, his hands moving quickly down his body, checking his pockets and inside his shirt, before grabbing the pack that lay beside the man and moving back towards Tasim. Without looking back Axel scooped up his own bag as well.

'What are you waiting for?' he said, already hurrying away, his head down as if willing anybody to stop him. 'Let's get out of here.'

Tasim looked around. Other people were sitting up now, watching; he could feel their anger and disapproval. He took a step back and then jogged after Axel.

A block from the park Axel knelt down in an alley and began to rifle through the bag. He pulled out a stained baseball cap and a battered paperback book, a bundle of papers held together with a rubber band and a plastic razor, a solar charger, an old pair of lenses. He discarded most of it without a second look, but the charger and the lenses he shoved into his own bag. When he was done he stood up and threw the man's bag against the wall and headed on up the alley.

Tasim did his best to keep up with Axel as the other man led him through the narrow streets. As they walked Axel talked constantly, wheeling through a seemingly endless and only tangentially related stream of stories about people who had tried to betray him or hurt him, and how he'd shown them the error of their actions in one way or another. The more he talked the less comfortable Tasim felt. Before long the towers gave way to smaller apartment blocks and a jumble of old terrace houses and converted industrial buildings, and shortly after that they turned onto a wide street lined with shopfronts and businesses, many of them standing empty. Axel stopped outside a mini-mart, its painted glass frontage bisected by a huge crack.

'Wait here,' he said, and disappeared inside. Tasim stood in the shade near the wall. Overnight the temperature had barely dropped, and although it was still early it was already hotter than it had been the day before, the sun ferocious against his skin, its heat like pressure. Closing his eyes, he took a deep breath, pushing his anxiety down, willing his hand not to tremble. When he opened them again Axel was standing in front of him. He shoved a sandwich into Tasim's hand, its plastic covering cool, then tilted his chin to indicate an alley opposite, before heading out across the street without stopping.

Tasim followed him, glancing up at the camera on one of the poles overhead, uncomfortably aware he was being watched. In the alley, Axel tore into his sandwich.

'Can you show me where my phone is?' Tasim asked, trying to keep his voice unthreatening.

Axel looked up, as if focusing on him for the first time. He made a dismissive motion with his hand.

'Yeah, yeah. Soon.'

Tasim clenched his fists, trying to steady himself. He knew he couldn't let this go on much longer, that if he stayed there would be danger, but he needed the information Axel had. Opening his sandwich, he took out a portion and bit into it; as he did Axel met his gaze, and in that moment, Tasim realised he had made some kind of commitment.

*

While they drove towards the city Sadiya called Nguyen to argue that Nina's death should be handled by her and Findlay rather than Homicide.

'She's a person of interest in the Mitchell disappearance,' she said.

Nguyen was silent for a moment. 'And you're confident her death has something to do with whatever happened to the girl?'

'I am.'

'But you still don't have any leads on who it might have been?'

'I think if we can find out what happened to Lukic we'll know what happened to Casey.'

Nguyen paused. 'Okay. I'll see what I can do. Given everything else that's going on they may well be happy not to have another case on their hands.'

'Thank you,' said Sadiya.

In the city they parked and headed for Horizon's offices. But when they arrived the guard informed them Manning wasn't there.

'Perhaps we could speak to somebody who might know his whereabouts?' said Sadiya.

The guard flicked them a link. 'His assistant will be able to help you.'

Sadiya opened the link and the AI appeared in her lenses.

'I'm afraid Mr Manning isn't in the office today,' they said. 'Is there something I can help you with?'

'Do you know where we could find him?'

'I'm afraid I'm not able to provide you with that information. Would you like his contact details so you can reach out to him directly?'

'We're police officers. It's important we speak with him,' said Sadiya. There was a moment's hesitation while the system checked her credentials and the relevant protocols.

'He's working at home today,' said the assistant.

'Great. Thank you.'

'Would you like me to tell him you want to see him?'

'No,' she said. 'That won't be necessary.'

'Have we got an address for him?' she asked Findlay as she hung up.

'He's in Wollstonecraft.'

'Great. Let's get over there now.'

Manning's apartment was in a complex of three towers constructed high above Gore Bay, where drowned tanks and gantries sat in the still water alongside the dead limbs of the trees from the Reserve. The three towers were connected by a circular platform, the undersides of which shimmered with mirrored panels. Once they had been admitted they stepped into the lobby, its climate-controlled air cool. An aquarium took up one wall, its water filled with darting fish and coral; Sadiya glanced at them, remembering images of the algae-covered ruin of the Barrier Reef.

'Nice place,' Findlay said.

'Building refugee camps is clearly good business,' Sadiya replied as her assistant gave the building's systems the apartment number. There was a long beep and a moment later, a girl's voice answered.

'We're looking for Oliver Manning,' Sadiya said.

Instead of replying the girl shouted, 'Dad!' A few seconds later Manning's voice took over.

'Hello, Mr Manning,' Sadiya said. 'This is Detective Sergeant Azad. We spoke to you the other day. Would it be possible to come up?'

There was a moment of silence. 'Of course,' he said. In front of them the lock clicked.

The apartment was on one of the upper floors. Manning opened the door almost as soon as they knocked. He was dressed in suit pants and a shirt.

'Detectives,' he said as he ushered them in. They stepped into a short hall that opened onto a long, open space, bordered on one side by a wide balcony. Creepers trailed down from the balcony above, shading the area from the sun, and filling the space with a soft, verdant light; through them the harbour could be seen, and beyond it the heads. A violin case and a navy-blue schoolbag with an elaborate school crest on its flap sat by the door.

'Will this take long?' he asked. 'I'm due at my daughter's school in half an hour.'

'We'll be as quick as we can. Is it all right if we talk here?'

Manning glanced around. 'I suppose.'

'I'm afraid we have some bad news.'

Manning fell still. 'About Nina?'

'Yes. Her car was found this morning. It had been set on fire.'

'Deliberately?'

'We believe so. But that's not all. There was a body in the vehicle.'

Manning's mouth fell open in surprise. 'Is it ... I mean, do you know ... Is it Nina?'

'We're don't know for sure yet,' Findlay said. 'But we believe so.'

Manning took a step back and sank down on a chair. 'Oh, god. That's awful. Do you know how ... did somebody do this to her?'

'That's what we're trying to establish,' Sadiya said.

'When did it happen? How long has she been dead?'

'We're not sure, exactly,' Findlay said.

'But if you could tell us where you were on Sunday night, that would be very helpful,' said Sadiya.

'I'm sorry?' said Manning.

'It's just a formality.'

Manning stared at her for a second or two. Sadiya recognised the look, the shock that somebody like them might have the nerve to suggest somebody like him might not be able to do whatever they want. Then his practised ease reasserted itself.

'Of course. I was here most of the evening.'

'And somebody can confirm that?'

'My wife.'

'Thank you,' said Sadiya. 'We'll need to speak to her. Is she here?'

'No, she's at work. I can send you her details.' He paused. 'Do you have any idea what happened?'

'At this point we're just trying to establish the facts of the matter. But there is one thing we could use your assistance with.'

'Of course, anything.'

'The car's security systems were damaged in the fire, so we need access to its cloud data. We can put a request through the company for access, but that often takes a while. Is there any chance you might know whether she made arrangements for somebody to have access to her accounts if something happened to her?'

'I can check, but I doubt human resources would hold information like that. They'd see it as a breach of privacy.'

Sadiya was about to reply when a girl appeared through the door on the far side of the room. Eight, maybe nine, same blond looks as Manning, blue private-school uniform.

'Daddy?' she said, her voice tentative but clear, precise. The girl who had answered the door.

Manning turned. 'Beatrix. I thought you were getting ready.'

'What's going on?'

'Nothing. Just something to do with work. These people were just leaving.'

The girl regarded them warily, obviously unsatisfied by her father's answer. Findlay took a step towards her and smiled. 'Is that your violin by the door?' he asked.

Beatrix nodded uncertainly.

'My sister used to play,' he said. 'What grade are you?'

'Four.'

'Impressive. You must practise a lot.'

'She should practise more,' said Manning before his daughter could answer.

Sadiya looked at him, surprised by the coldness in his tone.

Perhaps noticing her surprise, Manning turned to her. 'She needs to understand there's a connection between effort and outcome,' he said, then turned back to Beatrix. 'Go grab your hat. We're leaving in two minutes.'

As soon as the girl was gone he stood up. 'I'm sorry,' he said. 'I really have to go.'

'Of course. Just before you do, it would be helpful to know whether you think anybody might have wished Nina harm.'

Manning shook his head. 'I'm afraid not. But as I said the other day, I didn't really know her outside of work – and she was a very private person.'

'If you think of anybody, you'll let us know?' said Sadiya.

'Of course. Immediately.' He hesitated. 'Actually, there is something. She has – she had – a brother. I think they were estranged – he'd had problems with drugs or alcohol and had spent time in jail – but a few months ago she said he'd made contact with her.' He stopped, as if uncomfortable about continuing.

'Mr Manning?'

'I don't want to make accusations, but I know their relationship was tense. She said he'd demanded money, and I got the feeling she was frightened of him.'

'Do you know what he said?' asked Sadiya.

Manning shook his head. 'I'm afraid I don't.'

'Do you happen to know this brother's name?' Findlay asked.

'If she told me I've forgotten it. But she had to take some time off to deal with him.' His daughter appeared, holding her hat. 'I really am sorry,' he said. 'But it's her violin exam.'

'Of course,' Sadiya said. 'We're sorry to hold you up.'

'Not at all. Anything I can do to help, just say. Such an awful situation.'

'What did you think of that?' Findlay asked as they rode the lift back down to the car park.

'I think he thinks he can manage us,' said Sadiya. 'Did you notice how he behaved when he let us in?'

'What do you mean?'

'Usually when the police turn up on their doorstep people are anxious. Even if they haven't done anything they're worried they're in trouble for something.'

'And?'

'He wasn't worried at all.'

'Perhaps he knows none of this has anything to do with him.'

Sadiya pursed her lips as if she'd tasted something she wasn't sure she liked. 'Or maybe he thinks he's safe.'

*

As the morning drew on, Axel seemed to be deliberately trying to find excuses for not taking Tasim to his phone, instead dragging him from one place to another to talk to people or to conduct inscrutable surveillances of people or places. With each new delay Tasim grew more frustrated and uncomfortable. He had learned to stay out of people's way, but Axel seemed not to care about that. Quite the opposite: even crossing the road with Axel was a performance, as Axel eyeballed passers-by and stalked in front of moving cars, shouting and gesticulating at the drivers as they slowed down to avoid hitting him. Part of Tasim understood these provocations came from a place of weakness. But they still frightened him, because he knew it meant Axel might explode into violence at any moment.

Around midday, Axel seemed to grow tired of whatever it was he had been doing, and led Tasim to a bus stop. When the bus arrived he climbed on, indicating to Tasim to follow, shouting abuse at the driver when he told him to tap on, and stalking to a seat at the back. Tasim followed him and sat down on the seat opposite Axel's. After half-a-dozen stops Axel got up and jumped off, then stalked off down a side street, Tasim behind him, until they came to a block of flats.

'This is it,' he said.

Tasim's heart sank as he looked up at the building. It was old and nondescript, its façade broken up by balconies behind which stood glass doors, all sealed against the heat.

'How do I know which apartment it is?' he said.

'Did you see the guy who took it?' asked Axel.

Tasim shuddered, remembering the man's face and the girl staring at him. 'I think so.'

'We can wait, then. Catch the prick as he goes in or out.'

Tasim didn't reply. The thought of seeing the man again terrified him, but he knew he didn't want Axel to stay with him.

'I'll be all right on my own,' he said. 'Thank you for bringing me.'

Axel smiled. 'No way. If you stay, I stay.'

And so Tasim ended up seated in the shade of the entrance with Axel. At first he tried to be polite, and to humour him, but as the afternoon wore on, and the heat grew more intense, Axel's manner shifted, his aggression giving way to a sort of twitchy distraction. For his part, Tasim tried to ignore the heaviness of the heat and to focus on the street and the passing cars. Finally, in the middle of the day he tried to distract himself by asking Axel about the cyclone, and what he knew about it. Axel laughed bitterly. 'The weather guys don't know shit. They said there was going to be a big-arse storm a few weeks back, but then it never happened.'

'But if it hits the city, what will you do?'

'I'll find somewhere. Last time I was in a place in Waterloo, one of the old towers.'

'The storms. Are they very dangerous?'

Axel looked around and stood up. 'You just need to make sure you're somewhere safe. Are you thirsty? I'm thirsty.'

'No,' said Tasim. 'What if he comes while we are away?'

'You'll be fine.'

Tasim shook his head. 'I have to stay.'

Axel jiggled his leg. 'Wait here, then,' he said.

Tasim stood, watching as Axel crossed the road and vaulted the fence of the house opposite. Moving quickly, he ran to a tap and twisted it. A thin trickle of water filled the bottle. He ran back to the fence and leapt over again. A moment later the screen door swung open and a man in a singlet emerged.

'Hey!' he shouted. 'What do you think you're doing?'

Axel swung around. 'What was that?'

'What are you doing in my yard?'

'None of your fucking business!' Axel shouted.

Tasim stood up, his heart beating fast. The man took a step forward, bringing his arm around to reveal a baseball bat. Tasim froze, but Axel seemed unfazed.

'Yeah, that's right. Just try it, you fat cunt!' he shouted, rattling the gate and staring at the man.

'Get away from my fence,' the man said, stopping midway between the house and the gate.

'You gonna make me?' Axel demanded.

'Just go.'

Axel rattled the gate again, and the man took a step forward and lifted the bat.

'Come on!' Axel shouted, but the man didn't move. 'Yeah, that's what I thought. Ya fuckin' soft cunt,' he said, pushing himself back from the fence. Windmilling his arms, he smacked his hands together and threw his arms out wide. 'Cunt!' he shouted at the top of his voice.

Tasim stepped out into the heat, following Axel along the footpath.

'Let's get out of here,' Axel said. Tasim was about to protest when a white van turned the corner and pulled into the driveway of the building. Its driver's face was hidden behind dark lenses, but Tasim's stomach lurched as he came to a halt at the gate. It was him.

*

Arman could hear the girl in the living room arguing with somebody on her phone. He felt like he knew her, or had once known her, but he couldn't remember where from. Earlier she had come in to talk to him, helped him adjust his screen; she had been warm, gentle, and he had almost remembered then, but listening to the anger in her voice now he wondered whether she might have been deceiving him. Was it a man she was shouting at? Should he know? Was he supposed to help in some way? He didn't know.

In some part of himself he knew it hadn't always been like this, although it was getting harder and harder to hold onto that version of himself. Once he had walked through the world on his own, looked after himself. Fragments of that remained: he could picture the inside of a shop, the screen of a checkout, the taste of jhalmuri in a noisy space, heat and light. Mostly, though, what he remembered were fragments of feeling, moments of fear and confusion that recurred and then slipped out of reach. He remembered the first time he forgot his keys when he went outside, the way he had lied and laughed it off, the first time he got lost on his way home, his fear when somebody asked him if something was wrong. He remembered a fire in his kitchen – his kitchen? – the way the flames seemed to leap upwards and steal his ability to think, the shouting as his daughter – he had a daughter? – shoved him aside and extinguished them before grabbing his arms and shouting in his face. All of them slipping away like water when he tried to hold onto them.

Outside a siren blared, the heat coming at him through the glass, something tangible. A smell in the air – woodsmoke, burning, fire – so real but he knew enough not to trust it. He stood up, moved to the window. Outside the sky was clear, but he could still smell the smoke. Going to the door he stood, listening. She needed to know. But what if she already knew? He opened the door. She was standing with her back to him, her voice low, urgent. Who was she speaking to? Was there somebody else in the house? He tightened his grip on the handle, but then she turned to one side, her hand raised to emphasise a point, and he understood. On the phone. He took a breath. There was something he needed to tell her, something she needed to know, but it was gone, vanished like everything else.

*

As they drove away from the apartment Sadiya instructed her assistant to find Manning's wife's details and call her. A moment later the other woman accepted the call and her face appeared in Sadiya's lenses. Although the background was blurred, Sadiya guessed she was in a car. She looked older than she had in the photo on Oliver's desk, more careworn.

'Yes?'

'Ms Manning,' said Sadiya. 'My name is Sadiya Azad. I'm a detective. I was wondering whether you could tell me where your husband was on Sunday evening.'

'Of course. Oliver was at home with me,' she said, her voice barely disguising her irritation.

'You're sure about that? He didn't go out at any point?'

'No.'

'You have two daughters, don't you, Ms Manning?'

'Yes, although I don't see what that has to do with this.'

'Would it be possible for us to speak to your older daughter, confirm this with her as well?'

Sarah glanced sideways.

'Is she there with you now?' Sadiya asked.

The other woman nodded, and a moment later a girl of about sixteen appeared. Like her parents she was blond, with a teenager's scowl of permanent disapproval. Sadiya had little difficulty imagining her policing the behaviour of her schoolmates.

'This is Ava,' said Sarah.

'Hi Ava,' said Sadiya. 'I'm a detective. I just wanted to ask whether you know where your father was on Sunday night.'

The girl stared at her sullenly.

'Are you sure you're up to this?' asked Sarah.

Ava pushed her mother's hand off her shoulder. 'He was at home with us,' she said.

'Great, thank you,' said Sadiya. 'We appreciate your help.'

'If that's everything, we need to go,' said Sarah.

'Apparently Manning was at home with her on Sunday night,' she said to Findlay as she ended the call.

'Good. I've spoken to Novak. She's put in a priority request for the security footage from the car. I've also run a search for Nina's brother. It turns out she's listed as next-of-kin for a Stefan Lukic, who's done time for theft, disorderly conduct, fraud. I've requested an address.'

'Great,' she said. While she was on the phone they'd travelled onto the Bridge. To the west the broken roofs of the wharfs and the flats on Ballast Point protruded from the water, gleaming in the glare.

Findlay followed her gaze. 'Do you ever wonder what it was like before it all went to shit?'

When Sadiya didn't reply Findlay continued, his voice distant. 'My mum was born in Sydney. She used to talk about going to the beach in summer. About how beautiful it was back then.'

'You didn't grow up in Sydney?' said Sadiya.

'We were down south for a while. After that we ...' He hesitated. When he spoke again his voice was quieter. 'We moved around.'

Sadiya glanced across, surprised by the emotion in his voice. But before she could reply he straightened in his seat.

'Bingo. We've got an address for Stefan.'

'Where?'

'Enmore.'

'Okay. Let's go find him.'

The address was an old terrace on a street just back from Stanmore Road. At some point in the not-too-distant past the building had been painted grey, the newness of the paint contrasting with the rusting bars of the old metal fence that separated the front veranda from the street. Sadiya and Findlay climbed the three steps to the front door and knocked. Sadiya could feel the sun on her back as the door opened to reveal a skinny man with the sideways, twitchy manner of the ex-addict.

'We're looking for Stefan Lukic,' she said. The man regarded them with studied uninterest.

'Down the hall,' he said.

Stefan's room was the second door on the left. Sadiya knocked, and a moment later the lock released and a shirtless man in loose shorts appeared. He had a square face with high cheekbones and his thin chest was dusted with dark hair.

'Stefan Lukic?' Sadiya asked.

'Yep. Who are you?'

Sadiya produced her ID. 'I'm Detective Sergeant Sadiya Azad, and this is Detective Senior Constable Paul Findlay. Could we come in?'

He didn't move. 'What's it about?'

'It's better if we speak in private,' Findlay said.

Stefan looked at Sadiya's ID one more time and then stepped aside to let them enter.

The room was so small the bed in one corner and the small desk that sat under the window almost filled it. An old ceiling fan spun ineffectually overhead, barely affecting the thick heat in the space. Stefan pulled out the chair that was pushed under the desk and sat down.

'Is there a problem?'

'Are you related to Nina Lukic?' Sadiya asked.

Stefan didn't move, but Sadiya saw the way he tensed at the mention of Nina's name. 'Sure. She's my sister. Why? Has something happened?'

'I'm afraid it has.'

'What do you mean?'

'We've recovered a body. We're still waiting for confirmation, but we think it's her.'

Stefan sat forward. 'What? No.'

'I'm afraid so, Mr Lukic.'

'How? Where?'

'That's what we're trying to establish,' Sadiya said.

Stefan's records said that he was in his early thirties, but he looked older, his features drawn and blurred by years of drugs or alcohol, his hair unkempt, in the manner of somebody who didn't operate in a world where his appearance mattered.

'You think somebody killed her?'

'We don't know for certain, but it looks that way,' said Sadiya.

Stefan didn't reply, his face pale and hollowed out.

'I wonder whether you could tell me where you were on Sunday night. Perhaps between the hours of six and midnight,' Findlay said.

Stefan looked at Findlay with sudden dislike, his grief switching suddenly to anger.

'I was here.'

'Alone?'

'Yes.'

'And when was the last time you were in contact with your sister?'

'I don't know,' he said. 'A couple of weeks ago, maybe.'

'You don't remember?' Findlay asked.

'Not really.' Something about the way he spoke told Sadiya he was lying.

'Are you sure?'

Stefan looked at her. 'I had a message from her last week, I think.'

'And what was that about?'

'I don't know. How was I? Normal stuff.'

'So, nothing that seemed out of the ordinary?'

'No. But we didn't see each other much.' He straightened. 'What is this?'

'We've heard you and your sister had a somewhat tense relationship. That you'd had ... disagreements.'

His gaze shifted from one of them to the other. 'Are you saying you think I had something to do with whatever happened to her?'

'Did you?' asked Findlay.

Stefan got to his feet. 'No! Of course not!' Sadiya was familiar with the moods of addicts. She recognised the aggrieved dignity, the shallow affect.

Sadiya regarded him coolly. 'Have you ever heard of a girl called Casey Mitchell?'

Stefan looked at her blankly. 'Who?'

'Casey Mitchell. She went missing from the Floodline two days ago.'

'No. Why would I?' He hesitated. 'Do you think Nina's death could be connected to her in some way?'

'It's one of our lines of enquiry,' Sadiya said.

Stefan stared at her. 'What would Nina have had to do with some kid from the Floodline going missing?'

'That's what we're trying to find out.'

'If you think she could have done something to this girl you're barking up the wrong tree. Nina would never do anything like that.'

'Would you have any idea about her movements over the past week or so?'

'Like I said, it's a while since we spoke.'

'Are there people you think might have wished her harm?'

Stefan paused, staring at them. Then he shook his head.

'What about her personal life? Was she involved with anyone?'

'Not that I know of.'

'In the past?'

He looked uncomfortable. 'I'm sorry, I don't know.'

'Not anybody?'

Stefan looked away, and for a moment Sadiya could see that he was frightened.

'Mr Lukic?'

'I said I didn't know,' he snapped. 'I'd like you to leave.'

'Of course,' said Sadiya. 'Thank you for your time, Mr Lukic.'

As they opened the door to leave, Findlay stopped. 'What was it you and your sister argued about?' he asked.

Stefan shrugged. 'Nothing important. Family stuff.'

'What kind of family stuff?' asked Sadiya.

He looked away, his face suddenly full of loathing. 'Just stuff.'

Outside they climbed back into the car, its interior already baking.

'Did you see how he reacted when I asked him about her personal life?' said Sadiya.

'Everybody we've spoken to says they knew almost nothing about her personal life,' said Findlay. 'But he clearly knew something.

And Manning was right: there was clearly tension between the two of them.'

'But was it was enough for him to kill her?'

'Could there be a medical angle?'

'What do you mean?'

'Stefan has drug and alcohol problems; perhaps that has something to do with it?'

'You mean delusions or psychosis? Perhaps. It's hard to know with addicts. We need to get his records, see if he's telling the truth about where he was on Sunday night. And we can check with the system, see whether it can throw up any connections we might have missed.'

'But?'

'But I don't see how he connects to Casey.' She leaned back and closed her eyes, trying to ignore the heat. 'We need to go back, talk to the parents again, see if there's anything we missed. And we have to dig into Stefan, find out what was going on between him and Nina. If we can work out what happened to her, we'll know what happened to Casey. I'm sure of it.'

Sadiya was quiet as they drove back towards the Floodline. The conversation with Stefan and the discovery of Nina's body had unsettled her, reminding her of the anger and violence, cruelty and entitlement that often lurked just beneath the surface of the city.

Down by the Cooks River trucks were parked on the kerb, and men and women in hi-vis were heaving sandbags around the base of the buildings, their arms and shoulders shiny with sweat.

'What's the latest on the storm?' Findlay asked.

'They're still saying it should make landfall sometime before noon on Friday. And they're worried about the tides; even if it misses us, the storm surge could be big.'

Findlay shook his head. 'She could be anywhere,' he said, his voice tight.

Sadiya glanced across, startled by the vehemence in his voice.

Perhaps he was surprised as well, because instead of continuing he seemed to withdraw, his eyes focused on the road out his window.

Down in the Floodline people were filling sandbags and heaping them in doorways, or fixing sheets of tin or plywood over windows. But despite that an eerie calm prevailed, the streets oddly quiet and people hidden inside, away from the heat. In an empty lot not far from the highway an old woman in a faded floral bathing suit sat on a deckchair under an umbrella while three kids splashed in a plastic paddle pool, as if this were just any day.

Sadiya took a detour past the site where Casey had last been seen. Outside the shell of the building she slowed down and stared up at its crumbling exterior. It can't have been accidental Nina was there, but what was the connection? She turned to look at the block of apartments opposite, the flimsy tin and plywood blocking the windows, the sun-bleached tarpaulin lashed to the roof. This place always seemed about to wash away, but it never did: instead the inhabitants repaired and rebuilt, finding new ways to adapt.

Larkin met them at the base of the stairs at Emma and Jay's place. Sadiya checked they weren't being observed from the balcony above, then stepped in to speak to him privately.

'How are they?' she asked.

'Pretty tense. Emma keeps checking the reports about the storm.'

'And Jay?'

'Agitated and angry. He's tried to get into it with me a couple of times now. When that didn't work he tried to act as if we were buddies, started bitching about the investigation ...'

'What?' asked Sadiya.

Larkin looked uncomfortable. 'I'm afraid he doesn't like you, Detective Sergeant. He keeps talking about you not being prepared to go after the people you should be looking into.'

'And who would they be?'

'He's never specific about that.'

'Of course not,' said Sadiya drily. 'And how are they with each other? What's the dynamic like?'

'Not great. He keeps hounding her, telling her she shouldn't have let Casey go with those kids, that she's careless about who she spends time with.'

Findlay shook his head in disbelief.

'That sounds about right,' said Sadiya. 'How has Emma been responding?'

Larkin made a face. 'Like she thinks she deserves it.'

'Is there anything else we should know? Any visitors? People they're messaging or speaking to on the phone?'

'Not that I'm aware of. Hamida came by this morning, but she didn't stay long.'

Sadiya nodded, reminded of how alone Emma had seemed every time they had visited her. 'Okay,' she said. 'We have to speak to her about a development in the case. Make sure you keep an eye on them after we leave. If they race to communicate with somebody we need to know.'

Inside the apartment Emma sat down on the sofa and Sadiya took a seat opposite her while Larkin and Findlay hung back by the door. A moment later Jay came through from the bedroom and stood behind Emma. Emma stiffened and leaned forward slightly, as if afraid he would touch her. She looked thinner, the lines etched along each side of her mouth making her look a decade older than she was.

'Still nothing?' Emma asked, her voice tight.

'I'm afraid not.'

Emma gave a small nod. There was a moment when parents had to admit to themselves the worst might be true, a moment they might never come back from; Emma wasn't there yet, or not quite, but Sadiya suspected she was close.

'We need to ask you a few more questions relating to Nina Lukic.'

'The woman you asked about yesterday?'

'That's right.'

'Why? Have you arrested her?'

'No. But we found a body this morning. We think it's hers.'

Emma gasped. But it wasn't her reaction that interested Sadiya, it was Jay's. He fell still, an indecipherable look passing across his face.

'You don't think somebody might have done the same to Casey?' said Emma, her voice shaking.

'We don't have any reason to think that,' said Sadiya. 'But we suspect Nina's death is connected to Casey's disappearance. You both said yesterday that you'd never heard of her. That hasn't changed? You haven't remembered anything?'

'No, nothing,' said Emma, stifling a sob. She looked around at Jay. He shook his head.

'What about Stefan Lukic?' asked Findlay.

Jay narrowed his eyes. 'Who's he?'

'Nina's brother.'

'Do you think he killed her?'

'We're not ruling anything out at present,' said Findlay.

'What about Horizon, the company that owns the site where Casey went missing? Do either of you have any connection to it?'

'No,' said Emma. 'But I know who they are. Everybody down here does.'

'And you, Mr Markley?'

Jay sneered. 'How could I not?'

'What do you mean by that?' asked Findlay.

'Horizon has the contract to build this new development down here. But they also handle almost every aspect of relief work in the area. They're responsible for repairs and clean-up after storms, they truck in the water, they even fund the medical centre.'

'You sound like you don't approve,' Sadiya said.

'They make billions out of government contracts and relief work. But the work they get paid for, how often does it actually happen? The Badangi development is years behind schedule, and last time there was a storm there was supposed to be work done to protect people around here. Instead Horizon got subcontractors like Laurent to clear the roads so their trucks could get through, and then what? Nothing! And now we have another storm on the way, and where's the help they promised us? They're sandbagging the barriers upstream, but have you seen anybody from Horizon down here?'

Sadiya watched him without speaking for a second or two. 'You say your friend Laurent worked with them after the last storm. Did you work for him then as well?' said Sadiya.

Jay hesitated for a fraction of a second. 'For a few days, sure.'

'And did you have any contact with Horizon employees or management?'

'I had a conversation with one of their foremen that he won't forget in a hurry.'

'What do you mean?'

'Just the usual bullshit. They wanted us to do stuff that wasn't safe.'

'Do you remember the name of this foreman?'

'No. His name was Tran or Tan or something.'

'What about more senior people? Have you ever met any of them?'

'Management? They don't talk to people like me.'

'Are you aware Horizon owns the site where Casey disappeared?' Findlay asked.

Jay shrugged. 'Of course. They've been buying up land around here for the past few years. They own pretty much everything now.' He made a contemptuous noise. 'It's good business for them. The government rezoned this whole area a few years back, so Horizon gets tax breaks and subsidies on anything it buys, and the government will help fund the development. It's a sweet deal.'

'Why are you asking us about Horizon?' asked Emma.

Sadiya glanced at Findlay. 'Nina Lukic worked for them.'

'Why would Horizon or this Nina woman have anything to do with all of this?' said Jay. He folded his arms and regarded her with dislike, although Sadiya thought there was an element of anxiety in his manner. 'You're just looking for excuses not to focus on the people most likely to do something like this.'

'And who might they be?' asked Sadiya with exaggerated politeness.

Jay regarded her for a long moment and then smiled. 'Don't think we don't see you, Detective,' he said.

Sadiya walked fast as they left, hurrying down the stairs and out onto the duckboard.

'Are you okay?' Findlay asked when he caught up with her.

She spun around, about to snap at him, and then caught herself. She forced herself to take a breath, trying to ignore the sun beating down on her scalp and focus on staying calm. 'He's lying to us,' she said.

'About what?'

'Nina, Horizon. I'm not sure.'

'You don't think it's just that he hates cops?'

Sadiya was about to reply when she noticed a girl on a balcony of the building opposite, her lenses dark in the sun.

'Am I being videoed at the moment?' she asked her assistant.

There was a brief pause. *There seems to be a stream from your location.*

'Show me,' Sadiya said, and a moment later the feed of her and Findlay appeared in her lenses, a caption reading 'Cops doing nothing' beneath it. She watched Findlay and herself move away, their dark lenses making them look uncomfortable and guilty, like public figures hounded in disgrace while comments and emojis streamed past in the overlays. Then she flicked it off.

'You don't think we might be getting our wires crossed, do you? That whatever happened to Nina has nothing to do with what happened to Casey?'

'So, it's just a coincidence Nina was last seen in the same place Casey went missing?' asked Findlay.

'That's right.'

'Pretty big coincidence.'

'What say we have another talk to Morrison? We need to know whether he had some connection to Nina.'

'Good idea.'

*

Tasim sprinted through the gate after the van and darted into the shadows on the far side, keeping low to stay out of sight. Ahead of him the van swung into a parking space beside an expensive-looking black car. A moment later the door opened and the man stepped out, a bag in one hand. Tasim dropped down behind a car on the opposite side of the car park and pressed himself against the wall. Axel and the man with the baseball bat were still shouting at each other in the street above; warily the man walked a little way back towards the gate and stared up the ramp for a second or two until their voices stopped. Then he walked back to the car beside the van and, opening the driver's door, threw the bag onto the passenger seat and clambered in after it. A moment later the car hummed into life and pulled out.

As the gate closed behind the car Tasim stood up and ran towards the van. He didn't know how long he had until the man came back, and he didn't want to find out. Stopping by the passenger window he cupped his hand to the glass to peer inside, but his bag wasn't there. Frantically he pressed his face closer, trying to see down beside the seat, then moved to the rear door to look in the back. It wasn't there, either.

He took a breath and stood up. Outside he could hear Axel shouting his name, his voice increasingly agitated, but he blocked it out and tried to think. As well as half-a-dozen other cars and several e-bikes locked in a cage, there was a lift to the upper levels. If the man had parked down here it stood to reason one of the apartments overhead was his; perhaps his bag was there? But which apartment? He stepped back, looking around, and then noticed the number '405' painted on the concrete where the car had been. He dropped down and peered under the van, and saw it was also marked 405.

With a last glance around he hurried towards the lift and pressed the button. When the doors opened he ducked inside and touched the screen for level four, but the lift ignored his command. He tried the level above it and the same thing happened. Stepping out again he saw a door off to one side. Crossing to it he pressed the handle but it was locked. Noticing another door at the far end of the space he ran towards it, only to discover it opened onto a narrow space filled with bins, the smell of the garbage in the heat so intense he almost retched. As he closed it again a door slammed overhead. He froze. A moment later he heard footsteps; without thinking he sprinted back towards the lift, rounding the corner just as a woman stepped out the door. She looked up, startled, her dark eyes wide above the surgical mask that covered her mouth and nose. Tasim smiled, and with as much confidence as he could muster moved forward and caught the door for her. She hesitated uncertainly, but then stepped aside to let him pass.

Tasim didn't stop to give her time to reconsider. Instead he bounded up the stairs two at a time, his legs still shaking beneath him. When he reached the fourth floor he opened the door and hurried along the corridor until he came to 405. He stopped, uncertain of what to do. He didn't know how long he had until the man came back, but he also didn't know who else might be inside. Taking a breath he placed his ear against the door, but there was no sound. He stood there for a long while, his face close to the door, not sure what to do. What if he knocked and somebody answered? What was he supposed to say? 'Give me my phone'? And what if the girl was there? He took a breath, then, before he had time to change his mind, lifted his hand

and rapped his knuckles on the painted surface, the sound alarmingly loud in the quiet of the corridor.

For a long moment he waited. Reassured the apartment was empty he tried the handle, but it was locked. He looked up and down the corridor. Music was playing behind one door, a woman's voice came from behind another. He considered knocking on one of them and asking them to help, but he was afraid they'd just call Border Force or the police. Finally, he noticed a window at the end of the corridor. An idea forming in his mind, he walked towards it. It was closed, but there was a winder unit. He turned the handle and to his surprise the window opened, the frame popping as it slid free. He wound faster and the gap continued to expand, but then it stopped. He pushed on the winder again but it wouldn't budge. He jiggled the winder unit, and to his surprise it came loose, one of the screws connecting it to the frame slipping free. He twisted the unit and felt the metal at the other end bend. Grasping it with both hands he twisted it back and forth, working at the metal until all of a sudden it tore free and the window swung open. He looked back at the door to apartment 406 in alarm, worried they might have heard something, but nobody appeared. Leaning out he saw a narrow ledge running along the side of the building below the window. It was less than 30 centimetres wide and the wall behind it was smooth, with nothing to hang on to, but it was only ten metres or so to the far end. With a quick glance behind he hoisted himself up onto the windowsill, and then, after a moment's hesitation, closed his eyes and slid out the window onto the ledge.

Willing himself not to look down, he flattened his back against the wall and began to inch his way slowly along. It couldn't have taken more than a couple of minutes, but by the time he reached the far end he was dripping with sweat. He stopped, a sick feeling in his stomach as he realised he had miscalculated, and that in order to get around the corner he would have to turn, so his back was facing outwards and his face was against the wall.

Closing his eyes he pushed his right arm around the corner, hoping to find something he could grab hold of, only to lose his balance and pitch forward. Twisting wildly, he pulled himself back up and pressed himself against the wall, panting. When his heart had slowed down a bit, he opened his eyes and slowly, carefully, began to turn, shifting his feet bit by bit until he was facing in. Then he slipped his arm around the corner again. At first there was nothing, but then he found the other side of the wall, and running his hand down, hit what he guessed was a handrail. Taking a breath he grasped it, and slid himself slowly outward, pulling the top part of his body out until he could see around the corner. Balanced there he saw there was a ledge in front of the guard rail, so he swung one leg out and managed to get his foot onto it, then scrambled after it and pulled himself over the rail and onto the balcony.

For a few seconds he lay on the tiled floor of the balcony, his heart pounding and his breath coming fast. He got to his feet, and froze. Behind the glass doors a woman was standing with her back to him. In one fluid movement he darted across the balcony to the far end and swung over onto the balcony of 405. The doors were locked and the glass was blocked by sheets of black plastic stuck to the inside. An old concrete pot stood in the corner of the balcony, whatever plant it had once held long since dead. Picking it up he raised it in front of himself and then brought it down against the glass, but it bounced back, the impact jarring his arm painfully. He tried again. This time the glass cracked, so he struck it again, harder this time, and a sheet fell inwards and slid down the plastic.

He stood, not moving. He half-expected to hear voices, somebody attracted by the sound of breaking glass, but nothing happened, so he leaned in and pushed the glass and plastic aside and stepped through the gap.

The space on the other side was almost empty, the only furniture a cheap table and two chairs and an old sofa against one wall. At the far end a small kitchen ran along the wall, and on the left a door led into a room in which a mattress was visible. Otherwise the space was bare, the tiled floor uncovered, the white walls blank.

Moving quickly, Tasim crossed to the table. There was a jumble of objects on it – a pair of drones fitted with cameras, their black bodies insectile and sinister, a camera and a pair of large lenses, three phones, a set of earbuds, a mess of batteries and cables – but his phone was not amongst them. There were more cables and cards and a couple of old screens scattered along the benchtop in the kitchen; he scratched through them with a quick motion then started opening the cupboards and drawers, but aside from a couple of glasses and some cups of instant noodles, they were empty.

Turning back to the living area he noticed several shopping bags against the wall. The first two held unopened boxes of various electronics, but in the third he found a bunch of ziplock ties designed for binding wrists and a roll of silver gaffer tape. He stopped, a sick feeling in his stomach at the reminder of the girl's eyes staring at him above the tape across her mouth.

Crossing to the bedroom, he stared around. Other than the mattress the room was unfurnished, but then he saw his backpack sticking out of a cardboard box in one corner. He grabbed it but even before he pulled it open he knew it was empty. He looked inside, unbelieving. His phone had to be here. It *had* to be. He tightened his grip on his bag and tried to focus. Then he noticed a wall of built-ins on the far side of the room. Yanking the door open he found another cardboard box with his hoodie stuffed into it. And under the hoodie, amidst a clutter of other small objects, was his phone.

He snatched it, relief flooding through him as the screen lit up to show Dewi and his mother smiling together. Still shaking, he stuck the phone in his pocket, then stuffed the rest of his possessions into his bag. But as he placed his sketchbook in the bag he paused. Along with his things the box contained several other objects. He picked up the first, a black glove shaped out of some kind of artificial fabric.

Reaching down he turned the other objects over, finding another glove, a black cloth mask emblazoned with a skull of the sort he had seen protesters using to confuse facial recognition, and, last of all, a child's hairclip. He hesitated, picked it up and turned it over. It was made of red plastic and was shaped like a butterfly, its wings decorated with tiny glittering plastic gems. He knew at once it belonged to the girl, but looking at it, he was reminded that Dewi had once owned a clip a little like it, and for a sudden, throat-clenching moment he was back there, with her, hearing her laugh and sing. He closed his eyes. Where was the girl from the other night? What had the man done with her? And how could he leave her if she was still alive?

He stood up, a plan forming in his mind. Slipping the hairclip in his pocket he went back to the shopping bags in the living room. In the second he found what he was looking for: a small box containing three tiny trackers. But as he shoved it into his backpack somebody knocked on the door. He froze, his heart pounding.

'Hello?' said a woman's voice. 'Is there somebody there?'

For a moment he didn't move. Then he turned and ran back through to the bedroom. Grabbing his hoodie and his water bottle he shoved them into his bag and closed the wardrobe door. The woman knocked again. Putting the bag on, he went back to the living room again. The balcony door was still open, the broken glass scattered on the floor with the sagging plastic. Reaching a decision, he approached the door and stopped just behind it. In the hall outside the woman was still knocking and calling out. He placed his hand on the handle, took a breath, and pulled it open. The woman he had seen through her balcony door was standing there.

'I'm sorry to disturb you,' she said. 'But I heard breaking glass, and I wanted to check you were all right.'

'Yes,' he said. 'Everything is fine.' As he spoke he stepped past her and into the corridor. The woman took a step back, confused.

'Wait. Who are you?'

Tasim smiled again. 'Thank you,' he said, pulling the door closed behind him. 'I have to go,' he said, and without waiting for a reply began to walk towards the lift. She called after him, but he didn't turn around. He stopped in front of the lift and hit the button once, and then again.

'Stop!' said the woman. He looked back and saw she was holding her screen up to video him. He swung around, covering his face with his arm, and bolted for the stairwell, slamming through the door and bounding down the stairs and away.

*

Outside Morrison's building Sadiya pressed the intercom and waited. A moment later a girl's voice answered.

'Hello?'

Sadiya and Findlay exchanged a look.

'Hello?' the girl said again.

'This is Detective Inspector Sadiya Azad,' Sadiya said. 'We're looking for David Morrison.'

There was a brief silence, then Morrison's voice replaced that of the girl. 'Yes?'

'We'd like to come up,' Sadiya said.

'Now?'

'Now,' said Findlay, his voice hard.

There was a long silence, then the lock released with a buzz.

When they reached the apartment Morrison was standing in the doorway. His face was sick, sweaty. He smiled weakly.

'Detectives,' he said, attempting and failing to project a cheerful bonhomie.

'Can we come in, Mr Morrison?' said Findlay. Once again Sadiya saw the anger in him she'd seen the day before.

Morrison stared at Findlay. 'Can't we talk out here?'

Findlay moved closer to him. 'Let us in,' he said, his voice low and hard.

Morrison seemed to be about to refuse, but then he stepped aside to let them enter.

A girl of ten or eleven was standing in the kitchen area, dressed in a bottle-green school polo and shorts. Her straight dark hair was tied back from her face.

'This is my partner's daughter, Lily,' Morrison said weakly. 'She just dropped in on her way home from school.'

Findlay smiled at her. 'Hi Lily.'

'Have you been here long?' Sadiya asked.

Lily glanced at Morrison. 'A while. Not long.'

'Where do you go to school?' Findlay asked.

'Green Square.'

'Do you come here often after school?'

Lily looked confused. 'I suppose.'

'And David looks after you?'

She nodded.

'Because your mum's at work?'

'Yeah.'

'And what time does she usually get home?'

'Six? Seven?' said Lily, speaking slowly, as if concerned she was making a mistake.

'I just need to help the detectives with something,' Morrison said. 'Perhaps you could go to your room while I speak to them.'

'Okay,' said Lily. There was something slightly odd about her affect, a slowness of response, or confusion.

The moment her door closed Findlay spun to face Morrison. 'You told us she didn't live here. And now we find you're alone with her every afternoon?'

Morrison flinched. 'Please, it's not how it looks. I promise I haven't touched her. I wouldn't ever do that to her.'

Findlay didn't move. Sadiya watched him warily, uncertain how much of his anger was performance, how much real.

'You appreciate how this looks, don't you? We come to speak to you about a missing child, and you tell us you don't know anything about it. But then we discover you've been lying about your relationship with another child.'

'Please,' Morrison said, his voice little more than a whisper. 'You can't tell Sienna.'

'We don't have any choice in the matter.'

Morrison sank down onto the sofa. 'You don't understand. I don't have anywhere else to go.'

Sadiya steps towards him. 'You say you're not like that anymore, yet we have evidence you were nearby when Casey went missing, and when we asked you what you were doing you told us you were seeing a friend, but you can't tell us who that friend is.'

Morrison lowered his head into his hands and whimpered.

'So, David,' said Findlay. 'Who was that friend? Will he vouch for your whereabouts? Or was he just a figment of your creepy, kiddie-fiddling imagination?'

'You don't understand,' David moaned. 'I can't tell you.'

'Did you take Casey, David? Did you hurt her?'

'No! I would never hurt a child.'

'But you had sex with a child.'

'She was fifteen.'

Sadiya let the comment hang in the air long enough for its grotesquerie to be tangible. 'And you were what? Twenty-seven? That's rape whichever way you cut it.'

'What would we find if we checked your internet history?' Findlay asked.

Morrison's mouth opened and closed, his face stricken. 'Nothing.'

'Then where were you?'

Morrison stared at the ground for several seconds, his hair falling over his face in a sweaty curtain. Finally, he looked up.

'Okay. There's this group online. They ... they share simulations.'

'What kind of simulations?' asked Findlay.

'The kind that's illegal.'

'You mean virtual deepfakes of children?'

'Not children,' said Morrison. 'Teenagers.'

Findlay was about to say something but Sadiya silenced him with a look. 'And you bought one of these simulations?'

Morrison nodded.

'Why did you have to go to the Floodline for that?'

'The guy I bought it from had it preloaded on a set of lenses that are disconnected from the net so they can't be detected by security systems.'

'So you went to pick these lenses up?'

'Yes.'

'Where are they now?'

'After we spoke yesterday I got rid of them.'

Findlay and Sadiya exchanged a glance. 'So this guy, it was him you were meeting on Sunday night?'

Morrison shook his head. 'No. I just went to pick the package up.'

'We'll need the address.'

'Of course.'

'And we'll need some information about this guy you say you bought the lenses from. How do we find him?'

'I don't know. All I know is the name he gave me.'

'Which is?'

'Josh.'

'You must have been in contact with him. Don't you have messages, some kind of contact information?'

'We met on Checkpoint.'

'So, the messages were immediately erased,' Sadiya said.

Morrison looked as if he was about to throw up. 'That's right.'

'We can get more details from you at the station.'

Morrison's face was pale. 'What?'

'You're a known paedophile who's admitted to the use of pornographic simulations of children. Even if that wasn't a crime, we couldn't leave you here with Lily.'

'Please. You can't. I helped you.'

'Get up,' Findlay said, his voice tight with anger.

While Findlay took Morrison down to the car, Sadiya spoke to Lily, asking her whether she could call her mother. Once she did, Sadiya took the call and explained that David had been arrested and she needed to come home as soon as possible. To her surprise Sienna was angry rather than concerned, reacting almost monosyllabically to each new piece of information. Before Sadiya hung up she paused, then told Sienna she needed to check something with her.

'What?' Sienna asked, her voice curdled with what sounded like contempt.

'We need to know David's whereabouts on Sunday night. Do you remember whether he was at home, or perhaps out somewhere?'

There was a brief pause. 'Why?' Her voice cold and hard.

'It relates to another investigation.'

Again there was a pause. 'He was out.'

'Do you happen to know where?'

'He said he was visiting a friend.'

'Do you remember when he got in?'

'Late. I'd already gone to bed.'

'So, you don't know what time he got home?'

'I'm afraid not.'

'And he didn't say anything the next day?'

'I'm pretty sure he was still asleep when I left the next morning.' She gave a short, bitter laugh. 'He usually is.'

'Did he say who this friend he was supposed to be seeing was?'

'Honestly? I don't remember. Probably one of the people he games with. He doesn't have any real friends.'

Sadiya waited to see whether Sienna would volunteer more. When she didn't, she said, 'One more thing. Have you ever heard of a woman called Nina Lukic?'

Again the silence. 'No, why?'

'You've never heard David mention her?'

'As I just said, I've never heard of her.'

Sadiya waited. Was Sienna's anger about the circumstances or her default setting? Something told her it was the latter. Carefully she thanked her for her time, explained what would happen next, and hung up. When she was done, she turned to Lily.

'We're going to take David with us, but some other police officers will come before we go and wait with you until your mum gets home,' she said.

'Is he in trouble?'

'Why? Do you think he should be?' said Sadiya.

But the girl just stared at her, her round face oddly expressionless.

Sadiya touched her hand. 'It'll be okay,' she said.

Back at the station they placed Morrison in one of the interview rooms and directed the staff in charge to keep him there. In the corridor outside Sadiya spoke to the detective from the unit that would be handling Morrison's case, and brought her up to date. Then she briefed one of the techs with what they had on Josh, and returned to the situation room. Gunasekera and Novak looked up as she came in.

'Where are we on Lukic's data?' she asked. 'Any luck accessing the car's systems? Or pinning down her movements?'

'I'm afraid not,' said Novak. 'It's all encrypted. We've requested access through the company, but their processes are slow.'

'Can you hurry them up?'

'We're trying,' said Novak.

'What about the kid who was supposed to have been seen running away? Anything there?'

Gunasekera shook his head. 'Not yet. I've checked the system in case somebody in a yellow t-shirt got picked up by any cameras in the area at the time, but there doesn't seem to be anything.'

'Keep trying.' Findlay was standing by the window at the back of the room, staring out, his arms folded. She walked towards him.

'Do you believe him?'

'It seems very convenient. Then again why confess to an offence you haven't committed?'

'To get yourself off the hook for one you have?'

'It's a risky move.'

'What if it's all a distraction? A way of making sure we're wasting our time searching for somebody who doesn't exist instead of digging through his life?'

'We still don't have anything connecting him to Nina, though,' Sadiya said. She turned to Novak. 'What about Nina's phone? Do we have any records of who she spoke to or when yet?'

'She used Checkpoint. So no records.'

Sadiya leaned back against the wall and folded her arms. 'Of course we don't.' She shook her head. 'Okay. Let's go over this again. We know Casey went missing around eight pm. At about the same time Nina's car was near where she disappeared. I think it's safe to assume that whoever drove Nina's car away from the building site took Casey.

'We know Morrison was in the area at the time, but we don't know of any connection between him and Nina, or him and Casey. Nor can we be sure the story he's telling us is true.'

'Casey's stepfather seems to know something about Nina. And he's had dealings with Horizon. But he's got an alibi.'

'There's also Nina's brother,' added Findlay. 'We don't have his whereabouts at the time she went missing locked down. And there's clearly history there.'

'But no connection to Casey,' said Sadiya.

'No.'

'Okay. After it was at the site, Nina and her car disappear until they turn up in Rosebery a couple of hours later. By that point Nina is dead, Casey has vanished, and somebody torches the car.'

'But we have no witnesses who saw whoever it was set light to the car, or saw anybody leaving,' said Findlay.

'Except for this kid.'

'Except the kid.'

'If Casey was there when the car was set on fire, whoever it was who took her must have had some way of moving her elsewhere.'

'So there was a second vehicle?' said Findlay.

'There must have been.'

'So let's look for that.'

'And how did whoever it was make the car burn? Parekh said there must have been an accelerant.'

'So whoever lit it came prepared?'

'Perhaps. Or they had some waiting. Do we know anything about the site where Nina was found? Who owns it? Who had access to it?'

Findlay paused, flicking through searches, then fell still.

'What?' Sadiya asked.

'The site is owned by a company called Egmont Holdings. But they're a subsidiary of Horizon.'

'You're kidding.'

'It could just be a coincidence,' said Findlay. 'Horizon owns a lot of sites.'

'Do you really think that?'

'No.'

Sadiya froze, staring at a message in her lenses.

'What is it?' Findlay asked.

'There's been another incident down in the Floodline,' said Sadiya, already on her feet. 'Jay's been arrested.'

*

Arman stood in the bathroom, trying to remember where he was. The light in the ceiling hummed, curving time. It was morning, afternoon, evening, last week, last year, a lifetime ago. Through the door the sound of voices, people shouting.

He took a step forward, trying to focus, but it was impossible. He couldn't remember. Placing his hand on the tap, he turned it and watched the water spill out, its movement across the basin and into the drain hypnotic in its shivering constancy. Fluid dynamics were a thing of beauty and yet a mystery, the movement of the water describable at large scales, but also unpredictable, nonlinear. Once, long ago, he had known the equations, understood how to use the software, but that was all gone now, swept away. Yet as the water spilled down, its stream coiling, he felt something there, something he almost understood. Reaching out he twisted the tap further so the water ran faster, and slipped his hand in, watching the water play across it, the movement mesmerisingly beautiful. He recalled the sheen of hair, the cool of a body beside his, but he couldn't summon her name or her face. He knew he should hold the memory of her, that forgetting her was like forgetting himself, but it had fled. All he remembered was the closeness of her, a warm morning, the sight of a storm approaching on the horizon. And then the sound of her weeping. She was holding the child, the one he lost, but was that before or after? She was saying they needed to go now, that they weren't safe. He could hear the rain outside, and knew it all connected – but how? And why had he not done as she asked and left? Not until it was too late. We have a duty to stay, he kept saying, a duty to help.

'No,' she said. 'Our duty is to Lina and Sadiya.'

And as she spoke he had understood something he hadn't before. That this life – their life – had never really been real to her. Instead it had been a place she had run to, a place she could hide from her past, her grief. And now it was no longer safe she wanted to leave again, to go back to what was, for her, the real world.

He had been angry, he knew that. But he had agreed, hadn't he? Or had he refused? All he remembered was going down to the river and watching the water move by. The water should have been full of life but instead it stank of death, of the corpses and rotting matter. Or was that afterwards? When the rain came, when the water rose. When he lost them both. He leaned forward, wishing, wishing. He knew he could hear the water, that it was the water that would take him there. That it was the water that would erase all this pain.

And then there was a knock behind him. He turned, startled. He was doing something, but he didn't know what.

'What are you doing in there?' demanded a voice. The girl.

He jerked around. He knew her voice, knew he must be careful of her, must avoid her.

'Mr Azad? Mr Azad?'

He looked down. Water was spilling across the floor and rising around his feet.

'I'm going to open the door!' the girl shouted. A moment later there was a scratching sound, then the door flew open, and the girl was standing there. What was her name?

For a brief moment he saw himself in the mirror: thin and frightened and old.

'What the fuck! The water! No! Sadiya will kill me.'

She shoved past him to the sink and twisted the tap off, the movement sending more water cascading off the vanity.

'Couldn't you see it was overflowing?' she said. 'What were you thinking?'

He took a step back and she seemed to catch herself. 'I'm sorry,' she said. 'It's okay. I shouldn't have shouted.' She reached past him and pulled a towel off the rail. 'Here,' she said. 'Let's dry your hands.'

He watched as she wound the towel about his hands, and then led him towards the door.

'You go wait out there. I'll clean this up.'

He looked back at the flooded bathroom, the water slopping across the tiles. And for a brief moment he thought he understood. It was the water. The water was at the heart of everything.

*

Half-a-dozen police vehicles were parked on a back street a little way back from the water. Twenty or thirty people had gathered near them, and were being kept back by two police officers.

Sadiya stopped the car and pushed her way through the crowd until she reached the first of the uniforms. She had her baton out, and one hand raised to the people around her.

'What's going on?' Sadiya demanded. The officer glanced towards her, clearly intending to tell her to back off, but then she saw it was Sadiya and caught herself. She smiled contemptuously, and for a brief moment Sadiya saw everything she hated about cops: the hostility to outsiders, the superiority. The stupidity.

'An incident with one of the locals. It's all under control.'

She was about to reply when Findlay stopped beside her.

'Sadiya, look,' he said.

She turned. The back of one of the police vehicles was open and Jay was seated inside, his hands restrained behind him.

'Shit,' she said. Ignoring the uniform, she turned and hurried towards him. Before she reached him Behrens appeared around the side of the van. She swore under her breath and strode towards him.

Findlay grabbed her arm. 'Sadiya . . .' he began.

She spun around and glared at him. He dropped his hand.

Behrens stopped and waited for her to reach him.

'What the fuck is going on here?' she demanded.

Behrens turned to face her. 'Detective,' he said. His smile made it clear he'd been expecting her.

'Well? I'm waiting,' she said.

Another uniformed officer appeared around the side of the van. Behrens exchanged a glance with him. 'I'm not sure what you mean,' he said.

'Don't give me that shit. You know perfectly well what I'm talking about. We're trying to find a missing kid and you've just arrested her stepfather.'

'You mean him?' Behrens asked, glancing around at Jay. He smiled again. 'He was involved in a disturbance.'

'What are you talking about?'

'He attempted to break into the home of a resident. He kicked the door in. When we got here he was inside throwing furniture around.'

Sadiya spun to face Jay. 'Is this true?' she demanded.

Jay glared back at her. 'Somebody said they'd seen Casey over this way. When I knocked he wouldn't let me in.'

'So, you tried to force your way in?'

Behind Behrens one of the other officers laughed. Sadiya glared at him. Male. Shaven head above a full beard. Japanese tattoos crawling up his muscled arms and the sides of his neck.

'Do you have any idea what he and Casey's mother are going through right now?'

'Perhaps they'd be coping better if her partner wasn't out here causing trouble,' said the tattooed officer.

Sadiya ignored him. 'Let him go,' she said to Behrens. 'Don't make this any harder than it has to be.'

'I'm sorry,' Behrens said. 'He's already in the system. You'll have to arrange bail back at the station.'

Sadiya tensed, but before she could say anything else Findlay placed a hand on her arm. 'He's right,' he said. 'We can sort it out back at the station.'

Sadiya didn't respond. Instead she stood, staring at Behrens.

'Fuck you,' she said at last. As she walked away she heard the two of them laughing behind her, but she didn't turn around.

They followed the vans back to the station. Larkin and Emma were in the waiting room when they got inside. When Emma saw Sadiya and Findlay she marched towards them. Her face was drawn, her eyes bruised with exhaustion, but she seemed to hum with a manic energy that was at odds with her loose dress and pinned-back hair.

'Where is he?' she demanded. 'I want to see him.'

'Of course. We'll have him out as soon as we can.'

'Did you have anything to do with this?'

'Of course not. It's just a mix-up. We'll sort it out.'

'These officers who arrested him. Why aren't they out there looking for Casey?'

'We're doing our best,' Findlay said.

Emma swung around to face him. 'You keep saying that.'

'Please,' Sadiya said. 'Just give us some time.' She looked at the officer behind the desk. 'Can you find Ms Mitchell somewhere to sit and make sure she has everything she needs?' Then she turned to Larkin. 'And you, come with me.'

They went through the door to the secure area of the station. As soon as the door closed behind them, Sadiya turned to Larkin.

'What the hell happened? Why didn't you let us know something was up before Behrens got there?'

Larkin looked flushed and embarrassed. 'I didn't know. He said he was going out to look for Casey again. The next thing I know Emma's getting a call from somebody telling her he's been arrested.'

'And there was no sign he was up to something?'

'He was on socials just before he went out. He seemed wound up. I should have realised something was going on.'

Sadiya stared at him in disbelief. 'You think?' she said, then shook her head. 'Okay. You go keep an eye on Emma. I'll deal with Jay.'

While she waited for Jay's arrest to be processed and bail to be arranged Sadiya read through the details of his arrest. The police had been called by a Mr Dhar after Jay came into their home demanding to know where Casey was. Dhar seemed to have no connection to the case, although the uniforms who conducted the search on the first day had spoken to him and his wife. When she eventually received word that Jay was being released she went back through to the waiting room, where Emma was waiting with Larkin and Findlay. A moment later Jay appeared. He walked towards Emma and put his arms around her, but she didn't lift her arms to return the embrace; instead she clenched her fists and turned her face away. Jay stepped back and turned to Sadiya and Findlay.

'So, you're not only not going to help us, you're going to stop us from helping ourselves,' he said.

'What you did down there today didn't help anything,' Sadiya said. 'It just made this harder for all of us.'

'Did somebody look in Dhar's place? Was there some sign of Casey?'

'We're going to talk to Dhar. But the initial report from the officers who responded said there's no sign of Casey and they couldn't see any evidence he might have been involved in her disappearance.'

'So that's it? You just let him go?'

'You said somebody said they saw her?'

'On socials. Somebody said there was a girl who looked like Casey down there this morning.'

'So, you went and kicked somebody's door in?'

'If you'd been doing your job I wouldn't have had to,' said Jay.

Emma pulled away from him. 'Stop it,' she said. 'Stop making this worse.'

Jay looked at her. 'I did it for us, for Casey.'

'No, you didn't. You did it for yourself.'

'I did it because they won't. You know that. It's one rule for people like us and another for people like Mahid and her.' As he spoke he pointed at Sadiya.

Emma took another step away from him. 'This isn't about them or you. It's about Casey.'

'Please, Emma,' said Jay. 'I'm sorry. Let me make it up to you.'

Emma turned away. 'Yeah. You're always sorry. Everybody's sorry.' And then all at once she was crying, tears streaming down her face. Jay reached out but she shook his hand off.

'Don't touch me,' she snapped, backing away from him.

Jay took a step towards her. 'Please, Emma,' he said.

'I said stay away!' said Emma, her voice trembling. Findlay moved towards the two of them, but Sadiya motioned to him to stay where he was. He stopped, surprised.

'Let me make this right.'

Emma put her hands over her ears. 'Shut up,' she said. 'Shut up, shut up, shut up.'

Sadiya stepped towards Emma and put a hand on her shoulder. Emma swung around and pressed her face into Sadiya's chest. 'I'm sorry,' she said. 'I just don't know what to do.'

'It's okay,' said Sadiya. 'Constable Larkin can take you home.'

Emma looked at Larkin, who was standing behind the two of them. 'Thank you,' she said.

Sadiya and Larkin led Emma down to the car park, while Findlay followed with Jay. When they reached the car Sadiya opened the door for Emma. Jay stepped forward. 'Please...' he began, but Emma lifted a hand to silence him.

'Just don't,' she said, and climbed into the car. Jay, his face flushed and furious, waited a moment and got in the other side. Emma leaned against her door, her face turned away from him.

As the car pulled out of the car park, Sadiya leaned back on the wall and closed her eyes. The heat pressed in on her face, her eyelids.

'What now?' Findlay asked.

She took a breath. 'We go back there, talk to the guy Jay assaulted. Find out what happened.'

The crowd had dispersed by the time they arrived back at the house. As they walked towards the front door Sadiya catalogued the place. Grass grew high and green behind a low fence, and fronds from the dead palm tree that stood in the front yard lay here and there. A tideline on the walls marked out the storm surge from Brigitta. Taking off her lenses, Sadiya knocked on the door. A moment later a thin man appeared.

'Mr Dhar?' Sadiya said.

He regarded her carefully and then gave a small nod.

'I'm Detective Azad and this is Detective Findlay. We were wondering whether we could talk to you about the incident earlier.'

'I've already spoken to the officers who were here before,' he replied.

'I know. But we'd just like to ask a couple more questions.'

He didn't move from the doorway. 'Of course.'

'Could you tell us what happened?'

'He knocked on the door and said he wanted to come in to look for the missing girl. I told him he couldn't and he started threatening me, and when I closed the door he started kicking on it and shouting. Then he came around the back. My son and I went out to try to stop him and he attacked my son. That was when my wife called the police.'

'And you don't know why he came to your house?'

'I've never seen him before in my life.'

'And Casey? You haven't seen her?'

'No. I already told the officers who were here the other day that we didn't know the little girl.'

'And you definitely can't think of any reason he might have thought she was here?'

Dhar shrugged. 'Who knows? People say all kinds of crazy things.'

Back out in the street the sun was getting low, but the temperature had not dropped.

'Do you think somebody really saw her?' she said.

Findlay shrugged. 'Who knows? We can get Gunasekera and Khoury down here to talk to people and see.'

'Good thought.' Up ahead a dog trotted across the street and flopped down beside a pile of refuse in the lengthening shadow of a block of flats. Sadiya stopped and sighed. 'This mess with Behrens is my fault,' she said.

Findlay looked at her but didn't speak.

'He has a friend called Hayden. They've been mates forever. Hayden is like Behrens but worse: violent, thinks he's a law unto himself. We were all at the same station in my first couple of years out, and back then they used to run scavenger hunts where they earned points for popping illegals or bedding witnesses. They were smart enough to make sure it was always deniable, but they also made sure I knew about it.'

'Did you complain?'

'Guys like them, it's like fighting smoke. You complain and they say it was a joke. And I had too many fights already. Anyway, I managed to avoid the two of them as much as I could until last year, when we ended up back at the same station. One night I got called to a disturbance. There was a kid there who had been beaten senseless. Behrens and Hayden said he'd been like that when they arrived, but I knew they were lying and I made a complaint. It turned out Hayden had forgotten to turn off his camera, and they had it all. He was charged and suspended. Behrens has had it in for me ever since, and so have a number of the others. Every chance they get they mess with my shit.'

'You did the right thing,' said Findlay.

'I know that,' she said with sudden vehemence. 'The kid, he was only fifteen. But now Behrens is causing trouble, making it harder to find Casey. So did it make things better? I don't know.'

'You're not responsible for Behrens,' he said.

Sadiya nodded. 'We should get back, go over what we have. Perhaps there's something we missed.'

Gunasekera and Khoury were in the situation room when they arrived back at the station. After Sadiya asked for an update she told the two of them to head down to the Floodline and talk to the Dhars' neighbours in case any of them had seen anything. Left alone in the room she and Findlay set to work reviewing the materials one more time.

It was after eight before the two uniformed officers returned, their faces flushed with the heat. Sadiya knew from their expressions as they entered that they had found nothing. As they fed their notes into the predictives for review Sadiya noticed Gunasekera glancing at the door.

'Is there somewhere you need to be?' she asked.

Gunasekera looked uncomfortable. 'My mother needs help preparing for the storm,' he said.

Sadiya hesitated, suddenly aware he had already worked six hours overtime both yesterday and the day before. 'Of course. You should go help her. We'll be okay here.' She turned to Khoury. 'What about you? Do you need to go as well?'

'I'm okay.'

Sadiya regarded her for a moment. 'No. There's nothing more to be done tonight. You should leave.'

Khoury stood up. 'I'm available if you need me,' she said.

Sadiya met the other woman's gaze. Khoury did not look away.

'I know. Thank you.'

Once they were gone Sadiya sat down and leaned back in her chair, a wave of exhaustion sweeping over her.

'You should go home as well,' said Findlay. 'I can hold the fort and be the point of contact for tonight. You need the rest.'

Sadiya was about to reply when her assistant interrupted her.

I have Dr Parekh on the line.

Sadiya lifted a finger to indicate to Findlay that he should wait. 'Put her on.'

'Sorry to call so late,' said Parekh. 'I'll get you a full report in the morning, but I thought you'd want the results of the autopsy as soon as possible.'

'Of course,' said Sadiya. 'What have you got?'

'We've got a positive ID on the victim. It's definitely Nina Lukic.'

Sadiya felt the room go still, as if a weight was settling upon her.

'Okay. What about cause of death?'

'She was strangled. Probably somewhere else, because there's some settling of blood on the side of her body, which suggests she was in the boot for a while after she died.'

'So she was dead when the car was set on fire?'

'It looks that way.'

Sadiya didn't move. A cold fury was coiling in her gut. 'I suppose that's something.'

'Her skin was too badly burned to be absolutely certain, but it looks like whoever killed her used some kind of cord. I'll try to match it to some of our samples tomorrow, but my guess would be polypropylene, probably six millimetres in diameter.'

'What about the building? Did you find anything there?'

'Nothing useful. I'm sorry.'

Sadiya thanked Parekh and hung up. 'It's definitely Nina,' she said.

Findlay sat back and nodded. Sadiya took a breath, trying to calm herself.

'I need to go see her brother again,' she said. 'Tell him there's been a formal identification.'

'I'll come with you,' said Findlay.

She hesitated, then nodded. 'That would be good,' she said. 'Thank you.'

A man they didn't recognise answered the door when they reached Stefan's. He was older, with a grizzled beard and the edgy manner of somebody who had spent too long on the streets. They found Stefan in the small kitchen at the back of the building; he fell still when he saw them in the doorway.

'Mr Lukic,' said Sadiya. 'We're sorry to bother you so late, but we wanted to let you know that we've identified the body we found. It's Nina.'

Stefan didn't reply.

'Mr Lukic?' said Findlay.

Stefan seemed to flinch. He looked downwards. 'Do you know how she died?'

'I'm afraid we can't release those details yet,' said Sadiya. 'But we wanted to ask you again whether there's anybody you can think of who might have done this to her?'

Stefan shook his head. 'She used to visit me in hospital, did you know that? Nobody else did, ever, but Nina came.' He wiped his hand across his face with a quick motion. 'She didn't have to do that,' he said, and began to weep.

In the hot dark outside they stood under a streetlamp. 'What do you think?' said Findlay.

'He seems upset but guys like him, they're always sorry. And just because he's upset doesn't mean he didn't do it.' She paused. 'I'm sorry. It's been a long day.'

'It's okay. I understand,' said Findlay.

Sadiya glanced across at him. 'I have to get back, deal with my father. I'm going to order takeaway. If you're hungry I can feed you. We can go over the files again while we eat.'

Findlay stared at her for a moment. Then he smiled. 'Sure,' he said. 'Sounds good.'

They drove separately. Findlay was there before her, waiting outside the building in the street. She buzzed him in and they rode up together. Malila was in the kitchen when they entered, flicking through something on her screen. She looked up as the door opened, and for a fraction of a second Sadiya wondered whether they'd interrupted her doing something Malila would prefer she didn't know about. She shoved her phone into the back pocket of her shorts and smiled a little too brightly. 'You're back!'

'Sorry I'm late,' said Sadiya. She stopped, noticing wet towels hung over the backs of the dining chairs. 'Did something happen?'

Malila looked uncomfortable. 'He was in the bathroom and some water got spilled, but it's fine, I sorted it out.'

Sadiya glanced towards the bathroom door. The carpet was damp but it seemed okay otherwise. Malila shifted from foot to foot, her discomfort telling Sadiya there was more here than she was telling her. Remembering she needed her again the next day she forced herself to ignore the needle of concern she could feel in her belly. She smiled. 'Great. Thanks. Where is he now?'

'In his room.'

'Has he eaten?'

'He had a sandwich earlier.'

Sadiya smiled again, forcing a brightness into her face she knew must seem brittle, false. 'Fantastic. You're still okay for tomorrow?'

'Of course,' Malila said.

'Give me a moment,' Sadiya said once the door closed behind Malila. 'I just need to check on him.'

Arman was dozing when she opened the door, so she switched the light off and closed the door again

Back in the kitchen she opened the fridge and handed Findlay a beer, then walked out onto the balcony. Findlay followed her and leaned on the rail. He took a sip of his beer. 'It's just you and your father here?'

She regarded him carefully, aware of the cost of confiding too much. 'There was somebody a while back, but she left.'

'And you don't have family? Somebody to help you with him?'

She knew better than to tell him about Lina: people always wanted to sympathise, when the truth was she barely remembered her.

'No. It's just me. And he needs somebody with him all the time.'

'That's hard.'

She shrugged. 'What about you? Do you have somebody?'

He smiled. 'No. Not for a while. Hard to make it work with the hours.'

'The nights, particularly.'

To her surprise he laughed. 'You know I do private work?'

'I guessed. Not tonight, obviously.'

'Not tonight,' he said, and took a long sip from his bottle. She smiled. She liked that he seemed genuinely amused she had guessed he was moonlighting – it suggested his failure to mention it wasn't an attempt to deceive her.

'Who is it for?'

'A private company. We do security on some of the gated

communities on the North Shore. I help coordinate three nights a week.'

'Long hours.'

'I need the money. And they've been good to me. You don't disapprove?'

'Would it make any difference if I did?'

He laughed. 'Touché. So, this somebody who left. What did she do?'

Findlay didn't reply immediately. When he did his voice was gentler. 'She was a nurse. We met at the hospital one night after I brought somebody in.'

'You haven't run into her since you broke up?'

He shook his head. 'I'm not sure she's there anymore. She had a sister in Tasmania. Wanted to get resettlement down there.'

'Did she?'

He shrugged. 'Don't know.'

'Really?'

He laughed. 'Okay. Fair enough. Last I heard she was still trying.' He smiled at something, his face momentarily closing off.

'And you?'

'Do I want to go to Tasmania?' He looked at her for a second or two. 'I don't know. I'd like ...' – he gestured around himself – 'I'd like to think things here will get better.'

'But?'

'But I'm not sure it's likely to be all that much different down there in the end.'

'Do you ever wonder what it might be like to live in a world that wasn't so irretrievably fucked?' said Sadiya.

Findlay stared out at the city lights. 'I don't know,' he said. 'There's still beer.'

Sadiya laughed, surprising herself. She lifted her bottle. 'To silver linings.'

'To silver linings,' repeated Findlay, smiling.

Sadiya drained her beer. 'How do you think Horizon connects to all this?'

'I'm not sure they do.'

'It's too much of a coincidence. Horizon buying the land. Nina being down there. Her body turning up at another property owned by the company.'

'You think it might have been another employee?' said Findlay.

'Perhaps. Or something more complicated. You saw how the stepfather responded when we asked him about Horizon. Perhaps we should be looking into some of these land purchases.'

Findlay didn't reply.

'What is it?' asked Sadiya.

'Novak said you'd had trouble with Horizon before.'

Sadiya stared at him. 'Did she say what kind of trouble?'

'No. Just that you'd made things difficult for yourself.'

Sadiya snorted mirthlessly. 'Right.' She put her bottle down. 'There was a death down in the Floodline a couple of years ago. A woman called Nishat Hazra. She was twenty-five. Smart, thoughtful, caring. Horizon had bought a block of land they were planning to develop, but people were living on it. She'd organised protests and made things difficult for the company. And then she turned up dead. It looked like an accident – she'd fallen in the water and hit her head – but something about it didn't add up for me. There was a guy managing the project for Horizon, very plausible on paper, but with connections to some seriously bad people. I was sure he had something to do with it, and that people higher up at Horizon knew. I went after him, tried to make it stick, but he lawyered up and Horizon made complaints about me harassing employees.'

'So, you backed off?'

Sadiya laughed bleakly. 'No. I went to the house of one of the senior people. A guy called Proud, a real sleazebag, and confronted him. I spent six months on desk duty after that. They only let me come back last year, and then all the shit with Behrens and Hayden happened.'

'And that's why Nguyen was on the phone as soon as we spoke to Manning?'

'That's right.'

'But you don't think all that has anything to do with Casey, do you?'

Sadiya paused for a moment and then shook her head. 'This isn't about what happened to Nishat.'

'But you think it might have something to do with Horizon?' As he spoke an alert pinged on his screen. He looked at her. 'It's the video from Nina's car's security system.'

He stood next to her and held his screen up. Extending a finger, Sadiya scrolled through the video until they reached Sunday night. The car's security system was motion-activated, a series of brief grabs. First it was Nina closing the door and standing beside it looking around. Behind her the site was almost dark, but the gate stood open. Sadiya suppressed a tremor at the sight of Nina alive again. She looked cooler than she would have guessed from the photos, more self-possessed. Dark hair swept back off her face. The way she moved: was she apprehensive? Concerned?

After a moment she walked through the gate. As she moved out of sight the video continued for a few seconds and then cut out. Several minutes later something must have activated the system again. The same view through the gate. And in it a child.

'Casey,' Findlay said, his voice almost breaking, but Sadiya didn't reply. Casey was walking alone, twirling something in her hand as if absorbed in some game. She passed out of shot, moving in the same direction as Nina. A few seconds later she appeared again, running, a man's figure in pursuit. The man was dressed in black and had a hood pulled up over his head, then the image cut out. When the security system reactivated again five more minutes had passed: this time the man's figure strode towards the car, his body filling the camera as he opened the door and climbed in. A moment later the recording ended.

'What the fuck?' said Sadiya.

'Perhaps the footage has been damaged in some way.'

'No. This is before the car was burned. He must have deactivated the security system.'

'Wouldn't he have needed Nina's security codes for that?' said Findlay.

'Not if she had them stored in some kind of personal device and he had that.'

'Did we see his face?' Findlay asked.

Sadiya scrolled back through the footage. As the man passed the car there was a moment when he turned his head partway towards it, but his face was unrecognisable, a darkened blur. 'I think he's wearing a mask. Something holographic.'

'Who does that?'

'Somebody who went there intending to do something like this?'

'Or somebody for whom wearing a mask is second nature.'

'What do you mean?'

'He could be security. Or the kind of person who's used to avoiding cameras.'

'Like a paedophile.'

'Like a paedophile.'

'Fuck.'

Sadiya zoomed in on the image. 'I don't think it's Jay – he's too slim.'

'Could it be Morrison? Or Stefan?'

'Maybe. We need to get the video analysed, see if we can find out how tall he is or some kind of weight range.' She paused. 'We know one thing for sure now, though.'

'What's that?'

'Whoever killed Nina also took Casey.'

'So, the kid who ran away?'

'I think we can assume he didn't have anything to do with whatever happened to Casey.'

'But?'

'But perhaps he saw something, and that's why he was running.'
'That's a big perhaps.'
'It's all we have at present.'

*

When Tasim dreamed, he didn't dream of home, or his mother, or Dewi. He dreamed of the boat. It was hot the day they departed, the water turquoise. He had been told it was dangerous to cross in the monsoon, but that year the rain had been late to arrive and he knew he wouldn't last another wet season alive. He had paid the money to a man in Mataram, seated in a small room behind a shop, watched by an officer in a Polisi uniform. The man had been friendly and businesslike, smiling and asking him where he had come from, what it was like there, but the man in the uniform didn't move, didn't speak, just watched him, so Tasim kept his eyes down and hardly spoke.

After Tasim paid the money he became frightened it was a trick, that they would never come for him. He had got the man's details from one of the other passengers on the ferry that had taken him from Tanjung Perak to Lembar, a thin man with a livid bruise on his cheek who spent most of the journey standing outside smoking. The man on the ferry had said he was planning to make the journey himself, but that he had to wait for his wife to arrive. But what if he was part of it? What if it was all a ruse?

The man in the shop told him to come to an address by the docks, which turned out to be an old government building. Behind its façade there was a courtyard, the centre of which was shaded by a shabby tree. It was already full when he arrived, its space crowded with people leaning against the walls and lying on the ground on pieces of cardboard.

Many were in groups – families with children, or older couples. As Tasim picked his way across the space several of them smiled at him or nodded, but he kept his distance and found a spot by the wall out of the way.

They waited all afternoon and into the evening. When darkness fell somebody flicked on a spotlight, its harsh light illuminating the courtyard in stark white and casting long shadows. Just before midnight a man appeared. He was tall, with a wide face and hard eyes, but when he spoke he was brisk and efficient, informing them they would leave in the morning.

After he had gone Tasim tried to sleep but couldn't. He had come so far, yet now he was here he was afraid. He didn't know what lay ahead. Everybody knew the Australians were turning back boats, and socials were crowded with videos and advertisements warning that even if they did make it to land they would be placed in camps until they could be deported. But he had also heard stories about people who had made it to the cities and now lived illegally. Either way it had to be better than here. It had to be better than waiting to die in the next heatwave or storm.

It wasn't yet light when they came for them. A pair of men in shorts and t-shirts, cigarettes in their mouths, their skin dark and battered. One had a lazy eye, and he kept laughing as he walked through the room, telling them to move quickly.

Out on the street two trucks were waiting. People shoved and fought to be the first in line, no doubt afraid they would be left behind, but they got them all in. Tasim rode in the second truck, bouncing over the broken asphalt in the grey of the pre-dawn, the call to prayer echoing out around them.

Down by the water it stank of rotting fish and salt and diesel. The men unloaded them from the trucks, the one with the lazy eye herding them out along a long, curving jetty. At its end a boat was moored. It was painted a bright shade of green and sat low, the red of its lower hull almost hidden below the tideline.

Tasim climbed on board and found a place against the hull. He had to hold his backpack on his lap because there was no room beside him or in front of him. Towards the prow a baby was crying; Tasim leaned forward to try to see it. The mother was older than he expected, her face worn and tight.

Once they were all on board one of the men appeared with an armful of lifejackets that he started to hand out, but there were nowhere near enough. Several of the men stood and argued with them, but then a pair of other men appeared and produced a gun. The two men backed away, hands raised.

A few minutes later the engine coughed into life, and the man with the lazy eye cast them off. The sun was up now, huge and yellow on the horizon, its heat already unbearable.

The boat chugged ahead slowly, heavy in the water, and the fumes from the diesel settled over them as they motored out into the ocean. Although the sky was blue, to the east clouds were visible, heavy and grey, their vast weight like an explosion. As they cleared the breakwater the swell grew larger, so the boat bounced and rolled, and spray flew up from time to time. Tasim had been on boats before so he was prepared for it, but many of the others clearly weren't, and their faces grew drawn and frightened as the boat pitched and yawed.

They had been told the journey would take four days, but now they were on the boat Tasim couldn't see how that was going to work. Where was the water, to start with? Or the food? There were no toilets, either, only a bucket they had to use huddled in the corner, the contents of which were pitched overboard.

As the day wore on people began to faint in the still, heavy heat, or fight over the paltry shade in the wales. In the middle of the day the two men who had loaded them onto the boat moved between them, handing out plastic bottles of water; Tasim snatched his and pressed it to his lips. He tried to pace himself, but it was gone in a couple of sips, and he was still impossibly thirsty.

Late in the afternoon, as the sun began to sink, a breeze came up. At first the movement of air was a relief. But as the sun sank towards the horizon the breeze grew stronger and the swell began to rise, throwing the boat here and there and dousing Tasim and the others with spray, while ahead of them clouds loomed above the horizon.

Nobody spoke, but Tasim knew the others were watching the clouds as well. When at last darkness fell, the flicker of the lightning was visible on three sides. In the bleak glow of the light over the deck the faces of his fellow passengers were ashen.

There wasn't enough room to lie down so Tasim leaned forward, trying to rest his head on his knees. His stomach muscles ached, and finally he twisted sideways and tried to curl up on his side. He was so tired he could barely keep his eyes open, yet he couldn't sleep. The baby was crying, and people were sobbing and moaning. Closing his eyes, he tried to blot it all out and surrender to his exhaustion.

Although he didn't remember falling asleep he must have, because at some point, deep in the night, he woke. The water around them was black, the night heat heavy. But overhead the clouds had cleared, and the Milky Way dusted the moonless sky. Nearby somebody was panting in distress; he couldn't bear to look.

The second day was worse than the first. The sea was calmer, but it was hotter, and people were thirstier. A few hours after sunrise there was a wail from a middle-aged man near the wheelhouse. Tasim remembered him from the dock, where his expensive trousers and shirt had stood out. He was kneeling over a woman, his face pressed close to her and shaking her. He looked around, tears on his cheeks, and cried out for help. But nobody responded. Instead the people closest to him turned away, as if his pain embarrassed them. After a few minutes two of the sailors appeared. One rolled the woman from side to side, her body lolling loosely, while the sailor with the lazy eye placed a hand on the man's shoulder and leaned in to speak to him. The man shook his head violently and pushed the sailor's hand away. The sailor with the lazy eye just laughed his peculiar laugh and turned to his companion and pointed to the side of the boat.

Realising what they were suggesting, Tasim caught his breath. The husband cried out, telling them they couldn't, but they ignored him, and the other sailor bent down and threw the woman's body over his shoulder. The husband got to his feet, grabbing at her and shouting, but the man with the lazy eye stepped between his companion and the husband. He was still smiling, his expression oddly jovial, but suddenly Tasim realised his laughter was in fact a kind of threat, something the husband clearly hadn't understood, because he kept shouting and pushing, until, without warning, the man with the lazy eye punched him in the side of the head, sending him tumbling onto the others seated around him.

The man landed awkwardly, and there were cries of anger and pain. Meanwhile the sailor with the body had reached the side of the boat, and with a grunt, heaved the woman's body over. Behind him the man had stumbled back to his feet and was scrambling towards them; as the woman's body hit the water with a heavy splash and slid beneath the surface he reached over the side in an effort to grab her, but it was too late.

For a few seconds the man hung there, staring after her, but then he turned and slid down, murmuring something – a prayer, perhaps – while the two crewmen turned away and headed back towards the wheelhouse, the man with the lazy eye surveying the deck with his loose, slightly unhinged grin as if nothing had happened.

By nightfall two more had died, an older woman and a girl of six or seven. Both times they were thrown overboard without ceremony or delay, their loved ones left to mourn in silence. At dusk the sailors brought more water, although there wasn't enough to go around. Tasim was one of the lucky ones – he drained half his bottle and then stopped and handed the rest to a family near him. Despite those few mouthfuls the second night was worse than the first. In the darkness people moaned and sobbed, while one woman kept wailing in grief. Tasim was dizzy with thirst, his lips and skin so burned by the sun he could hardly keep his eyes open, but when he slept his dreams were dreadful, nightmares of loss and pain. By dawn there were half-a-dozen more dead; one by one they were hefted over the side and left behind, their bodies floating in the dark water, clothing spread out.

There was no water that morning. Around them the ocean spread out to the horizon, as if they were adrift in the middle of nowhere. As the sun rose higher Tasim put his t-shirt over his head to try to keep it off and lay down on the deck. He must have slept for a time, for in the middle of the afternoon he woke to shouting and, pulling the t-shirt away, squinted around. Two of the crewmen were pointing up into the sky and yelling. Tasim tried to make out what they were looking at. At first he saw nothing; then, a flash of something white. A drone.

One of the crewmen disappeared back into the wheelhouse, and a moment later the pitch of the engine changed, and the boat sped up. Tasim tried to think through what it meant, what would come now. He had heard the Australians disabled ships like theirs, left them drifting, but how could that be worse than this? Dazedly he got to his feet. Perhaps a dozen people were already gone; those that were left looked half-dead. But on every side the ocean was blue and empty, an immensity without beginning or end.

As the afternoon wore on the mood on the boat changed. There were more deaths, but nobody came to throw the bodies over. Instead, the crewmen came down every now and then and walked about on the deck, scanning the horizon with binoculars. Then, a couple of hours before sunset, there was a shout from the side, and the sailor who had thrown the first woman overboard turned to the wheelhouse, pointing to the north-west. Tasim got to his feet, his legs unsteady and weak beneath him. In the distance the dark shape of a ship was visible on the horizon. The crewman with the binoculars waved his arm, spinning it as if winding something up, and the boat pushed forward.

They motored hard for the next hour, the engine straining and smoking. Behind them the ship had grown larger, its outline visible. But as dark approached clouds began to gather to the south and the east, and a fitful wind began to blow. Around Tasim the passengers who were still conscious began to murmur with concern. As the clouds rose up above them the sky turned green, and the water grew dark. And then, with a sudden crack of thunder, the squall hit them, the wind slamming into the boat and flinging spray across them.

The storm grew worse as night overtook them, rain and wind lashing the boat. Tasim held his face up and drank the falling water, then squeezed his soaking t-shirt into his mouth. Around him people slipped and sprawled as the boat pitched and rolled in the dark, vomit and other fluids mingling with the water on the deck.

An hour passed, then another, and then a beam of light cut through the rain and a ship loomed out of the darkness beside them. An amplified voice shouted unintelligibly, the sense of the words torn away by the keening wind. He wondered whether they were planning to board them, but then the ship was gone again, and they were alone.

Finally the rain stopped, and the lightning and thunder moved off. The engine was quiet, although whether because the crew had turned it off or because it was damaged wasn't clear. Although he didn't mean to, Tasim must have slept, because the next thing he knew he was jolted awake by a cry. The sky overhead was grey, and people were shouting and crawling about. Looking down, he saw water rising around his legs. He stood up unsteadily, confused. A bearded man grabbed him by the arms and shouted something in his face, but a wave washed over while he was talking, and when it passed he was no longer there. Looking around in confusion Tasim realised they were sinking. Beside the boat three of the crewmen were clambering into a Zodiac; Tasim splashed towards them, but the water was up to his thighs now, and a moment later another wave washed over the deck, bearing him over the side and into the water.

There was a moment as he sank beneath the surface when he felt total calm. There was no up, no down, no sound besides the groan of the ship in the water and the echo of voices in the distance. And then he was up, in the air again, floundering. There were people all around him in the water, shouting and screaming. Something collided with him; he grabbed at it and found it was a hunk of wood with a piece of rope attached to it. He pulled himself up onto it and wrapped the rope around his wrist, refusing to let go. Pressing his face into the wet surface of the wood he closed his eyes and slid down into darkness. When he slept he dreamed of the boat, and when he woke he dreamed of it again. He was there now. He would always be there.

THURSDAY

Sadiya was checking her messages when the shouting began. The room was dim, the sun not yet risen. Standing, she crossed to the landing and stepped out. Down in the street a man was walking in circles, raving and hollering, his finger jabbing angrily at some imaginary antagonist only he could see. Although it was difficult to tell for certain in the half-light of the pre-dawn, his feet were bare, and his long hair and straggly beard matted. In the block opposite, lights were coming on as people sleeping with their doors open because of the heat woke up; a woman stepped out and screamed at the raving man to piss off. At first he didn't seem to have heard her, but then he spun around and began pointing and shouting in her direction. On the balcony above the woman, a heavyset man appeared, a towel around his waist, and repeated her directive; down in the street the man wheeled away, muttering to himself, before beginning to shout at nobody again. Sadiya looked up and tried to blot out the argument. Behind the building the sky was lightening, high bands of cloud luminous against the pearl grey. More people emerged and stood shouting at the man in the street, so with one last look at the sky she went back inside and closed the door.

Out in the hall she stopped beside Arman's door. Most days he woke before her, and she often found him pacing restlessly around his room or making a mess in the kitchen, but this morning he was quiet, seemingly asleep despite the disturbance outside.

In the kitchen half-a-dozen beer bottles stood on the bench. She ignored them and instead drank first one and then two glasses of water, grateful for its cool wetness. It had been years since she allowed one of her colleagues into her home, yet the night before she had been surprised by how grateful she had been to Findlay for his preparedness to spend a few hours with her, and the feeling that she wasn't alone. While she drank, she pulled up the latest reports on Nasreen. Her feeds were crowded with updates and news items, posts and videos on socials that had been voted up or down, but she ignored them, and instead paused over a satellite image of the storm, gazing at its immense wheel, the vast spiral of cloud bulging outwards from the planet's surface like a blister.

For a moment or two she tried to think through what its effects would be when it hit, but she couldn't make sense of it, so instead she flicked the images away and pulled up the video from the car once more, in the hope she might notice something she had missed the night before. The fact the man had been masked suggested he had come prepared, but for which of them? Casey or Nina? And the mask's holographic fabric meant he was probably somebody who understood how to evade security. Thinking back to her encounters with Morrison, she found it difficult to imagine him possessing that sort of expertise. But it was never safe to assume anything about men like him: dig a bit deeper and you often found levels of planning and scheming that were completely at odds with their outward appearance. On the other hand, she had little doubt some of the people he knew would be familiar with techniques designed to confuse security systems, and it was entirely possible Nina's brother Stefan did as well. But why would Morrison or Jay's associates have wanted to harm Nina? Scrolling the video forward she paused on the frozen image of Casey running from her assailant, the look of fear on her face. What had she just seen?

Lowering her screen she leaned back. The night before, the forecast for today had been 47 degrees, with humidity in the territory that could kill. Yet they still didn't have a clue where Casey was, or even whether she was still alive. What they did know was that whoever killed Nina took Casey. And if they were going to kill her they could have done it then, and left her body with the car. Which meant it was at least possible she was alive. And, perhaps more importantly, that the key to finding out where she was lay in understanding what happened to Nina.

There was a clatter from Arman's room. She fell still, listening. But whatever it was had stopped. She went back out to the balcony. The man in the street was gone. In the early morning light, the city was peaceful. The sky was apricot to the east, the air heavy with the smell of salt and the approaching heat, the soft shadows still lingering in the lee of the buildings. Casey was out there somewhere. She needed to find her.

Her assistant interrupted to tell her Findlay was calling. She answered immediately.

'They released Morrison.'

'What the fuck? When? Why?'

'Last night, around midnight. They're saying it was a mistake. The place is in chaos with everybody trying to get ready for the storm.'

'Was he fitted with a tracker?'

'Apparently not.'

'Have you spoken to Lily's mother?'

'No. I called you as soon as I found out.'

'Right. I'll call her now. Then we need to get over to the station and work out what happened.'

'Agreed.'

Sadiya hung up and swore to herself. Glancing at the time again she saw it was only just after six. She dashed off a message to Malila.

Can you come as soon as possible? Have to get to work right away.

For a second or two she waited, watching the receipts, hoping for some sign Malila might be awake and able to reply. When none came, she took a deep breath and went through to her bedroom and began to pull on her clothes.

*

Tasim woke at first light. Sitting up he looked around, relieved to see he was still alone. Axel had been nowhere to be seen when he emerged from the apartment building the day before; relieved to be rid of him he had fled in the opposite direction to the way he had arrived, only slowing down when he was several blocks away.

Unwilling to go back to Central, he had found another park and waited for dark, doing his best to ignore the pangs of hunger and the constant fear that Axel was going to find him as he waited for sleep. He knew he would have to try to find food today, but for now he wanted to be ready the moment the man got back in the van.

Out on the road three army trucks swept by, troops seated inside them alongside bundles of construction gear. The night before there had been men in uniform in the park, taking people's details and offering to evacuate them before the storm arrived, but Tasim had stayed out of their way in case they decided to take him by force.

He knew he could not risk taking the bus, and so he walked, but as the minutes ticked by he felt himself growing more and more uneasy. The tracker he had stolen from the man's apartment and placed under the van as he left the building the day before showed it had not moved, but he did not know how long he had until that changed. He sped up, walking faster and trying not to think too hard about what lay ahead. Was he really capable of doing this? What if the man caught him before he worked out where the girl was?

Here and there beside the road there were mobile alert systems telling people to find shelter and to make sure their details on the emergency notification and location systems were up to date. He had just passed one when an alert pinged on his phone. He opened it and saw the van was moving. Not taking his eyes off the screen he started to run.

*

Sadiya was in the car park at the station when Sienna finally answered. She explained the situation and apologised before asking Sienna to contact her immediately if Morrison turned up on her doorstep or tried to contact her.

'I have enough to deal with getting ready for the storm without wasting time on David,' said Sienna.

Sadiya hesitated, surprised by the other woman's tone. 'It's important we find him. He's a person of interest in the disappearance of a five-year-old girl.'

'I know that,' said Sienna. 'But I'm not the one who let him go.'

Findlay was waiting in reception.

'Anything?' she asked as she hurried towards him.

'Not yet,' he said. 'How did it go with his partner?'

'She said she hadn't seen him.'

'Did you believe her?'

'I did. And I'm pretty sure I woke her up, which suggests that if he's going there, he's not there yet.'

In the back room they found the officer responsible for the cells, who told them he didn't know what had gone wrong, and that the officer in charge was now off duty.

'And you're sure nobody placed a trace on him?'

'There doesn't seem to be a request for that.'

'Because why would anybody follow basic procedure?' Sadiya said, making sure her anger was clear.

As they left, she noticed Findlay look back and catch the officer's eye. For a brief second, she half-expected him to give the idiot a look that suggested she was being unreasonable, womanly, and found herself steeling herself for the tiny betrayal, but instead he stared at the other man coldly.

'I'm going to make sure whoever did this ends up on report,' he said.

The officer laughed. 'You do that,' he said.

'Do you think somebody had him released on purpose?' she said once they were back in the lift.

'It's more likely it was some kind of mistake,' said Findlay. 'You've seen what it's like in there: nobody has any idea what's going on.'

'So you think it was a cock-up?'

Again the hesitation. 'Perhaps.'

'Or perhaps what?'

'I think cock-ups tend to happen when people think cases aren't important.'

'Or when detectives aren't popular, and people see a chance to fuck with them,' she said grimly.

'That too.'

Before she could reply they rounded the corner to the situation room and found Khoury and Gunasekera waiting outside.

Sadiya stopped. 'What is it?'

Khoury and the younger officer exchanged a glance. 'We wanted to wait, to tell you in person,' said Khoury.

'Tell me what?'

'We've been taken off the investigation,' said Khoury. 'Reassigned to disaster prep.'

'On whose authority?'

'Don't know,' said Khoury. 'But it's official.'

'What about Larkin and Novak?'

'Them as well,' said Gunasekera.

'Wait here. I'm going to talk to Nguyen and get to the bottom of this.'

Khoury stepped after her as she turned away. 'Detective Sergeant?' she said. Sadiya stopped and looked back. 'I want you to know this wouldn't have been our choice. Not any of us.'

'Thank you,' she said.

Although it was only just seven, Nguyen was in her office. She stood up as they walked in. 'Sadiya, Paul, I'm glad you're here.'

'You can't be serious,' Sadiya declared. 'Casey is still missing. If we don't find her by tomorrow we probably won't.'

'I'm aware of that,' said Nguyen.

'So you're closing us down?'

'No. I'm leaving the two of you on the case.' She sighed. 'I understand what this means. But you must have seen the projections for what the storm is going to do. We need all the resources we can muster to deal with that.'

Sadiya regarded the other woman coldly. 'Thanks for nothing,' she said.

Outside in the hall Sadiya stopped. 'We don't have time for this shit. If we don't find her by tomorrow we never will.'

'So what do we do?' said Findlay.

She took a breath, tried to think. 'There's no point chasing after Morrison now. We have to concentrate on what happened to Nina, work out who was behind that. Let's begin by talking to Emma again. See whether we know everything about what happened with Jay. Then we need to talk to Manning again, see if we can get something more out of him. If there's some connection to Horizon or the Badangi development I want to know what it is.'

They took Sadiya's car. Although it was early the streets were already busy, crowded with people trying to get out of the city or to pick up supplies. Down in the Floodline they parked near the tideline and set off for Emma and Jay's. The tide was high, and water covered the road and footpaths in many places, a smell of effluent and rotting food filling the air. As they followed the walkway out through the half-submerged buildings Sadiya remembered her father talking about the sea, the impossibility of holding it back.

Neither Emma nor Jay answered the door. Sadiya knocked for a second time and then asked her assistant to call Emma. The call went through almost immediately.

'She's at the clinic,' she said as she hung up.

'What's she doing there?' asked Findlay.

'Let's find out,' said Sadiya.

She called Larkin while they were on the way.

'You've heard?' he said when he answered.

'I have,' said Sadiya.

'I'm sorry. I only found out myself an hour ago.'

'That's okay. I'm grateful for what you've done. We're at Emma and Jay's place now, but he's not here, and she says she's at the clinic. Do you know anything about that?'

Larkin was silent for a moment. 'No, although it doesn't surprise me. She was very wound up when I dropped her home last night. Almost manic.'

'And how were things with Jay?'

'Messy. She was furious with him.'

'That's good to know,' said Sadiya. 'You haven't told either of them you've been reassigned?'

'No. I thought that was better coming from you.' He paused, and when he spoke again his voice cracked. 'I hope you find her.'

The clinic's windows were already covered with sheets of plywood and somebody had piled sandbags across the entrance. Sadiya and Findlay opened the door and stepped over them. The reception area was crowded with people, many of them holding children on their knees or sitting with older relatives. Than was standing behind the desk talking to a thin woman in a yellow dress. He lifted a hand to interrupt her when he saw them.

'Detectives,' he said.

'Emma said she was here,' said Sadiya.

Than's face was flushed and he seemed flustered, uneasy. 'Yes. She's out the back.'

He told the woman in the yellow dress he'd be back in a moment and led them through the door. At the end of the corridor he stopped in front of a second door. 'We told her she didn't have to come in,' he said, then knocked twice and ushered them through.

The room had once been a kitchen, but had been converted into a storeroom with two beds in it. Shelves stacked with medical supplies lined the walls, and boxes and packets were spread across the floor.

Emma was crouched at one end, packing rolls of bandages into one of the boxes. She looked around, and seeing it was Sadiya and Findlay, stood up.

Her face was drawn and her eyes large. Sadiya knew immediately she hadn't slept. She had seen this before, the way people began to slip free of themselves, to lose their moorings.

'I didn't expect to find you here,' Sadiya said.

'I couldn't sit around anymore. The last time a storm came through this whole area flooded. Dr Ballard and Dr Shibli are trying to move people who need medical care away from the water, but I wanted to help make sure the clinic is prepared.'

'Where will the doctors take everybody?' asked Sadiya.

Emma pulled another box down and began to fill it with bottles of antiseptic. 'There's a school hall not far from here. They're setting up there in case anybody needs care. Other people have got friends inland they can shelter with. Some will probably take their chances here.'

Sadiya nodded. She knew what that meant. 'And you? Where will you go?'

'I'll stay.' She fixed Sadiya with a look of frightening intensity. 'I need to, in case Casey comes back.' As she spoke, she kept packing, faster and faster. Packets began to spill and fall. Finally, she reached for another packet, but knocked the box. She grabbed at it, but only succeeded in sending it flying, spilling packets of bandages all over the floor. She clenched and unclenched her fists, then let out a sort of whimper. 'I can't do this. What if you don't find her before the storm? What then?' She slumped to the floor and began to weep.

Sadiya knelt down and put an arm around her. She was thinner than Sadiya had realised, and her skin was warm to the touch, as if she were on fire. At Sadiya's touch she crumpled sideways and pressed her face into Sadiya's shoulder. Sadiya stroked her hair in silence while Emma sobbed. After a minute or so Emma pulled away and tried to compose herself.

'She's going to be okay, isn't she? You're going to find her?'

'We're doing our best.'

Emma stared at her. 'This is my fault.'

'Why's that?' Sadiya asked carefully.

Emma squeezed her fists tighter. 'I was the one who wanted to move down here. After the floods up north I couldn't be there anymore. Every time it rained I started to panic. Our neighbours, they died when the levee broke. All five of them, drowned in their house. Jay found their bodies in the upstairs room; they'd been trapped there when the water rose. I said I couldn't do it anymore, that we had to leave. But if we'd stayed up there none of this would have happened. Casey would be okay.'

'You couldn't have known,' said Sadiya.

'I'm her mother. It's my job to keep her safe. I can't stop thinking about the night she went missing. Why did I let her go out? Why didn't I tell her she had to stay close?'

'You can't plan for this kind of thing,' said Sadiya.

'Jay says she's careless, that she won't do what she's told, but that's not it. She's just a little girl. She trusts people.'

'Does Jay get angry when she's careless?' said Findlay.

Emma looked at him for a long moment. Then she nodded.

'Does that happen a lot?' asked Sadiya.

'You have to understand, he wouldn't do anything to her. At least nothing like this.'

'Are you sure about that?' asked Sadiya.

Emma hesitated for brief moment. 'Yes,' she said.

'But is it possible something he did or somebody he knows might have put her at risk?'

Emma was quiet for a second or two. 'I don't know. Maybe,' she said at last.

'What about Nina Lukic?' said Sadiya. 'Is there any chance he knew her?'

'I don't see how.'

'What about the place Casey went missing? Nina worked for Horizon, who own that building and a lot of the properties around it. Is it possible Jay had some contact with them he hasn't told us about? Or that somebody wanted to keep something there hidden?'

'Like what?' She shook her head. 'None of it makes any sense.'

Sadiya was about to press her when Findlay caught her eye. She paused for a moment and then placed a hand on Emma's arm. 'Thank you,' she said. 'I promise we're doing everything we can.'

Emma didn't reply.

'What do you think?' said Findlay when they were out in the car park.

'I think she's in a bad way, but I'm not sure she knows more than she's already told us.'

'And Jay?'

'I don't trust him, but he has an alibi for when Casey went missing. And it wasn't him in the video.'

'Then who was it? Could it have been somebody he knows, or who knows him?'

'Perhaps. But what's the connection to Nina?'

Findlay didn't reply.

'Come on. I want to talk to Manning again,' she said.

*

Arman emerged from his room to find the apartment empty. He stopped, the gnawing certainty he had forgotten something rising in him. He couldn't shake the feeling there was somewhere he needed to be. Was it Pandit he was supposed to be meeting? Or the other one, the Australian? No, that was before, he hadn't seen Pandit in years. The houses, the painting, the apartments, they blurred into one, the details slipping from his grasp, like wind. Like water.

He looked at the open door behind him. This apartment. Whose was it? Why was he here? Suddenly something occurred to him.

What if this was a trick? What if they were keeping him here? What if they were watching him? He shuffled back into his room, staring around. Were there cameras? He couldn't see any, but that didn't mean they weren't there. A pair of trousers hung over a chair: he pulled them on and went back out into the living area. He knew there was something he was afraid of, something he must not forget, but it had already gone, leaving only the knowledge that he had forgotten. There was a rattle as a key turned in the lock. He dropped back against the wall. A woman called out hello. He knew that voice. She was the one who talked with the other woman, the one who sometimes reminded him of his daughter. Where was she now? He heard a clatter – her bag on the table? Then she called his name again and crossed towards his bedroom door. She knocked, once, twice, then pushed it open.

Arman ignored her, trying to hold onto memories that kept slipping away from him. But now one was there, and he held onto it. It wasn't long before the monsoon in the year after everything began to unravel, the year that the Melt really began. It hadn't been a surprise. The disasters had been accelerating for a decade or more, droughts in India and Africa followed by hurricanes in the Atlantic and floods in Pakistan and Europe and fires across Australia and equatorial Africa and America and Russia. In Siberia and the Yukon, the earth had begun to buckle and split as methane poured forth, further accelerating the seemingly unstoppable heating of the planet. But as that year had rolled on it had begun to seem increasingly clear that the planet had passed some kind of point of no return. In Brazil the Amazon burned, the once-lush rainforest consumed in a vast conflagration that spread halfway across the continent, while in southern Africa, Australia and India, a series of heatwaves pushed temperatures past 50 degrees and left tens of thousands dead. Finally, in December, temperatures in parts of the Antarctic reached 30 degrees, and stayed there. As the world watched in disbelief, the meltwater atop the ice sheets began to form vast rivers that flowed downwards towards the ocean, carving an expanding network of canyons. In places where the coast was exposed, these torrents swept churning cascades of sediment into the ocean; elsewhere they crashed down off the face of the glaciers like a thousand Niagaras. Yet it was the movement of water lower down they should have been watching, the influx of warm water beneath the ice. Under Thwaites and Pine Island, Lambert and other glaciers, vast caves began to form, the water spreading deeper, lubricating the ice, until these huge rivers of ice began to tumble forward, collapsing under their own weight, and as they did, the immense weight of the ice sheet behind them began to slip forward, crashing into the ocean.

The scientists called it Marine Ice Cliff Instability, a strangely anodyne name for a process so immense in its scale and implication; on footage filmed by drones, huge walls of ice – some hundreds of metres high – collapsed into the ocean, sending waves rolling outwards, the newly calved icebergs, some the size of cities, rolling and roiling in the water like logs tumbling into a river. For a time, there was a fad for memes featuring videos of the process, slow-motion images of the explosions as they struck the water, sending spumes of spray shooting kilometres into the air.

There had been an air of unreality in those months, a sense the future had come unmoored. Of course the truth was things had come unstuck long before, and this unstoppable tide of catastrophe was just the future that had been created decades before catching up with the world. It felt like standing on a beach waiting for a tsunami to strike, or like they were falling but hadn't yet hit the ground, Leah said to him one morning as they lay in bed listening to the sound of the building waking up. Arman didn't answer, and after a few seconds she turned and pressed her body against his, her skin cool, her breath moving on his neck. For a moment it felt like a truce, an interregnum in the argument they had been having for weeks. She wanted to return to Australia, to make sure the four of them were safe; he was resisting.

He wasn't certain why: he knew she was right, that they would be safer there, that when the disaster really arrived it would strike here faster and harder. But even knowing what was on its way didn't change his sense of loss, or the feeling that leaving was a sort of betrayal.

While Leah made breakfast for Lina and Sadiya, he went down to the tide gauge the ministry had installed on the beach not far from their building to check the level. It had become an obsession of his, a daily ritual. Yet it wasn't calming, nor reassuring; instead, it was more like worrying at a scab, a compulsion he didn't seem able to control. The gauge showed the water had risen another two millimetres over the past week, an increase that would have been thought impossible even a year before, yet which now seemed quite routine. When he was done he looked around. At first glance the sea appeared still, its surface like grey silk in the early morning light, yet small waves broke softly on the dirty sand, and farther out the water moved gently, its surface creased by tiny perturbations, the constantly shifting pattern of interference and refraction driven by the wind and tides and currents, a reminder that water was the source of all life, the medium that connected everything. But Arman also knew the water was a force no human could resist, a destroyer that swept all before it. How could he reconcile these two?

He heard a rumble of thunder. The sky was grey, heavy, the first rain of the monsoon almost here. It was already raining inland, and there were heavy falls forecast for later in the day here as well. The year before, the rains had come late or not at all, causing crops to fail and leaving many hungry and desperate; this year they were hoping for better. Overhead the thunder rumbled again, and a moment later a drop of rain struck the water, ripples breaking its dark surface, followed by another and another. He turned and sprinted back towards the cover of the building, one hand held above his head to keep the rain at bay.

*

Tasim was almost at the corner of the street where the apartment building stood when the van swung around the corner ahead and towards him. Worried the man might recognise him, he ducked behind a pole until it passed, then took off after it.

Although the traffic was slow the van soon left him behind, but Tasim jogged on, his phone held in front of him so he could keep track of its movements. At first its route made little sense: after driving for a short distance along the main road it had turned aside and started weaving through a series of back streets. But Tasim quickly realised its curious path must be designed to avoid passing through traffic cameras.

After about ten minutes the van stopped near a train station. Tasim slowed down, watching to see if it was going to stay where it was, but after a few minutes it resumed its crabwise motion through the streets, this time heading towards the tideline, where it stopped again. Tasim came to a halt, sweat pouring down his face. The van was now only a couple of kilometres from where he was. Checking the map again he tried to decide whether he should head towards the place the van had stopped the first time, or to where it was now. After a moment he decided he would aim at its current location.

The van remained stationary as he cut across the streets towards it. The area he was passing through seemed to be mostly residential – blocks of apartments and gardens – but it was difficult to mistake the air of agitation. In many of the driveways people were packing bags and boxes into cars, while on the balconies of the apartment blocks many of the doors and windows had been covered with tape. At one point he passed a supermarket with people queued outside; a little farther on two men were filling plastic tanks with water and loading them into the back of a ute.

After about twenty minutes his screen buzzed, alerting him to the fact the van was in motion again. He stopped, blinking and swaying in the heat, uncertain whether he should change direction again, but after a minute or so he realised it was heading back towards the apartment. Opening his bag he took out his water and drank the last of it, then headed on.

Eventually he reached a highway, which he crossed and then followed for a while before turning down the side street where the van had been parked. The street sloped down, away from the highway; at its end the water gleamed malignantly in the sun. On both sides were an assortment of abandoned industrial buildings, many still bearing signs advertising businesses long since closed or relocated: a car repair shop, a courier depot adorned with a cartoon figure of a man in a uniform, an empty gym, its windows smashed in and cabling hanging from its ceiling. He stared in the windows as he passed, searching for something that might lead him to the girl, until at last he reached the point where the street disappeared into the water. Ahead of him a makeshift duckboard connected to the last couple of buildings; beyond them dead trees lined a half-submerged fence and a tangle of rusting machinery.

Hot and exhausted, he slumped against the wall. There was no way to know which of these buildings the man had been visiting. And he had no idea who or what might be waiting inside if he attempted to force his way into any of them. But if he was going to find her, he had to try.

*

'You were good with her,' said Findlay as they accelerated away from the clinic.

'I can't imagine what she's going through.'

'Neither can I. But it's obvious you care.'

'Caring won't be much help if we don't find Casey before the storm hits,' she said, uncomfortably aware of the anger in her voice.

'We'll find her.'

Sadiya tightened her grip on the steering wheel. She knew he was trying to convince himself as much as her, but what scared her was that she wasn't certain she believed it herself anymore.

The young woman who had met them on Tuesday was waiting for them again when they stepped out of the lift on Manning's floor.

'Ariana, right?' said Findlay.

She smiled uncertainly. Although she was dressed as precisely as the first time they had met, her face was drawn and her hair was tied back and looked unwashed.

'That's right. Are you looking for Oliver again?'

'Is he here?'

'He should be back any minute. Would you like to wait?'

'Thank you,' said Sadiya.

'I'll let him know you're here,' she said. But as she turned to go Findlay stepped after her.

'Did you know Nina?' he asked.

She didn't answer. Suddenly she looked very young.

'Well?'

'Not really. I'm not sure any of us did.'

'But?'

'She was always good to me, to all of us. One time I made a mistake, with some documents. It was nothing huge: it was just that I sent some things to a client they shouldn't have seen. Oliver was furious: he screamed at me in front of everybody. Nobody did anything, except for Nina: she told him to calm down and leave me alone. Afterwards she came and found me in the bathroom, just to check I was all right.'

'Does Oliver act like that a lot?' Findlay asked.

Ariana folded her arms. 'Not at me so much, but sure. He gets angry.'

'At Nina?'

She looked uneasy. 'No. Or I don't think so.' She stopped, clearly uncomfortable. When neither of them replied she continued. 'It was different with her. They ... I don't know.'

Sadiya moved closer. 'Different how?'

Ariana shook her head. 'It's nothing. I'm probably wrong anyway.'

'Are you saying there was something between them?'

Before Ariana could answer the door behind her opened and Manning appeared. He was tieless, and his face was damp with sweat.

'Detectives. I wasn't expecting you.'

Sadiya stepped away from Ariana, careful to keep her face composed. 'We're sorry to interrupt. We just have a few more questions.'

Manning hesitated and then smiled. 'Of course,' he said. 'Come through.'

As he turned to usher them in, Sadiya caught Findlay's eye and gave a small shake of her head to warn him not to say anything until she did.

Manning showed them to a conference room. Once they were inside he motioned to them to sit and pulled out a chair for himself. Sadiya took a chair, but Findlay remained standing, his arms folded.

'I'm sorry but this will need to be quick,' Manning said. 'We've got a number of sites that still need to be secured before the storm gets here.'

'We wanted you to know we've recovered the security video from the car Nina was driving,' Sadiya said.

There was a flicker of hesitation. 'Really?' he said. 'Then you got access to the car's backups?'

'We did.'

Manning sat forward. 'That's good news, isn't it? If the video is intact, won't it show you who it was?'

'We're still waiting for the analysis, but we hope so.'

Manning's eyes flicked from her to Findlay and back again. 'That's great.'

Sadiya watched him carefully, waiting to see if he might say more. When he didn't she leaned back, keeping her eyes on him. She wasn't quite sure what to make of what Ariana had told them, but her gut told her the other woman was right, and Manning had been hiding something from them.

'When we spoke to you the other day you said you hardly knew Nina, that she was just a colleague,' she said.

This time Manning tensed slightly. 'That's right.'

'But that's not true, is it?'

'What do you mean?'

'We spoke to somebody who knew Nina. They said the two of you were close.'

Manning opened his mouth but didn't reply. Sadiya decided to take a chance.

'Were you in a relationship with Nina Lukic, Mr Manning?'

Manning's eyes slid away from theirs for a moment, something feral suddenly visible beneath his bland handsomeness before his control reasserted itself. 'It's not what you think.'

'We haven't told you what we think,' Findlay said.

Manning looked up at him with sudden dislike. But then he seemed to recover, and smiled, the crack in his composure disappearing as quickly as it had appeared. 'Nina and I were involved, last year, for a few months. But then it ended. I ended it. She was needy, difficult.'

'She didn't take it well?'

'You could say that. She threatened to tell my wife, to report me to Human Resources.'

'But she didn't?'

'Eventually we talked. She ... she saw reason.'

'And since then?'

'We've done our best to avoid each other. To be civil in the office. A complaint would be bad for both of us. I offered to have her assigned to a different unit, but she refused.'

'So, you haven't seen her outside the office since then?' Findlay asked.

'Last week she asked me if I'd have a drink with her after work. She said she wanted to talk.'

'And you went?'

'I knew I shouldn't have. But she seemed on edge. I was worried about her.'

'And what did she say?'

'We talked. She'd been having some trouble here and was thinking about applying for a new position, but that wasn't what was really on her mind. She wanted to talk about the situation with her brother.'

'Stefan?' asked Sadiya.

'That's right' said Manning, an edge of contempt in his voice. 'I mentioned him the other day, but he's trouble. He's always been trouble. Nina and he had money, their parents left it to them. She used hers to buy her flat. His ...' He shook his head. 'Nina said he pissed it away almost as soon as he got it.'

'Did she say how?'

'How do you think? Drinking, drugs, gambling. She bailed him out more than once, but eventually she couldn't help him anymore, and he ended up in prison. Since his release he's been in and out of rehab and on and off the streets. She stayed in contact with him and visited him as often as she could, but I don't know if that helped. He was so angry with her.' His voice slowed and grew gentler. 'My sister is an addict. I understand the way they resent you. It's not easy.' He smiled sadly. 'It was one of the things that drew us together, I think.'

'Was there something in particular she was concerned about that day?'

'She said that after he got out he started demanding money.' Manning swallowed. 'Making threats.'

'Threats?' said Sadiya. 'What kind of threats?'

'I don't think it was specific. He told her she'd be sorry if she didn't pay him what he was owed.'

'And she thought he was serious?' said Findlay.

'She didn't know what to think. She was very forgiving, and she loved him. I told her she should tell the police.'

'But she didn't?'

'I don't think so.' His face creased in pain. 'Do you suppose that if she had, she might still be alive? I should have insisted.'

'You said she'd been having trouble at work,' Findlay said. 'What kind of trouble?'

Manning shrugged. 'Oh, you know. Just work stuff. Personalities. Nothing major.'

'And you hadn't seen her outside of work other than that night?' Sadiya asked.

'No. It was only that one time.'

'And why didn't you tell us this last time we spoke?'

Manning looked uneasy. 'I'm sorry. I should have. But I ... I knew how it would look, and I can't afford to lose this job.'

'A guy like you must have plenty of options,' Findlay said.

'You think it's easy holding down a position like this? It's not. All these people, they rely on me. If I mess up, they suffer. And if I lose this job ...' He shrugged. 'My wife, my kids – what happens to them? We've been trying to get to New Zealand. You know that? Three years running we've entered the lottery. But we only meet the criteria if I keep working, if we've got the money when we get picked.'

Sadiya let his words hang in the air. 'We'll need to talk to anybody who knew her,' she said at last.

For a moment she thought Manning was going to refuse. But then he nodded. 'Of course,' he said. 'Anything I can do to help. Who would you like to begin with?'

Findlay smiled. 'Perhaps you could tell us who she worked with most closely?'

'That would be Marieke. She reported to Nina and they were friendly.'

'Is Marieke here?'

'Not today. She took disaster leave. I assume she's at home or on her way out of the city somewhere.'

Sadiya stood up and pushed her chair in. 'Perhaps you can send us her details?'

Manning's fingers tapped his screen. 'Already done. And, Detective Azad?'

Sadiya looked at him. His face was serious.

'I hope you understand why I held back. I hope I haven't made things harder. If there's anything I can do to help, if there's anything any of us can do to help, just say. Things between us didn't end well, but Nina is ...' He caught himself. 'I know I didn't treat her as well as I should have, but I really cared about her.'

At the lift Sadiya stopped and glanced back.

'What is it?' Findlay asked.

'Did you see the way Ariana reacted when Manning appeared?'

'Do you think she's frightened of him?'

'There's definitely something off about him. And he's been lying to us about Nina since the beginning.'

'He has an alibi.'

'His wife. We should talk to her again. And we need to access his phone records, find out where he was when Casey went missing. But before that we need to find Stefan again. See what he says about these threats Manning alleges he made. Then we track down this Marieke and see whether she knows anything. And I want to speak to Jay again.'

Findlay stopped.

'Why? We've seen the video. It wasn't him.'

She turned back towards him. 'His stepdaughter is missing. He's been aggressive and difficult, and he's got connections to white supremacists. I think that's enough reason to check we haven't missed anything.'

It was almost midday by the time they got to Stefan's place. Sadiya hammered on the door until a balding man in a white shirt appeared. Circles of moisture ringed his armpits and sweat beaded the flushed dome of his head.

'Yes?' he asked, his bulky form filling the doorway.

Sadiya held up her ID. 'We're looking for Stefan Lukic.'

The man lifted the pair of reading glasses that hung on a cord around his neck to his nose and examined her ID through them, blinking owlishly. Lowering his glasses again he regarded the two of them carefully. 'Can I ask why? Has something happened?'

'Perhaps you could start by telling us who you are,' said Findlay.

The man regarded them for another moment or two. 'My name's Brian Darcy. I'm a priest. I work with the men who live here, support them. When I arrived this morning they told me Stefan went out last night and hasn't been seen since. One of them told me he said his sister had been killed.'

'That's right. We were here yesterday evening, and we told him his sister had been murdered. Do you know where he might have gone?'

'I wish I did. He shouldn't be on his own at a time like this.'

'You think he's relapsed? That he's on some kind of bender?'

'I do. Stefan can be difficult and even quite aggressive, but he's surprisingly fragile underneath that, and very isolated. I know from my conversations with him that he and his sister have had their issues, but he also really depended on her. She was the only family he had left. Losing her ...' Darcy turned his hands upwards.

'Somebody told us Stefan had threatened her. Does that sound likely to you?'

Darcy shook his head. 'Obviously I can't be certain, but I don't think Stefan would have threatened his sister. And if he had, I can't believe he'd follow through.'

'Do you have any kind of tracking on residents?' Findlay asked.

Darcy looked at him in surprise. 'Of course not. That would be a terrible violation of their privacy.'

'So, you have no idea where Stefan is?'

'I'm afraid not.'

'If you hear anything – anything at all – please let us know,' said Sadiya. As she spoke, she sent him her contact details.

'Of course,' said Darcy. 'We're trying to get everybody somewhere safe, so hopefully he'll turn up.'

Darcy stood watching them as they walked back to the car. As they climbed in Findlay peered through the windscreen at him.

'Did you believe what he said about Stefan not being capable of hurting Nina?'

Sadiya started the car. 'I think people often do things in the moment that surprise others.'

'But?'

'But this wasn't in the moment. Whoever killed Nina planned it. They had gear there with them.'

'And that doesn't sound like Stefan.'

'No. It doesn't.'

While Findlay logged a request for sightings of Stefan with the facial rec systems, Sadiya drove them towards Marieke's. The traffic heading west and out of the city was heavy, the streets crowded with people trying to leave. Several times they passed army vehicles and teams of emergency workers loading sandbags and clearing drains. Sadiya watched them without speaking, trying not to think about what was coming.

Marieke's house was in Ashbury. The Cooks River had long since spilled its banks and submerged the racecourse and the area around it, but despite its proximity to the water, Marieke's street seemed as if it had changed little since the Melt. Red-brick houses with tiled roofs, white Federation trim, tree-lined footpaths. It was only on closer examination that the damage became apparent: old tarpaulins lashed to roofs, broken windows, plastic-covered piles of boxes and other garbage in yards.

A car was parked in the driveway when they pulled up, its rear hatch open. As Sadiya and Findlay approached the gate a woman emerged from the front door and hefted a suitcase into the back of the car. She was small, slim, her dark hair tied up in a scarf as if she had just stepped out of the 1950s.

'Ms Schoff?' Sadiya said, pausing at the gate.

The woman closed the back of the car and turned towards them. 'That's right. Who are you?'

Sadiya produced her ID. Marieke examined it. 'Is this about Nina?' she said, her face suddenly tired.

'It is. Is there somewhere we could talk?'

Marieke glanced towards the front door, shaded under the shallow veranda. 'Of course. But you'll need to be quick.'

She led them in. The hall was stacked with bags and boxes. A pet carrier was balanced on top of the nearest: as Marieke led them past it a cat let out a long howl.

In the living area at the back Marieke gestured to the dining table and the three of them sat down.

'I'm sorry if I sounded rude outside. I'm very happy to help. But I'm in a hurry.'

'Are you going somewhere?' Findlay asked.

'I have a friend who has a place in the Mountains. We're going to head up there before the storm hits.'

'We?' Sadiya asked.

'Me and my mother. She's sick. Cancer.'

'I'm sorry.'

'Thank you,' said Marieke. Although her tone was polite it suggested her mother's illness wasn't a topic she was interested in discussing further.

'We understand you worked with Nina,' Findlay said.

'That's right. I report to her.' Her mouth tightened. 'Reported.'

'Would you say you knew her well?' Sadiya asked.

'Not really. She was always easy to deal with, but she kept her personal life very separate from her work life.'

'Do you have any idea why that was?'

Marieke looked at them for a second or two. Then she seemed to come to some kind of decision. 'I don't know a lot about her background, but it was pretty complicated. Her mother died a few years ago, and there is – or was – a stepfather, but she wasn't in contact with him. There's a brother as well, but he's had problems.'

'She told you that?' Findlay asked.

'Not really. Last year she used to visit somebody every week. One day I called her when she was out of the office and because I recognised the waiting room, I realised she was at the rehab centre at the Marie Bashir. When she got back, I asked her whether there was anything to talk about, but she said it was fine, she'd just been visiting her brother.'

'You mean Stefan?'

She nodded.

'Do you know anything else about her relationship with him?' Sadiya asked.

Marieke looked at her for a moment, clearly considering what to say. 'I know it was difficult. But I think she felt responsible for him. She told me her stepfather was violent, and Stefan was stuck with him a lot longer than her. I think she felt guilty about that, like she'd let him down. And Stefan was angry with her and blamed a lot of his problems on her. She said his anger frightened her, but also that she thought she owed him.'

Sadiya made a note. 'Can you think of anybody who might have wished her harm? An ex-lover, perhaps?'

Marieke shook her head. 'I wish I could. I've been racking my brains ever since I heard what happened, but she always seemed so self-contained, so in control that it was hard to know what was really going on with her.'

'What about at work? Any tension there?'

Again, the hesitation.

'Ms Schoff?'

'Over the past couple of weeks, it seemed like something was bothering her. I'm not sure what it was, but she was in her office a lot. And one day last week she disappeared all day. I assumed it had something to do with her brother, but now I'm not sure.'

'Do you remember what day?'

Marieke thought for a moment. 'Thursday. I remember because she was supposed to be in a meeting and she didn't turn up.'

'And do you have any idea where she was?'

'I'm afraid not.'

'But she turned up on Friday as normal?'

'No. She worked from home on Friday.'

'What can you tell us about your boss, Oliver Manning?' Findlay asked.

A look of contempt flickered across Marieke's face. 'Oliver? What do you want to know?'

'You don't like him?'

She shrugged. 'He's fine.'

'Not exactly a rousing endorsement.'

'Have you ever seen his wife?' When neither of them answered, she shrugged. 'She looks like she'd shatter if you touched her.'

'Did he and Nina get along?' Sadiya asked.

Marieke gave her a sharp look. 'Do you think he had something to do with what happened to her?'

'Would that surprise you?'

Marieke paused, thinking. 'I don't like him, but the notion he could do something like this . . .' She hesitated, as if an idea she didn't like had lodged itself in her brain. 'It doesn't seem possible.'

'And Nina? What did she think of him?'

'Nina never said anything, but I'm pretty sure something happened between the two of them last year. When I asked Nina about it she said they'd had an argument, and it was fine, but I wondered whether it was more than that. And recently . . .'

'What?'

'I don't know. Nina seemed to start going out of her way to avoid being with him in the office, but one evening I saw the two of them talking around the corner from the building. It looked like they were arguing.'

'Do you have any idea what about?'

Marieke shook her head.

'Is there anything else you could tell us?' Sadiya asked. 'Anything at all?'

'I wish there was, but that's all I know.' She stood up. 'I'm sorry, but if there's nothing else, I really have to go.'

Marieke stopped in the doorway as they stepped out into the heat. 'You're going to find who did this, aren't you?' she said.

'We're going to try,' Sadiya said.

Marieke stared at her for a long moment and then nodded. But when she reached the gate Sadiya glanced back to find Marieke was still standing in the shadowed space of her doorway, watching them.

'Where do you suppose Nina went last Thursday?' Findlay asked when they were back in the car.

'Good question.'

'I'll put in a request, see whether we can find anything about where her car was.'

Sadiya was about to reply when an alert pinged. She scanned it and began to run towards the car.

'What is it?' said Findlay.

'It's Morrison. There's been some kind of incident at Lily's school. We need to get over there right away.'

They took the back way, cutting through Marrickville and Tempe to the Princes Highway and then up to Green Square. A small knot of people were gathered outside the school in the shade of the tree at its front when they arrived, parents and children talking and staring across the road, where Morrison sat with his face to the wall, his hands secured behind his back with zip cuffs, a heavyset male uniform standing just to one side of him. A short way down the street a female uniform stood with Lily and a woman in business clothes Sadiya recognised as Lily's mother, Sienna.

They jogged across the road towards them. Lily turned to look at them as they approached. Findlay smiled at her.

'Hi Lily,' he said.

The woman turned to face them. 'Who are you?' she demanded.

'I'm Detective Azad. We spoke on the phone.'

'Where were you? Why was this allowed to happen?' she demanded, her thin face furious.

'We got here as fast as we could,' Sadiya said. 'Could you tell us what's going on? Is Lily all right?'

'Lily is fine, no thanks to you.'

'David is aware he's not supposed to try to contact Lily,' said Sadiya.

'Well he has. So what are you going to do about it?' said Sienna.

Sadiya took a step away. 'I'm happy to speak to you afterwards,' she said. 'For now, we need to speak to David.' Sienna opened her mouth as if to continue her tirade, but behind her Lily coughed. Sienna glanced at her.

'Just keep him away from me and Lily,' she said.

Morrison twisted around to look up at them as they walked towards him. His face was tearstained and dirty. 'Detective,' he said. 'This is all a misunderstanding.'

Sadiya ignored him. 'Walk me through what happened,' she said to the uniform.

'One of the teachers saw him hanging around; they called us and we arrived just as the kids were chucking out. He was with the girl when we got here, but when we approached him, he made a run for it.'

'It wasn't like that,' said Morrison. 'I just wanted to talk to Lily. To explain.'

'Did he attempt to take the girl with him when he ran?'

At this the uniform, who had been studiously avoiding looking at Morrison, looked down.

'He did.'

'No,' moaned Morrison. 'I just wanted to talk to her.'

'And the mother?'

'She arrived just after we arrested him.'

Sadiya went and stood over Morrison. 'You know it's a term of your bail that you stay away from Lily?'

'And from schools,' Findlay said, stepping in beside her.

Morrison shrank away from him. 'I didn't hurt anybody. I just wanted to see her.'

'Don't give me that shit,' Findlay said. 'You know the rules.'

Morrison's eyes widened. 'I never touched her. I promise.'

Findlay made a sound of disgust and turned away.

'Please,' Morrison said.

Sadiya knelt down next to him. 'How did you get out?'

Morrison looked surprised. 'What are you talking about?'

'Your bail. Who arranged it?'

'I don't know. They just told me I could go.'

'And where have you been?'

Morrison began to sob, tears streaming down his cheeks. 'Sienna threw me out. All my stuff. She put it in the street.'

Sadiya didn't move, remembering Lily's mother's fury. Perhaps she'd misunderstood.

'You know you couldn't go there anyway.'

Morrison nodded hopelessly.

Sadiya stood up and straightened her shirt. The heat made it difficult to think straight. 'Process him,' she said. 'And find somebody to take the mother and the girl home.'

'Please,' Morrison sobbed. 'Don't do this. I didn't do anything.'

'What do you think?' Findlay asked as they crossed back through the traffic towards their car.

'I don't fucking care,' Sadiya said.

'You don't think he had anything to do with Casey?'

'No. And we can't waste any more time on him.'

Back in the car, she cracked open a bottle of water and gulped it down. Overhead the sky shimmered, the glare blinding. Her head was pounding.

'None of this makes any sense.'

Findlay sat down beside her. 'Perhaps there's something we missed. Someone we missed.'

'No. One of them knows who killed Nina, and whoever that is knows where Casey is.'

Findlay didn't reply.

'What?' Sadiya demanded.

He looked uncomfortable. 'Unless she's got water there's no way she can still be alive.'

'You think I don't know that?' Sadiya snapped.

Findlay lifted his hands in surrender. 'I'm not the enemy here.'

Before she could reply her assistant interrupted her to say she had a call from Brian Darcy. She answered immediately.

'Detective Azad?' said Darcy. 'We spoke earlier about Stefan Lukic?'

'Yes, Reverend Darcy. Of course.'

'I've had a message from one of our residents. He says he saw Stefan up near Broadway a few minutes ago.'

'Where exactly?'

'In the Sports Hotel under the shopping centre. Do you know it?'

'Of course. Did he say anything else?'

'I'm afraid not. Only that he was in the bar.'

'What is it?' Findlay asked as she hung up.

Still angry, she didn't look at him. 'Stefan's been seen near Broadway.'

Sadiya accelerated away through the traffic, leaning on the horn as they fought to get through the lines of cars choking the streets and ignoring the angry stares of the people they passed. They pulled up on Bay Street. The building that housed the shopping centre had started life as a department store in the first half of the twentieth century, and while its interior had been refitted several times over the years, its clocktower-topped exterior still spoke to the solidity of an earlier age.

The Sports Hotel was at street level, nestled behind the escalators. The footpath in front of it was crowded with shoppers pushing trolleys laden with bottles of water and other supplies. As they pushed their way through towards the door Sadiya's phone chimed: glancing at her messages in her lenses she saw it was Nguyen and flicked it away.

It was cooler inside, the air filled with the sweet stink of spilled beer and fried food. Behind the bar a woman was loading bags of ice into a fridge, while an older man sat in one corner nursing a drink. Sadiya approached the woman and flashed her ID.

'Police,' she said, then held up her phone to show the woman an image of Stefan.

'Have you seen this man?'

The woman leaned closer. Her head was shaved on one side, and a pale tattoo of a coiling vine snaked across her scalp.

'Sure. He just left.'

'Do you know where he went?' she asked, looking back towards the street.

'He was drunk. When I told him I couldn't keep serving him he abused me. If you find him you can tell him he's barred.'

'Thanks,' Sadiya said, flicking the woman her number. 'If he comes back, call me.'

'Sure,' the woman said.

Findlay paused, looking over the bar. 'That's a lot of ice,' he said.

'If the power goes it might stop some of the food from spoiling.'

'Good luck,' Findlay said.

The woman looked at him, her manner softening suddenly. 'You too,' she said.

They walked back out into the heat and glare. Sadiya pointed down Bay Street. 'I'll check out here. You look inside.'

While Findlay pushed his way up the escalators, Sadiya shoved her way through the crowd to the next corner, where a narrow street ran between the centre and the car park next door. She jogged down it until she reached a small area of empty ground at the far end. A couple of tents had been set up beside a garden bed on one side of the space, while on the other half a dozen men and women sat slumped on bedrolls in the shade of a large tree. Sadiya checked Stefan was not among them, then headed on down the street behind them. At the next corner, more tents and shelters clogged the road; she paused, staring down the street towards the flood barriers at its end, but there was no sign of him. Sweat pouring down her face, she jogged on, ducking down to look through the open flaps of the tents. She had almost reached the tideline when there was a shout behind her. She stopped and turned around. Back near the corner a man shoved another against a wall, then slammed his arm into his neck, pinning him against the bricks. Even at a distance she recognised the man against the wall as Stefan.

'Hey!' she shouted, as she sprinted towards them. The man holding Stefan turned. His dirty brown hair was cut in a close-cropped mullet and his face was wasted and raw from years on the streets. He took in her appearance and paused just long enough to show he didn't have to stop if he didn't want to. Then he dropped his arm and stepped back, his hands raised in the air. Stefan slumped to the ground, his hands on his neck.

'What's going on here?' Sadiya demanded when she reached the pair of them.

'This cunt tried to take our water,' said Stefan's assailant.

Sadiya stared down at Stefan curled up on the asphalt. He was vilely drunk, his curly hair flat with sweat. Reaching down, she grabbed his shirt and dragged him to his feet.

'I'll deal with him,' she said. The man who had assaulted Stefan spat on the ground beside her. 'Fucking maggots,' he said, and turned away.

Sadiya waited for a moment and then pulled Stefan around to face her. 'We need to talk,' she said.

She dragged Stefan into a doorway out of the sun. Propping him against the wall she sent her location to Findlay and then knelt down.

'What are you doing here?' she said. 'Is this about Nina?'

Stefan turned his face away. 'Piss off,' he slurred.

'Because if it is, the best thing you can do is talk to me. Help me find out who did this to her.'

He didn't move.

'I don't have time for this shit,' she said. 'Are you upset because she's gone, or because you did something to her?'

Stefan swivelled around and tried to focus on her. 'I didn't do anything to her. I wouldn't. I couldn't.'

Findlay appeared at the corner. Sadiya waved to him and waited for him to join her.

'Are you sure about that? Because we spoke to her boss, and he seemed to think you were quite capable of hurting her.'

'Oliver?' Stefan spat. 'Oliver? That fucking arsehole. He was the one telling her not to help me. We were fine until he came along.' As he spoke Sadiya glimpsed the anger in him she had suspected was there all along.

'So, you've met Oliver?' Findlay asked.

'What? He didn't mention that? I bet he didn't tell you he threatened me either.'

'What?' Sadiya said. 'Oliver threatened you?'

Stefan laughed bitterly. 'He's got you fooled as well, hasn't he? Seems like such a great guy, but he's not.'

'Why don't you tell us about him?' Findlay said.

Stefan focused on Findlay as if searching for some indication Findlay was mocking him. Finally, he nodded.

'Sure. I met him last year. I was just out of hospital. I'd been trying to reconnect with Nina, to make some kind of amends. I . . .' He shrugged. 'I fucked things up. A lot. Anyway, I sent her a message, asked if she would meet me. Just to talk. She said yes, so we met for a coffee. I didn't really expect her to come, but she was Nina, so she did.' He sniffed, wiping his eyes. 'She didn't deserve any of this.'

Sadiya didn't reply. She knew enough addicts to know their displays of sentiment were usually about absolving themselves.

'So, we were talking and then this guy turned up and sat down with us. I didn't know him then, he was just some guy in a suit, but I could see Nina knew him, and she wasn't comfortable with him being there.

'Anyway, as we were leaving he got in front of me, and stopped, and when I looked up he was all up in my face, and told me to leave Nina alone – that she didn't need trash like me in her life, and that if I contacted her again he'd make sure I disappeared forever.'

'Did you take him seriously?' Sadiya asked.

Stefan sneered. 'Wouldn't you? He's a fucking psycho.'

'But you didn't leave her alone, did you?'

He shifted uneasily. 'What do you mean?'

'You were in contact until a week ago.'

'Sure.'

'And how did she seem the last time you saw her?'

Stefan blinked blearily. 'I don't know. Okay. Stressed, perhaps.'

'About what?'

'I don't know.'

'Are you sure about that?'

He nodded, but Sadiya saw the hesitation.

'We have information that you'd threatened her. That you were demanding money.'

Stefan's eyes widened. 'What? That's bullshit,' he said, his voice wavering, slightly too high. 'I'd never hurt her.'

'So what did you say to her?'

Stefan looked away. For a brief moment she saw the way his mind slipped from subject to subject, the ease with which he lied when it suited his purposes. The bottomless self-loathing and costless self-recrimination. Then he seemed to reach a decision.

'At first I was trying to help her,' he said. 'A few months ago I met her one afternoon. I could see she was upset, so I asked her what was going on. She said she'd found out somebody at work was doing something illegal. I told her she needed to tell somebody, but she said she was worried he might do something, hurt her in some way.'

'So, what happened?'

'Next time I saw her I asked her what she'd decided to do. She told me she hadn't done anything, that she'd made a mistake. I knew she was lying.'

Sadiya leaned back and regarded him coldly. 'So, you threatened to tell?'

Stefan stared at the ground.

'After she came to see you in hospital? And helped you?' said Findlay, his voice icy with contempt.

Stefan twitched. 'She only helped me because she felt guilty about leaving me when I was a kid.'

Sadiya shot Findlay a look. 'This person she thought had been skimming money. Do you know who they were?'

'No.'

'Was it Manning?' Findlay asked.

'I don't know. Perhaps. Probably. She was frightened of him, but she kept seeing him. It was like he had a hold over her.'

'And you don't know anything else? What the contracts were? Anything that might help us?'

Stefan subsided sideways, his face sweaty and puffy with drink. 'No.' Turning his face to the wall he began to sob. 'I'm sorry. I fucked everything up. Nina was only ever good to me.' He thumped his head into the wall. 'It's all my fault.'

Sadiya stepped back.

'I'm going to contact Father Darcy, tell him where you are.'

Stefan didn't answer, just kept bashing his head against the wall and sobbing.

'You'll wait here until he comes?'

Stefan made a choking sound, then nodded feebly.

'You think he's telling the truth? That it was Manning?' said Findlay as they headed back to the car.

'After what he and Marieke told us I'm sure of it,' said Sadiya. 'But we need something concrete before we can arrest him. Where are we on Nina's movements? Any update on where she was on Thursday when she disappeared from work?'

Findlay checked his screen. 'Nothing. But our request has to go through human oversight: if they're already closed due to the storm we may not get anything until they come back online.'

'Shit,' said Sadiya, throwing the car into gear and accelerating out into the traffic. 'Keep trying. In the meantime let's find Manning, see what else we can get out of him.'

They pulled up outside Horizon's headquarters. But as they walked into the foyer the security guard stood up and walked towards them, his hand raised in warning.

'I'm sorry, I'm afraid I'm going to have to ask you to leave,' he said.

Sadiya stared at him in disbelief. 'I'm sorry?'

'I've got instructions you're not to be admitted.'

'We're here on police business,' said Findlay.

The guard didn't move. 'I'm afraid I've got my orders. You'll have to take it up with your superiors.'

'Did Manning tell you to do this?' she demanded, staring at the guard.

'I'm sorry. There's nothing I can do.'

'A little girl is missing. If we don't find her before tomorrow she'll die,' she said. 'Manning knows where she is.'

The guard shifted uneasily but didn't step aside.

'You realise you're protecting a murderer,' she said.

'I'm sorry. I have my orders,' said the guard. 'If you want to come in you'll have to have some kind of warrant.'

Sadiya stared at him for a second or two and then shook her head in disgust and turned away. Findlay fell in behind her as she stalked out.

'Did you hear what he said about taking it up with our superiors?' she demanded once they were outside. 'This was us. Police.'

Findlay stopped and looked back at the building. 'But why would they do that?'

'I'm going to find out,' she said. She pulled up Nguyen's contact. A moment later Nguyen's image appeared in her lenses.

'Do you know anything about us being turned away from Horizon?' she demanded.

'I gather you've been back to their offices?'

'So, you did know?'

'I'm sorry, Sadiya, but I had no choice. Horizon have accused you and Findlay of harassing their staff.'

'What?'

'You heard me.'

'That's bullshit, and you know it. We have reason to believe one of their executives is involved in the murder of Nina Lukic, and very likely the abduction of Casey Mitchell.'

'I'm sorry. But until you have enough evidence to arrest him you need to stay away from Horizon and their employees.'

'You can't do this. What if Casey's still alive? If we delay questioning Manning, we lose valuable time.'

'This isn't negotiable. If you want to talk to Manning or anybody else at Horizon you'll need to arrange for an interview with a solicitor present.'

'We don't have time for that. We've got less than twenty-four hours before the storm hits. If we don't find Casey before then she may not survive.'

'I don't like this any more than you do, but my hands are tied. Given your history with Horizon it was hard enough to convince the assistant commissioner to let me keep you on the case.'

Sadiya hung up. 'They've said we can't talk to Manning without a lawyer present.'

'Fuck. So, what do we do now?'

She glanced up at the sliver of sky visible between the buildings, the shimmering blue of it. 'We need to work out what it was Nina knew. If we can find that we'll have enough to arrest him. And if we can do that it will lead us to Casey.'

*

Tasim woke facedown, the light so bright he could barely see. Turning over, he held a hand up to shield his eyes and blinked against the glare. He was on a beach. Wreckage floated in the shallows, rolling slowly in the gentle movement of the water.

He got to his feet, swaying unsteadily. He felt dizzy, outside himself. His backpack was still on his back, heavy with water. Other people were sprawled on the sand nearby, clothes plastered to their bodies. He staggered towards the closest. It was a man who lay on his back with his face turned away. The remains of his shirt hung loose from one shoulder, exposing dark skin gone blotchy. He knew he should touch him, prod him or shake him, see if he was alive, but the sight of his battered skin, its puffy texture, was too much, and he couldn't. He turned. The sea was turquoise in the glaring sun. A few metres offshore a boy in a green t-shirt was floating in the water. Tasim splashed through the warm water towards him and turned him over and recoiled. He was about ten, his thin limbs loose, his eyes open but unseeing. Something had struck him in the head, and the skin was puckered open in a great contusion above one ear, the edges turned pale in the water, what looked like white bone exposed beneath it.

He turned. Another body was floating nearby. He waded over to it. It was a woman, her dark hair fanning out around her head. He looked around dazedly, and then staggered back towards the sand. Further up the beach a man sat, staring out over the water, but Tasim ignored him, instead stumbling from one body to the next, searching for some sign of life. Finally, he came to a woman of his mother's age lying by the waterline. On the sand by her mouth the water trembled, her breath moving in and out. Tasim knelt beside her and, grabbing her shoulder, shook her until she opened her eyes. He was crying, he realised, although he hadn't noticed until that very moment, tears streaming down his face as he sank to the sand beside her and lay down, staring up.

He couldn't have said how long he lay there, but eventually he became aware of something overhead, a glinting dot in the impossible blue of the sky. Blinking, he sat up. Dimly, he realised it must be a drone, that the Australians had found them. He turned to look at the woman beside him. She was sitting up now as well, staring at the sea, her face blank with exhaustion and grief. Elsewhere on the beach other figures had begun to move as well.

Standing up again he began to search amongst the wreckage. He found a half-empty bottle of water, its base buried in the sand, and tearing it open drank greedily, and later a lifejacket with an envelope stuffed into it. Pulling it open he found a wad of banknotes in a plastic bag and slipped them in the waistband of his pants.

Finally, in the middle of the day, a black inflatable appeared from the north and turned into the bay. There were six men in it, all dressed in black uniforms, their heads covered by caps. Tasim and the others walked down the beach towards it as it approached the shore, the water creasing like liquid light around it. In the shallows the engine guttered out, and the men jumped out and splashed towards them, their faces hidden behind dark lenses. The front one had an orange beard; the men behind him were darker-skinned and clean-shaven. The two at the back carried snub-nosed machine guns.

Tasim stopped when he saw the weapons, as did a man beside him and a couple of others. But most of the others continued to advance. As the men in uniforms reached the sand a heavyset man with a dark moustache and wiry, greying hair rushed towards the man with the orange beard and waved his passport in Orange Beard's face. 'We claim asylum,' he shouted in heavily accented English. Two other men joined him, waving and shouting. Orange Beard lifted his hand, gesturing them to back away.

'Please,' he said. 'Keep back and stay calm, or we'll have to restrain you.'

Tasim stiffened, unable to take his eyes off the guns. The men held them loosely and casually, but something about their manner told Tasim that could change quickly.

'I said get back!' Orange Beard said again, louder this time.

But the man with the moustache didn't listen. He had produced other papers now, and was shouting, 'We are refugees! We are refugees!'

Orange Beard leaned backwards to avoid the papers being thrust at him, his movements poised, like the boys who used to train at the silat gym near Tasim's school, his face wearing a mask of amusement that the other man seemed not to have understood was really a threat. The man with the moustache waved his papers and shouted one more time, then without warning Orange Beard grabbed his wrist, wrenching his arm downwards and pushing him back so he fell to the sand.

'I said get back!' he snapped. The other two men who had been shouting at Orange Beard fell quiet and backed away as well. Orange Beard looked at Tasim and the others.

'This landing is an unauthorised entry under Australian law. Your presence here constitutes an offence, and as such you will be transported to a holding facility for processing. Until that time, you are under our control.' He stopped and looked around. 'Do any of you not understand what I'm saying?'

Several of the people on the beach turned to each other, speaking rapidly in Bahasa. Orange Beard ignored them.

'Right,' he said, pointing towards a spot higher up the beach. 'If you can all line up, we'll begin.' He nodded to the men behind him, and they splashed forward. Tasim moved towards the spot Orange Beard had indicated, careful to stay ahead of the men with the guns, who were shouting as they herded them up the sand. They were smiling, but they weren't kind smiles; they were contemptuous, the smiles of men who had little regard for others.

Once they were lined up, Orange Beard ordered them to sit and then walked along, counting them and making notes on his screen. Then two of the others went back to the boat and returned with bottles of water, which they handed out to each of them.

They sat there in the sun for several hours, the heat growing ever more unbearable. One of the women had a broken arm and kept sobbing quietly, and several others had wounds and injuries, including one man who lay half-conscious in the sand, moaning. Orange Beard and the others gave their various wounds a perfunctory inspection, making notes on the screens that they carried, but beyond that they did little. As the day dragged on and the heat grew worse, even those in the line who had been complaining grew silent, until the only sounds were those of the injured man's wet, breathy moaning, and the sobbing of some of the others. Several times people fainted, slumping forwards or toppling back, lying unmoving on the sand.

Finally, a second boat appeared offshore and turned towards them. Tasim guessed it was about noon, because the sun was directly overhead. At first it was difficult to make out much, the glare of the sand and the salt too much for his eyes, so he had to peer through a crack in his eyelids. But as the boat grew closer, he saw it was a long, low vessel quite a bit larger than the inflatable Orange Beard and the others had arrived in.

The second boat moored a short way offshore, and Orange Beard and one of the others waited while a stocky woman in the same black uniform waded ashore to talk to them. Then Orange Beard returned and directed them to stand and walk in single file towards the water. Those who couldn't walk on their own were helped by the people next to them, and the moaning man was loaded onto a stretcher.

'Where are we going?' one of the men demanded.

'You'll find out soon enough,' Orange Beard said, a comment that provoked a laugh from one of the men with guns.

After so long in the sun it was a relief to wade out into the water. Now he was closer, Tasim saw the second boat had a tarpaulin stretched over the seats, and as he was dragged aboard by two of the crew he slumped down under it, grateful for the shade.

Once they were aboard the crew distributed more bottles of water, as well as sweet bars made of nuts and grains and dried fruit; Tasim swilled the water and stuffed the unfamiliar food into his mouth. And then, with a pre-emptory chug, as if it were clearing its throat, the boat reversed in a slow arc across the bay and headed out into deeper water.

They travelled south for a couple of hours, the whirr of the electric engine numbing Tasim's senses. He was so exhausted it was difficult to keep his head upright, but each time he slipped sideways the man next to him pushed him away, or his head hit the gunwale, the vibration and the concussion of the waves striking the hull jarring him awake again. Eventually they turned into another bay, a wide sandy beach, red dirt and low grass beyond. A number of boats lay at anchor in the gleaming water, while farther back from the shoreline low buildings were visible, blocky prefabricated boxes that sat squatly in the heat.

In the prow one of the crew stood up and cast the anchor overboard, then one of the others grabbed the nearest of the passengers under the arm and pulled him to his feet. 'Okay! Ride over!' he said, shoving him overboard, so he fell into the shallow water with a splash. As he reached for the next man, he shouted, 'Everybody off!' and laughed, as if this was a game, although the way he held himself made it clear it wasn't anything of the sort.

They waded through the shallow water to the beach, then the guards marched them over the low ridge towards the buildings they had seen from the boat. They found themselves in an open space. On one side there were about a dozen small, prefabricated pods about the size of a shipping container; on the other two slightly larger structures. A short distance beyond the two larger buildings were two wire enclosures six or seven metres square, over which faded shade sails had been suspended. A number of men stood inside the nearer of the fenced areas, staring out through the wire, while several women sat in the other.

The guards moved them towards the enclosures, then ordered the men to go to one side and the women to the other. A number of the men refused to leave their wives and children, but the guards ignored their protests and shoved them where they needed to go. One woman tried to hang onto a boy a few years younger than Tasim, shouting in a language Tasim didn't recognise and clinging to his arm, until at last one of the guards wrenched him away from her, sending her sprawling onto the red, dusty ground. The mother lay sobbing on the ground as the boy was led away from her, his face tight with fear. Nobody knelt to help her; instead, the other women moved away from her, as if her pain and grief might be infectious.

Once they were separated, the guards herded the men into the first enclosure and the women into the second and locked the gate behind them. The space was covered with scattered squares of foam and thin blankets, and despite the shade cloth overhead it was hot, the air thick with the reek of unwashed bodies. To one side were a row of taps, each fed from a tank that stood outside the wire; against the next fence over, a tarpaulin was stretched across the space, behind which buckets were visible. Later he would learn the concrete there covered a huge septic tank, the line of round, dark holes in the ground opening into it like gates into the underworld. On the far side of the fence behind the taps a stretch of red sand five or six metres wide separated the men's enclosure from that in which the women were confined.

At first Tasim and the other newcomers milled around, not sure where to go next. There were perhaps two dozen men in the space already, some Indonesian, others who seemed to be from India or Bangladesh, together with a small number of men who looked like they had come from Papua or perhaps the islands. They were unshaven, dirty, their faces hollow-eyed and gaunt, and several wore bandages or dressings. They hung back as Tasim and the other survivors from the boat spread out across the space. Most of the newcomers settled in groups of one or two against the fence or near the poles that held up the shade cloth, but several approached the guards as they locked the gate, demanding to know where they were and what was happening to them.

'You cannot do this to us!' shouted the man who had waved his papers in Orange Beard's face on the beach. 'We are refugees!' But the guards ignored them.

The next two days seemed endless. In the heat it was difficult to think, meaning that during the daylight hours there was little to do but sit and wait for sunset. The nights were worse, though. In the dark the men sobbed and moaned, or cried out in their sleep. When Tasim managed to sleep he found himself slipping down into images of confusion and heat and drowning, nightmares so vivid that he awoke gasping and weeping in the darkness.

On the third day three buses arrived, bumping down a trail towards them across the red emptiness of the landscape, their white shapes shimmering in the heat haze. They parked in the empty space behind the concrete areas, their drivers clambering out to stretch and talk to the guards. Tasim watched Orange Beard approach them and, after a few moments of conversation, point in their direction, the gesture followed by a brief ripple of laughter of the sort he had come to think of as distinctly Australian, a hard, humourless sound from which those it was directed at were excluded.

Once their conversation was done Orange Beard approached the gates and addressed them in English, then repeated the same words in Bahasa. 'Pursuant to Australian law you're being transferred to a designated processing centre. Once you're there you'll be assessed for refugee status.'

Several of the men and women began to shout, rattling the wire and gesticulating at the guard. Orange Beard regarded them for a few seconds and then, with a sort of smirk, turned away and walked back towards the buses.

Once Orange Beard was gone a young man joined Tasim by the fence. He wore a shirt that had once been white and was now stained with blood and seawater and the omnipresent red dust. Tasim had noticed him before: like Tasim he seemed to be unaccompanied, and although he sometimes spoke to the other men, he had a delicate, almost feminine manner that made him seem out of place. Tasim was surprised – over the past few days he had become aware how rarely the men looked at each other, as if each other's uncertainty and fear were catching.

'I'm Sigit,' he said.

'Tasim.'

Now they were speaking Tasim realised Sigit was only a year or two older than he was, and despite the way he held himself had a vulnerability his slightly preening manner couldn't quite disguise.

'One of the others said they have prison camps in the desert. Do you think that's true?' he asked.

Tasim regarded the black-clad guards outside the fence for a long moment. 'I don't know.'

Sigit nodded towards the area where the women and children were held. 'Do you have somebody in there? Your mother? Your sister?'

Tasim swallowed. 'No,' he said, his voice catching. 'You?'

Sigit was silent for a second or two. 'No,' he said at last.

*

'How do you think they got to Nguyen?' said Findlay once they were back in the car.

'Who knows?' said Sadiya. 'Horizon has connections at every level of government. Maybe somebody had a word with the minister on Manning's behalf.'

'Why would they do that for Manning?'

'It could be anything. Perhaps they owed him a favour. Perhaps he had something on somebody. It doesn't matter. All that matters is finding something concrete to link Manning to Nina's death. Some evidence that will let us arrest him.'

'So where do we start?'

'Manning has an alibi for the night Nina died. If it was him, that must be false. So, we begin by chipping away at that. We also need to work out what it was Nina knew about him. And we should find out any offences or irregularities in his past. If there's some kind of financial trouble, we may be able to find something useful.'

'Remember what he said about the lottery, and about people not understanding how difficult it is for him?' Findlay asked.

'Maybe he's not as wealthy as his lifestyle suggests.'

Findlay thought for a moment. 'If Casey is still alive, he must be keeping her somewhere. That means he would have to be feeding her, keeping an eye on her. Unless he has a second place in the complex where he lives, that means he'd have to be going there regularly.'

'We should be tracking his movements. And if he is keeping her somewhere perhaps there's some record of his connection to that property. We should check land titles and the tenancy database.'

'Good idea,' said Findlay.

'And I want to go back to the Floodline, look at the place Casey disappeared one more time. See if there's something we missed.'

While Findlay put in requests for location data and searched Manning's police records, Sadiya set up alerts on the facial-rec system in case he was caught on video somewhere. As she worked, she kept one eye on the passing streets. An hour earlier she had checked on Nasreen's progress. One of the rainbands had passed over Lord Howe a few hours earlier: photos taken as it approached showed walls of cloud that dwarfed the low-lying buildings and palms, great blue-black masses that seemed to float atop drifts of gauzy light and rain, but aside from a few scattered videos of hastening winds and rain as it made landfall there had been no contact with the island since it had hit. In the face of such power one might have expected the streets they were passing through to be filled with activity, but aside from the traffic choking the main roads out of the city and a few people walking dogs or watching children play on scooters the streets were empty.

They stopped outside the building site. The police tape was still strung across the gate. Sadiya unlatched the gate and ducked under the tape. Crossing towards the stained mattress she stopped beside it.

'What are you thinking?' Findlay asked.

'We know Horizon owns this site, as well as the one where Nina's body was found. If Manning was using them both, perhaps he's using another Horizon property to hide Casey.'

'Horizon must own hundreds of sites. We can't check them all.'

'But if we could link Manning to some of them it might narrow things down.'

'He's too smart for that. If he's stayed off our radar until now he knows how to avoid cameras.'

'How's he moving around?' she said.

Findlay thought for a moment. 'If it's by car there will be a record of him coming or going from his building.'

'Do you think he'd be that careless?'

Findlay shook his head.

'So, he must be using Swifts or public transport,' said Sadiya.

'Or a second vehicle.'

'If he's got a second vehicle perhaps it's registered in his name. But even if he doesn't have a second vehicle and he's getting around some other way, he would have to be coming and going from his building. And if he is, there should be a record of that.'

'We can apply to the building administrators to get that data.'

Half-a-dozen people had gathered by the gate when they emerged. Sadiya kept her head down and ignored them, walking briskly towards the car. But as she opened the door one of them called out.

'Why are you back here? Why aren't you out looking for Casey?'

Sadiya looked up. The speaker was a tall white woman with lank green hair and a hard mouth.

'What?'

'You heard me. Why aren't you out looking for her? Are you trying to pin this on one of us?'

Sadiya was about to reply when Findlay placed a hand on her arm. 'Leave it.'

Back in the car they drove slowly, staring out at the streets. As they reached the highway Findlay swore softly.

'What?'

'Manning was cautioned back when he was at university. There was a complaint about him stalking a woman, but it never went anywhere.'

'Of course he was,' said Sadiya with sudden vehemence. 'No doubt he did the same thing to Nina.'

'Probably. But if he did she never reported it, so we still have no evidence of any real connection between the two of them.'

'We need a motive. Some reason he would kill her.'

'Stefan said she'd discovered some kind of irregularity but hadn't reported it.'

'She was an auditor,' said Sadiya. 'If she found out Manning was involved in something illegal, why wouldn't she have reported it?'

'Because she was involved with him?'

'Or because she was afraid of him,' said Sadiya.

'Or both.'

'Or both,' Sadiya agreed. She took a breath, thinking. It was too much. She had to focus.

'We know Nina was anxious about something in the days before she died. Perhaps if we can find out where it was she went on the day she left the office it will tell us why Manning wanted her dead.'

'And without that?'

She sighed. 'His alibi. We have to find a hole in it. Some evidence he's lying. Then we have an excuse to bring him in.' She glanced over at him. 'You don't have to do this with me,' she said. 'There will be blowback, for sure.'

'No. I want to do it.'

Sadiya nodded. 'Okay. Let's start by talking to Emma and Jay again. Jay knows more than he's telling us. We have to find out what that is and whether it has anything to do with Nina or Manning.'

*

Tasim stopped in front of the nearest building. The door was set back in a small alcove. Bags of garbage were piled in the corner beside it, their sides split and torn and the mess that spilled from them dried and unrecognisable. He grabbed the handle and shook it, but the door didn't budge. Taking a step back he surveyed the building's exterior. Behind the broken panes of the ground-floor windows metal grilles were visible. Unwilling to waste time on a building he couldn't easily access he jogged across the road to the building opposite, but as he reached it a siren whooped behind him. He spun around to see a police van had pulled into the side street. The doors opened and two officers emerged.

'Hey!' one of them shouted, turning towards him. 'What are you doing?'

Tasim took a step back, and then bolted. Behind him somebody shouted 'Stop!', but he didn't look back, he just ran, vaulting over the refuse that littered the ground as he searched for an escape route. He was almost at the tideline when one of them caught up with him. He darted sideways, but his foot slipped and he fell. He lurched up again, but it was too late, and the officer crashed into him and slammed him into the ground. Before he could twist free she yanked his arm up behind him.

'Stay still,' she spat, pressing her knee into his back.

After they had handcuffed him they took his backpack and led him back towards the van. The officer who had captured him pressed him against the side of the vehicle.

'Illegal?' she said.

Her partner checked his lenses. 'Tasim Benakat. Indonesian. Seems to have walked out of one of the camps in Western Australia a while back. The system says he's a minor.'

The woman laughed humourlessly, as if her colleague had just confirmed something contemptible. 'What's in his bag?'

The other officer opened Tasim's backpack and rifled through it. 'It's clean.'

'Drop him off on the way back?'

'Sure,' the man said. 'Do you think he speaks any English?'

The woman looked at him. 'Well?' she said, but Tasim didn't reply.

'Nope,' she said. 'Let's get him back for processing.'

The male officer opened the back of the van and she pushed Tasim towards it. Just before he went inside he turned to the male cop. 'My bag,' he said.

The cop grinned. 'So, you do speak English?'

Tasim just stared back at him. 'Please.'

'You can have it once you're processed,' he said, and slammed the door.

Two other men sat at the back of the van, their hands restrained behind them. Tasim slumped down on the bench and eyed them warily. One was a small man in his forties, his square face slack with exhaustion; the other was only a little older than Tasim and tall and slim, with elegant features and a high forehead.

'You okay?' the taller one asked, smiling. Tasim looked down. His pants were ripped at the knee and he was bleeding. The wound was bright red, but the pain seemed far away.

He nodded. 'Where are we going?' he asked.

'Processing,' said the smaller one without looking around.

'And then?'

The smaller man shrugged.

'Perhaps it's good,' said the taller one. 'At least we'll be safe from the storm.'

Tasim didn't answer, just leaned back against the van and closed his eyes.

About fifteen minutes after Orange Beard explained where they were going the guards opened the gate of the men's enclosure and marched them in the direction of the buses. Several of the men tried to break free and run towards the enclosure where the women and children were being held, but the guards dragged them back into line and bundled them up the stairs onto the buses.

Despite the guards and their uncertainty about what came next, the atmosphere after they boarded was curiously informal, as if being in motion again had somehow released them from the torpor and misery of the preceding days. Men moved from seat to seat, leaning forward or twisting backwards and talking animatedly, like kids on a school excursion. Tasim found a seat near the front and climbed in, pressing himself against the window as one of the older men slumped down beside him, his face grey and his breath shallow. On each seat was a two-litre bottle of water and a box containing some kind of energy bar. Tasim took a sip of the water and put the rest away. Twisting around, he saw Sigit had been seated farther back; he caught Tasim watching him and lifted a hand in greeting then turned to stare out the window, his thin body tensed as if frightened of the men around him.

Once everybody was on board, one of the guards stepped in and closed the plexiglass shield that separated the front seat and the driver from the bus. The guard tapped his ear to show he couldn't hear them, then pointed up to one corner of the roof, where the red light of a camera shone. And then the bus jerked into motion.

While the other men talked and laughed, Tasim stared at the passing landscape. It was vast: red soil and patches of low grass and scrubby trees spreading out beneath an immensity of blue. In the distance, hills were sometimes visible, low and red or blue.

Occasionally they passed the wrecks of cars or trucks, but otherwise the landscape seemed devoid of human presence. Tasim hadn't realised there was this much space in the entire world.

Perhaps the others felt the same, because as the hours passed the other men fell silent or drifted off to sleep. Next to Tasim the older man snored, his breath coming in shallow, irregular pants. In the early afternoon the buses pulled off the road and stopped outside a small compound a little like the one they had just left. The guard and the driver disembarked, leaving the men alone on the bus. For a number of them it was too much, and they shouted and hit the glass, but nobody came, until half an hour later the guard and driver re-boarded and they headed off again.

After that first stop the mood was different. A sullen anger had overtaken the group, as it had dawned on them that they were now prisoners, and nobody cared where they were or what happened to them. In the front, the guard didn't look at them, even when they beat on the plexiglass; outside the bus the emptiness went on forever. Some of the men raged, others just sat, staring.

Near dark they turned off the road and drove inland. The country here was different: although the road ran dead straight, as if it had been marked on the map with a ruler, the hills were broken and craggy. After half an hour they passed the abandoned shell of some kind of mine, vast machines and skeletal structures marking out shadows on the broken earth, beyond which an enormous pit opened, a yawning scar in the earth. A little way beyond the pit the buses drew up outside some kind of camp, rows of white buildings laid out in a grid in the red soil. Once the dust had settled the guard opened the plexiglass barrier and they filed off. As they clambered back out into the heat Tasim heard the men asking each other where they were, whether this was a prison where the guards meant to leave them. Tasim hung back, trying to keep some space between himself and the others. A moment later Sigit appeared beside him.

'Will we stay here?' he asked.

Tasim looked around. People were filing off the other two buses, and the men were calling to their wives and children.

'Maybe we're going to sleep here tonight,' he said.

'But where?' said Sigit. He was even thinner than when they had arrived, his almond-shaped eyes puffy and bruised.

Tasim didn't reply.

The guards led the women to the cabins in groups of four, while the men were led to an open space just outside the camp and given bedrolls and blankets. In the centre of the space a circle of stones surrounded the remains of a fire. The guards directed them to spread themselves out, then one addressed them.

'We'll be back on the buses tomorrow morning. Until then you're to remain here. And if anybody gets any ideas about running off, just be aware there's nothing for hundreds of kilometres in any direction.'

While one of the guards built a fire and distributed food and water, Tasim and Sigit found a space on the far edge of the group and unrolled their bedrolls. The blankets stank of stale smoke, but Sigit didn't seem to care. Instead he sat, staring out at the empty land, unspeaking.

Darkness came quickly, the light draining away all at once, and although the ground held its warmth, the air quickly grew cooler. By the fire some of the men were talking; others lay around quietly. Tasim had hoped to speak to Sigit but he stayed silent. Overhead the Milky Way shone, a great girdle of light; once or twice Tasim saw meteors flare, and once the light of a satellite or one of the space stations shot past, slicing across the sky in a matter of minutes. How strange to think there were people up there, so far away. Did they wish they could forget the world, fly on and away? Or did they wish they were back here, on the ground? Tasim didn't know.

Eventually he slept, slipping deep into dreams of water and confusion; once he woke, a cry still in his mouth. As he fought to catch his breath he listened to the men around him, the sound of their snores and murmuring, one man's quiet sobs. When he woke again it was almost dawn, the landscape huge in the first light. Something moved beside him, and he turned, then froze. Suspended over him was the face of some kind of animal, a strange, cloven nose and huge dark eyes set into sandy-coloured fur. He jerked upright, but if it was surprised it didn't show it; instead it just tipped its head slightly. He reached towards Sigit, intending to wake him, but something in the animal's oddly gentle expression stopped him. Looking past it, he saw half-a-dozen more: great, pale creatures he now recognised as camels. The one in front of him blinked, long lashes moving over its deep, gentle eyes, and then shook its head, its small ears contracting. And suddenly Tasim was smiling, the camel regarding him with a benign indifference. He lifted his hand, thinking to touch it, but the camel swung its neck away and, with a curiously stately and silent movement, plodded slowly away into the half-light. Tasim watched them go, not quite sure what he had seen, but certain he would tell nobody.

*

As Sadiya and Findlay approached Emma and Jay's building they heard a man shouting in anger. Sadiya paused long enough to recognise Jay's voice before she took off down the duckboard and up the stairs. Jay was standing outside on the balcony pounding on the door.

'You can't do this!' he shouted, then registered Sadiya and Findlay's presence.

'What the fuck?' he demanded, straightening up. 'Did she call you?'

'Nobody called us,' said Sadiya. 'We came to speak to the two of you.'

He didn't move. She could see him thinking, calculating the odds.

'Is Emma inside?' she asked. She stepped towards the window, careful to keep her eyes on Jay. 'Emma? Are you okay?'

The door opened and Emma emerged. She was shaking and her face was blotchy and stained with tears. Jay swung around towards her.

'Did you call them?'

'No. But I should have.'

'What do you mean?' said Sadiya.

'Ask him,' Emma said, her voice icy.

'Ask him what?'

'About that woman. Nina. He knew her.'

'What?' Sadiya said.

'He spoke to her last week. They had some sort of meeting.'

'Is that true?' Sadiya asked.

'It's not what it looks like,' said Jay.

'Why would you lie?' Emma said, moving towards him. 'Why would you lie unless you had something to hide?'

'No,' Jay said. 'You know that's not true. I would never do something like that.' He lifted a hand, but she jerked away from him.

'Don't touch me!' she hissed, her face hard with rage and disgust.

'Was it him?' she said, turning towards Sadiya and Findlay. 'Did he do it?'

Behind the sunburn on Jay's cheeks and nose the blood had drained from his face and his eyes seemed unfocused as if he was in shock.

'Please. You can't think that.'

'I think you need to come with us,' Findlay said. Jay swivelled, tensing.

'I didn't do it,' he said. 'You have to believe me.'

Sadiya hesitated, startled by the shift in his demeanour. She would have expected rage, but he was genuinely horrified. For a brief instant a chink opened in her dislike of him.

'Come with us and we'll talk about it,' she said.

When Jay didn't move Findlay took a step towards him. Only then did Jay raise his hands and allow himself to be ushered away. Once they were gone, Sadiya approached Emma.

'What happened?'

'I knew he was lying about something, but this afternoon somebody I know messaged me to say she'd seen a picture of the woman who died, and that she'd seen Jay talking to her. When I confronted him he denied it at first, but then he admitted to it.' She stopped, shaking. 'He said he'd found out about weird payments to suppliers like his friend Laurent, and he'd contacted her. He said he thought he could use it to get us on the list for housing in the new development.' She stopped and stared at Sadiya. 'How can I believe him? What if he had something to do with it? What if he killed her? Or Casey? Oh, god ...' She began to sob.

Sadiya raised her hand, touched the other woman's arm. At first she thought Emma would shake her off, but she didn't. 'Let us talk to him,' she said.

'Please,' Emma said, looking up at her, her face drawn and terrified. 'You have to find Casey. If you don't, then tomorrow ...' She gestured hopelessly.

Sadiya took a breath, and gripped Emma's arm. 'I'll do everything I can to make sure that doesn't happen, that she's found.'

Sadiya squeezed the other woman's arm. 'Call somebody,' she said. 'You shouldn't be alone.'

Downstairs Jay was leaning against the car, one hand pressed to his forehead. Findlay stood a little way back, watching him.

'Is she telling the truth?' Sadiya demanded, as she reached them. 'You were in contact with Nina?'

Jay looked at her. Something vital had drained out of him.

'Why didn't you tell us?'

'Because I knew how it would look. If you found out I'd had dealings with Nina you'd focus on me, and not on finding Casey.'

Sadiya stepped towards him. 'So instead, you lied to us and hid information that might have helped us.' She heard the anger in her voice, tried to contain it.

'So, tell us now,' she said when he didn't reply. 'How did you know Nina Lukic?'

'I didn't. I searched for people who worked in auditing at Horizon, and I found her. After I contacted her, she agreed to meet me and I told her what I knew.'

'Which was?'

'Just what I said. Suppliers not getting paid. Materials that are supposed to have been delivered but never arrived. It was Laurent who told me about it.'

'When was this?'

'A few months ago.'

'And she came here to meet you?'

Jay nodded.

'And what did you want in return?'

He looked down. 'I wanted to be moved up the list for housing in the new development.'

'And you haven't seen her since?'

He didn't reply.

'Don't fucking lie to us again,' Sadiya said.

'Last week. On Wednesday afternoon. I went to her office.'

'Why?'

'It wasn't moving fast enough. I wanted to put some pressure on her.'

'What does that mean?' Findlay said.

Jay shrugged. 'I suggested I might talk to the police, see what they had to say about her not reporting it.'

'And what did she say?'

'She said she thought she knew who was behind it, and that she was going to do something about it. But...'

'But what?'

'She said it was complicated. She said she might be in trouble herself.'

'Did she say who was behind it?'

Jay shook his head. 'Whoever it was, you think they killed her? Took Casey?'

'If they did, then you should have told us this days ago. Instead, you've obstructed our investigation.' She paused, aware she was going to regret what she said next, but was unable to stop herself, her voice cold and hard. 'If we're too late to save Casey, that's on you.' When Jay didn't reply she shook her head in disgust. 'Get out of here. I don't want to look at you.'

Jay took a step back, swaying as if he might fall.

Sadiya wrenched the car door open.

'Where are you going?' Findlay said.

'We need to go there now, get Manning.'

Findlay grabbed her arm. She tensed, ready to throw him off, startled at the anger, the violence welling up in herself, the seductiveness of it. It would be easy to give way to it, to lash out, to let herself go, but she caught herself in time, held back.

'Don't do this,' he said. 'We can't risk it. You know that. We need the evidence, the connection. Without it he'll just get a lawyer, refuse to talk. We won't get anything.'

She could feel her breath coming fast and shallow. She knew how she must look to him, the anger she had been holding in all her life now on full display. With a sharp, violent gesture she pulled her arm free. He let his hand fall, careful to show he didn't mean her harm. Was she really that far gone? Did he think she was that out of control? *Was* she that far out of control?

'He knows where she is.'

'So let's make sure we have him where we want him, that he'll tell us.'

She took a step back. 'Don't touch me again,' she said.

Findlay didn't look away, but she saw the way he flinched, her brief flash of satisfaction giving way to guilt.

Back at the station they ran Manning through the predictives, searching for connections, information that might connect him to anything untoward at Horizon or give some sense of where he might have taken Casey. But there was nothing. If he had another vehicle it wasn't registered in his name, and his phone was on one of the satellite networks that allowed him to encrypt his location. And while his building's security was connected to the police system, with the exception of some gaps during the past week, his departures and returns aligned with his appearances at work and elsewhere. And during those gaps he seemed to be nowhere, as if he was careful to avoid driving or walking anywhere he might be picked up on a camera.

With each new failure Sadiya grew more frustrated. 'The guy is a ghost,' she snapped when the predictives failed to find any evidence of him having a second address. She turned to Findlay.

'What about Nina? What do we know about her movements last week?'

'Not much. Except that on the Thursday she wasn't at work her car was picked up exiting the M4 near Regentville at 10.37 am. She then re-enters the M4 at 12.11 pm, and heads back to her apartment in Bellevue Hill.'

'Regentville? That's 60 kilometres from her place. What on earth was she doing out there? Was she picked up anywhere in between those times?'

Findlay shook his head. 'And until we can get the locational data on her car we have no idea where she went.'

Sadiya leaned back in her seat. 'So Jay pays her a visit at the office on the Wednesday afternoon and tells her he's going to go to the cops if she doesn't do something about the discrepancies in the accounts. The next morning she doesn't turn up at work, but she drives out to Regentville. But why? What's out there?'

'Is it possible she went to meet Manning?'

Sadiya checked their timeline for Manning. 'No. He was in the office.' She thought for a moment. 'Do Horizon own land out there?'

Findlay checked his notes. 'I can see at least twelve properties in the area around Regentville with connections to Horizon.'

Sadiya exhaled. 'Shit. This is a nightmare. We've got twelve hours until the storm hits. If we can't find something to connect Manning to

Nina or to establish a motive we've got no way of finding Casey. She could be anywhere.'

She stood up. 'You keep looking. I'm going to go to where we found Nina's body, look at the crime scene again. Then I have to get home to deal with my father.'

'I can go to Manning's, keep an eye on the building,' said Findlay. 'If he's going in and out without turning up on the cameras he must have found a back entrance, but perhaps if he leaves I can spot him.'

Sadiya nodded. 'Meanwhile we just have to hope the locational data for her car turns up.'

Outside it was growing dark. When she pulled up outside the building where Nina's car had been found a number of the apartments in the buildings opposite and next door were unlit, their occupants presumably already gone. She paused for a moment and went in, walking down the side to where the burned-out shell of Nina's car still stood, police tape twisted around it. She circled it once or twice, hoping to spot something they'd missed. Then she went over to the building, and, turning on the light on her phone, pushed open the door and went inside. It smelled of mildew and piss, and there were pools of water lying here and there, but no sign of anything that might be connected to Manning.

Back outside she started pressing bells for the apartments next to the site, asking anybody who answered whether they had seen anybody on the night the car had been set on fire, but the handful of people she spoke to told her they'd been asleep or out. And when she was done she went back to her car, slumped down next to it and beat her head slowly against the door.

It was almost eleven by the time she got back to her apartment. Malila was on her feet when she opened the door.

Sadiya began to apologise, but Malila cut her off. 'I have to go. Zac has been calling all evening.'

'I'm sorry,' Sadiya said. 'It's late. Do you want to stay here tonight?'

'I can't. Zac says we have to get inland before the storm hits. He's waiting to leave as soon as I get back.'

'What if you get caught on the road?'

'He says that won't happen.' She hesitated. When she spoke again her voice shook. 'I was here last during the last storm. I can't do that again.'

Hearing the tremor in Malila's voice Sadiya was suddenly ashamed of how little she really knew about her or her life. 'Please, Malila, I need you. Tell Zac he can come here. This building is safe, the ground is high. I've filled the bath, we've got water and food. And I need you to help me with Arman. I can't leave him alone, but I also can't promise I'll be able to be here tomorrow.'

Malila stared at her. For a moment Sadiya thought she was going to refuse. But instead she sighed. 'Okay. I'll talk to Zac, see if he'll agree to come here.' She looked away, as if uncomfortable meeting Sadiya's gaze. 'I have to go.'

Once Malila had left Sadiya slipped into Arman's room to check on him. He lay on his side, snoring softly. His face was older in sleep, its angles gaunt, but the lines of fear and confusion she had come to know so well also melted away. She leaned down and drew the sheet higher and then slipped out again.

Back in the living area she searched for the latest on the storm. Its course hadn't changed, and neither had the prediction for when it would strike. For a few moments she gazed at the satellite image, its occluding mass covering much of the south-eastern Pacific. She knew she needed to work, to keep looking, but she also needed to make sure the apartment was ready for the storm. Going through to the bathroom she flicked on the light, checked the bath then, opened the cupboard in the laundry to check on food and other supplies. The water bottles were full, and there were rows of cans and dried foods.

When she had organised the supplies, she had made sure there was enough for her and Arman for a fortnight; with Zac and Malila here as well, they would only have a week, but that should be enough.

Returning to the lounge room she slumped down in her chair. The room was hot, as if the air conditioning was struggling. Calling up Malila's details she sent her a text, reiterating her invitation. *Safer than the road*, she wrote. Finally, she slumped back, remembering her argument with Findlay. She knew he had been right, that they couldn't risk it until they had more information: go in half-cocked and they risked Manning eluding them, or his solicitor pulling the plug; do that and he might not tell them what they needed, or just never go back to wherever he had Casey. She closed her eyes. What kind of person could do that, she wondered. What kind of twisted logic said you could kill a woman but not a child? No doubt it had been impulse, a spur of the moment thing, and once he had her he was too afraid to kill her. Oftentimes people had an idea of themselves, a strange moral accounting that insisted they weren't like that, even when it was obvious they were. But she also knew that if people were pushed, that squeamishness gave way, that once they felt threatened they could do anything.

FRIDAY

FRIDAY

She woke with a start, staring around herself, unsure where she was or how long she had been asleep. She was in the lounge room, on the sofa, the lights still on. Outside it was dark. Her screen buzzed again. She was on her feet before she finished reading the message, checking the time – 4.55 am – and calling Findlay.

He answered quickly, as if already awake.

'We've got it,' she said.

'Got what?'

'The location data for Nina's car on the day she left work.' As she spoke she flicked the message to Findlay. A moment later she heard the alert chime at his end. There was a moment's silence.

'I don't understand. What's out there?'

'I don't know. But we need to find out. Where are you?'

'Don't worry. I'll come to you.'

'How long?'

'Half an hour. No more.'

'Make it faster.'

Sadiya rang off. She was awake and alert but still felt disoriented, as if there was a kind of wrongness in the air, something palpable. The blinds were open; across the roofs opposite the huge bands of cloud blotted out the stars, mauve and grey where they caught the city's lights. She checked the news: they had less than seven hours before the storm hit.

She dressed quickly, then opened the safe and took out her gun and slipped it into its holster. Out in the hall she could hear Arman snoring in his room. Checking her messages again she saw that Malila hadn't responded to her offer for her and Zac to shelter with her. Not knowing what else to do she composed a message repeating the offer, and asking her to call as soon as she got up. She didn't like leaving Arman alone, especially today, but she couldn't see any alternative.

The air in the lift and lobby was hot, the air in the street hotter still and thick with the smell of saltwater. Someone had once told her that you could tell when a crocodile was close by the salty smell, something that sounded so unlikely that she thought it had to be true.

It was still dark when Findlay arrived. She told him to leave his car and come with her.

'Anything?' she asked as he climbed in.

He shook his head. His eyes were puffy and dark with lack of sleep. 'If he left I didn't see him.'

Although sunrise was still almost an hour away the streets were already busy, cars and people moving through them, gravitating towards the main roads like water flowing towards the sea. By the time they reached Parramatta Road the traffic was barely moving, the tail-lights of the cars and trucks a sea of red in the weird half-light of the cyclonic morning.

'Where do you think they're going?' Findlay asked, staring at a ute, its back piled high with bags and boxes, a family of six crowded into its cabin.

Sadiya shrugged. 'Who knows? South. North. Into the Mountains.'

'What if they're still on the road when it hits?'

Sadiya didn't reply, but as they approached the entrance to the motorway, the traffic slowed to a halt. Findlay checked his lenses.

'There's some kind of delay ahead,' he said.

'Fuck this,' she said, spinning the wheel and driving the car over the median strip, lights flashing they rolled forward, ignoring the blaring horns as they passed the stationary cars. A few hundred metres before they reached the intersection they saw the problem: a squad of Crisis officers had set up a roadblock and were checking IDs. To one side four men were seated on the ground, their arms secured behind their backs, an armed officer keeping guard over them.

As they reached the barriers one of the Crisis officers approached them, his hand raised to tell them to stop. Sadiya swore under her breath and rolled down the window.

'What's going on?' she asked.

The officer leaned down and looked in at the two of them, his face hidden beneath dark lenses and a black cap.

'I'm afraid all non-essential travel has been put on hold,' he said.

Sadiya held up her ID. 'We're police officers. We need to get past.'

'Can I ask why?'

Before Sadiya could reply Findlay placed a hand on her arm and leaned across. 'It's police business, part of a live investigation.'

The officer stared back without speaking, his face impassive. Sadiya saw the way he waited a moment longer than he needed to. Arsehole, she thought.

'You sure it's not something that can wait?'

'If we thought it could wait, we wouldn't be here now,' Findlay said.

The officer paused, then stood up and touched his earpiece. Turning slightly away he carried on a quick conversation. Then he turned back to them.

'Okay,' he said. 'You can go.'

Sadiya pressed down on the accelerator and angled the car around and down, into the tunnel. As they passed the people seated by the wall, she glanced across at them, wondered what would happen to them after this.

'What?' she asked, catching Findlay staring at the cars lined up behind them.

'Where will they all go? Back to their homes?'

'We can't worry about that now.'

Findlay was silent for a moment. Then he exhaled. 'Jesus,' he said.

The tunnel gave way to motorway. After another half an hour they took a turn off, dropping down into Regentville. As they swung out across the overpass they were briefly suspended above the trees and buildings, the vista of the city far behind them, the vast weight of cloud rising above it, then they were back down again, shooting past buildings and empty lots. At some point a fire had burned through here, leaving the ground scorched and scarred, blackened trunks scattered in the yellow grass, green leaves here and there sprouting already. Once, this would have been semi-rural, farmland; ravaged by the heat and fire, it was now a wasteland. Finally they headed onto Silverdale Road, and then out along a dirt side road that ran through a stand of dead trees and out into an empty space of ruined fields. A short distance from the trees a cyclone-wire fence and gate barred their way.

Sadiya stopped the car and got out. The sun was up now, and the heat was already ferocious.

'Are you sure this is where she came?' Findlay asked.

Sadiya nodded and approached the gate. It was chained shut. Turning, she walked back to the car and, opening the boot, took out a pair of boltcutters. Positioning the blades on the shank she cut the lock and pushed the gate open.

'What is this place?' said Findlay as they went in.

'It's the new refugee processing centre. The one Manning is managing the development of.'

She walked slowly out into the space. Dry grass and dust crunched underfoot. Back to the east, vast banks of cloud were building, their weight eclipsing the sun and leaving the space in a ghostly shadow. On one side of the field, a pile of building supplies lay jumbled under torn plastic sheeting. Sadiya walked slowly towards them and pulled back a flap to expose a pallet of timber.

Findlay pointed to another tear in the plastic. 'Look,' he said. 'It's ruined. Whoever left it here didn't secure it properly. The water ...' He opened his hands in resignation.

Sadiya turned and stared out across the field. For a brief instant it was almost silent, the only sound that of the wind gusting uncertainly around them shivering the grass, the slow creak and flap of the plastic.

'I don't understand. There's nothing here. What did she find? Why even come here?'

To the east, lightning stuttered high in the clouds. In the trees behind them a currawong cried, the peal of its song resonating in the weird light. Sadiya walked slowly towards a sign that lay on its back in the grass, and stood, staring down. Findlay came and stood next to her.

'Of course,' said Sadiya. 'How did I not see it?'

*

Arman woke to an eerie light, the sound of traffic and sirens in the distance. Standing up, he pulled on a shirt and shorts and shuffled out the door. The room outside was unfamiliar, somebody's home, but whose? His? He didn't know. Walking to the balcony doors he looked out. The sun was still low, the sky green and blue and banded with cloud. He swallowed and heard his ears pop. He was certain there was somewhere he needed to be, but he couldn't remember where it was. He walked across the living area to the apartment door. He didn't know why he had wanted to reach it, but now he was at it he reached out and turned the handle. The latch clicked and the door swung inwards.

He went out into the hall. He had been here before – he must have been – but it was unfamiliar. To his left the corridor ran on a little way before ending in three doors, one in each wall. To his right it ran past several more doors, then turned to one side. He was about to head that way when he heard the chime of an elevator and a man's voice;

he shrank back, then, hugging the wall for safety, he walked slowly to the door at the end of the corridor and, opening it, stepped into a stairwell. It was dim, the air hot and damp. His breath coming fast he began to descend, glancing back with each turn in case he was being followed.

He emerged into a back alley, broken furniture and an old mattress heaped against the wall. No longer certain where he was or what he was doing he hesitated for a few seconds, then made for the street beyond. Although the sun was still low it was already hot, the air thick with humidity. Cars snaked down the road in front of him. Confused, he set off down the footpath, looking for something familiar. Outside the next building a woman stood watching him. He glanced down at himself to see what might have attracted her attention, and realised he was barefoot, his nails yellow against the grey skin of his feet. This wasn't his body, wasn't him. Putting his head down he hurried on, but as he passed her she asked if he was all right. Without a word he took off down a side street, his breath coming fast, panic rising. Somewhere behind him somebody shouted, but he didn't slow down. He didn't know why he was running or who was after him, only that he had to get away. Somewhere ahead a dog began to bark. He stopped by a gate. The dog barked again. With a whimper of fear he opened the gate and shuffled in, searching for somewhere to hide.

He emerged in a narrow back yard. An old tree rose overhead, black seed pods hanging from it; on the far side vegetables grew in tubs along a raised concrete structure. Eager to put as much distance between himself and the dog as possible he hurried past them, but as he reached the back of the house he noticed an old hammer sitting on a wooden bench. He picked it up and hefted it in his hand. Its handle was wood, the worn grain smooth against his hand, the head heavy, the once-bright metal corroded almost black. Once, long before, he had held his father's hammer this same way, and for a moment he was there again, in the small shelter at the back of their house, the air bright and rich with the smell of the water and the flowers, the drifting scent of woodsmoke. He heard a bird whoop in the distance, its cry crazy, exultant, the thrum of insects, and for a brief moment he remembered his father, the feeling the world was there in front of him. Lowering the hammer he looked down at himself, the ruin of his body, the hot stain of piss on his pants, his sudden lucidity like a brief shaft of light and clarity, and in the moment before it slipped away again, he stumbled back, a strangled sob on his lips.

*

Back in the car, Sadiya wove through the traffic back towards the motorway. Ahead of them the clouds dwarfed the towers of the city, immense and uncanny as an alien spaceship breaching the atmosphere.

'Tell me what's going on,' said Findlay.

Sadiya blasted the horn at a car that was blocking their way. 'When we were in his office that first time we talked about the refugee processing centre, you remember? He said he was overseeing the project.'

'I remember.'

'But you saw when we were there. There is no project, only a few goods dumped there and left to rot.'

'So?'

'That's what Nina found out. She knew from Jay that there were irregularities, but she must not have had the evidence. After Jay threatened to go tell somebody what he knew she went back and looked again, and then came out here. This must have been the evidence she needed, so she confronted Manning with it.'

'So why meet at the site down in the Floodline?'

'It must have been his idea. Maybe she wanted to talk to him, get some kind of answer about what was going on. Or perhaps she had already told him, and he asked to meet her to talk about it. Either way he went there planning to kill her.'

'Why would she do that? Why not just go straight to the company legal team? Or somebody above both of them in the organisation?'

Sadiya leaned on the horn. 'Maybe she felt some kind of loyalty to him. They'd been lovers, after all. Or perhaps she was worried there might be other people involved and thought she'd gauge his reaction before she took it any further.'

'Do you think there are others?'

'Who knows? Possibly. Probably. You've seen the reports about waste of government money, failures in the tendering processes. But nothing ever happens. These arseholes just skate off.'

'So we were right: he took Casey because she saw something.'

'And now we have enough to question him.'

They reached Manning's apartment complex just after nine. Huge sandbags were piled around the front of the building, and tape covered all visible glass. Even the gardens had been prepared, the cordylines and palm trees bound up in tarpaulins to protect them from the wind. When they pulled up out the front a pair of SecurCorp officers approached the car. One stopped beside Sadiya's door.

'You can't stop here,' he said as she stepped out.

Sadiya held up her ID. 'We're police. We need to get inside.'

The guard ignored her ID. 'That's not possible. The entire complex is now under temporary private control. The only people allowed in are residents and essential staff.' His voice was careful, firm but polite.

'A child's life could be at stake,' Sadiya said.

The guard didn't move, but Sadiya saw the other shift slightly.

'I'm sorry. Our orders are clear.'

'Who's in command? Goodman?' said Findlay.

The officer looked at him in surprise. 'No. Morgan.'

Findlay glanced at Sadiya. 'Give me a minute,' he said. Turning away, he accessed something in his lenses. A few moments passed, then he spoke quickly, quietly. There was another silence, then he stood, staring into the distance for a few seconds. Then he turned and walked back to the SecurCorp guards, careful to avoid Sadiya's questioning stare.

'Check your system,' he said. 'You'll see I've got access.'

The second officer stared into his lenses for a few seconds and gave his colleague a quick nod. The first officer regarded Findlay with sudden dislike.

'Right,' he said. 'You can go in.'

In the lobby Findlay kept his eyes forward, avoiding Sadiya's gaze. Finally, by the video interface she caught up to him.

'What. The. Fuck. Was that?' she demanded.

He looked at her, visibly uncomfortable.

'You remember I said I do private work? It's for SecurCorp. My boss is pretty senior.'

Before she could reply there was a soft chime, and Manning's wife appeared on the screen.

'Detective Azad?'

'That's right. We need to see your husband.'

Sarah glanced at something they couldn't see. Findlay widened his eyes slightly and moved his lips soundlessly. 'He's there.'

Sadiya leaned closer to the screen. 'I need to warn you that if you obstruct us in our enquiries, we'll be forced to arrest you and charge you.'

On the screen Sarah's eyes widened in surprise, but then her expression hardened.

'You've got no right to threaten me.'

'Just let us in,' Sadiya said.

Sarah's image disappeared, and there was a long silence. Then there was a soft chime and Sarah opened the door. She looked angry, but also tired and frightened. The younger daughter, Beatrix, was standing behind her. Sarah put a hand on the girl's chest as if to protect her.

'Where is he?' said Sadiya.

Sarah didn't move. As she had been the first time they'd spoken, Sadiya was struck by the other woman's brittleness, the sense she was liable to shatter at any moment, but there was an anger to her now that was new.

'This isn't a good time.'

'This is the only time,' Sadiya said, pushing past her into the apartment. For a moment she wondered whether Sarah would resist her, but she didn't; instead she took a step back, shielding Beatrix with her body.

'We know he's here. There's no use pretending.'

In the doorway on the far side of the living area the older daughter, Ava, appeared. She stood with her arms at her side, her fists clenched, her face set in an odd mixture of fear and fury.

Sadiya took a step towards her. 'Ava,' she said. But the girl turned and fled down the hall.

Sadiya followed her. 'Is he through there?' she asked.

'Please,' said Sarah. 'Don't go in there.'

But it was too late: Sadiya and Findlay were already in the hall beyond. On the left a door led into a home office, one wall adorned with children's pictures, the other by a desk with shelving above it, beyond which glass doors opened onto a balcony, the city visible across the harbour. Manning was standing by the doors, Ava in front of him, his body turned slightly to one side as if he was concealing something behind his back. He was dishevelled, his face haggard and hollowed out.

He gave them a thin smile, and for a moment the violence in him was unmistakable. 'Detective Azad.'

Sarah appeared behind them. Sadiya raised a hand to hold her back. She took a step towards Manning. 'We know about Nina. About the refugee processing centre, the money. The girl.'

His smile took on a mocking edge. 'I don't have any idea what you're talking about.'

'Is she alive?' Sadiya demanded.

'Who?'

'Casey.'

He took a step back. 'How would I know that?'

Sadiya advanced slowly, her hand outheld and her eyes on the hand Manning was keeping out of sight. 'Please. We don't have time for this. If she's alive we need to know before the storm hits.'

'I've already said I don't know what you're talking about.'

'It's over, Oliver,' said Findlay. 'You're going to jail whatever happens. Don't let Casey die for nothing.'

The older daughter turned to stare at her father. 'Who's Casey?'

Manning's smile faltered for the first time. He looked at his daughter.

'He kidnapped a girl,' said Sadiya. 'She saw him murder a woman, so he took her. If she's alive we have to find her.'

'Please, Ava,' said Manning. 'You don't understand.'

For a long moment Ava didn't move or speak. Then she turned to stare at Sadiya. 'Is it true?'

Sadiya hesitated. 'You knew?'

'About the girl? No.'

'But you knew about Nina?' Findlay demanded.

Ava's mouth opened and closed in confusion. Then something reasserted itself. 'The other night, he came home late. I don't think he knew I was awake. But he was dressed in black and he was being so weird. When I heard about the woman at his work going missing, I realised ...' She fell silent.

'But you didn't tell anybody? A girl could be dead.'

'I'm sorry,' she said, tears running down her face. 'I didn't know.'

Sadiya felt a moment of revulsion for the girl, her good looks and fragile sense of self, and the fact that in the end it wouldn't matter: people like her move through the world without ever needing to reckon with themselves, without ever really having to grow up.

She turned to Sarah. 'And you? When did you find out?'

'Ava told me this morning.'

'But before that?'

Sarah stared at her, her blue-green eyes angry, although not, Sadiya suspected, at Manning for what he had done, but for the mess he had made.

'Oliver Manning,' she said, walking towards him. 'You're under arrest for the murder of Nina Lukic, and for the abduction of Casey Mitchell. You have the right to remain silent, but anything you do say may be used against you in a court of law.'

Manning backed away onto the balcony. There was something wild in his face. Sadiya had seen the look before, the moment when somebody realises the world doesn't operate the way they thought it did, when they understand they can no longer control things. He came to a halt on the balcony and glanced from side to side, searching for an escape route. Sadiya followed him carefully, but as she reached the door he swung the hand he had been keeping hidden up to reveal a taser. Sadiya froze.

'Oliver!' said Sarah. Findlay lifted his hand to tell her to keep back.

'Don't make this any harder than it needs to be,' Sadiya said.

'You don't know what it's like,' said Manning, staring at her. 'Trying to keep all of this together. Knowing you've only got so long before it all goes wrong.'

'You killed a woman,' Findlay said.

'It wasn't like that.'

'We've seen the video, Oliver,' said Sadiya. 'You went there to kill her.'

'I didn't want to. But she didn't leave me a choice.'

Sarah made a choking sound.

'None of that matters now,' Sadiya said. 'All that matters is finding Casey.'

Manning stared at her. 'I told her it didn't have to be this way.'

Behind her Sarah stepped forward. 'Just tell them, Oliver.'

Manning turned to her. 'You know I did all this for you, don't you? For us.'

Before Sarah could answer Ava turned to him. 'For us? You killed somebody, Dad. None of us wanted that.'

Sarah placed a hand on her daughter's arm, but Ava shook her off. 'Don't touch me!' she spat. She advanced on her father. 'Is it true? Did you take the girl? Where is she?'

For a moment Manning didn't move. Sadiya thought he was about to tell her. Not taking his eyes off his wife and daughter, he lowered the taser to the ground and straightened again. Then, quite suddenly, he smiled and, turning, vaulted over the balustrade and into the air.

There was a sickening moment when Manning seemed to hang, motionless, time slowing as Sadiya lunged forward and collided with the balustrade, her arms outstretched, but it was too late, and he was already falling, his body twisting around as he plummeted towards the ground, the interval between his departure and his impact stretching on and on, until all at once he struck the ground below with a sickening crunch. Sadiya stood, staring down, unable to move, until suddenly she became aware of a sound coming as if from far away, and turned to see Ava screaming beside her.

'No,' said Findlay, his face pale. 'No, no, no.'

Sarah turned to Beatrix. 'Stay there!' she said, then approached the balustrade and stared down. She swung around to face Sadiya. 'What have you done?' she screamed. Next to Sadiya, Ava was still wailing. Sadiya extended a hand towards her, but Sarah stepped between them and drew her into an embrace. Ava stopped screaming, her face blank, then began to weep. Sarah raised a hand to Beatrix and pulled her towards the two of them.

Findlay was still staring down. She approached him and looked down as well. Two guards were hurrying towards Manning's body. Sadiya watched as they knelt beside him, then stood and looked up.

'We need to call for backup.'

'No point,' Sadiya said. 'They'll be calling already.'

'Then what?'

'We have to work out where he took Casey.'

Findlay. 'How?'

Sadiya looked down again. The two black-uniformed guards had been joined by a third. She turned to Sarah.

'I'm sorry,' she said. 'I can't begin to imagine what you're going through right now. But we have to find the girl your husband kidnapped. Do you have any idea where he might have taken her?'

Sarah just looked at her, her eyes wild. For a moment Sadiya thought she hadn't understood the question, but then she shook her head.

'Anything?' Findlay said. 'Did he have access to somebody's house or apartment? Or a storage area somewhere?'

'No, nothing.'

'Please. A child's life might depend on it.'

Ava shook herself loose of her mother's embrace and turned to face them, her face wet with tears. 'He had a place. An apartment.'

Sarah looked at her. 'What?'

'I saw a message about it on his screen. He was behind on the rent.'

'Where was it?' Sadiya said.

The girl took out her phone and touched the screen. But before she could finish what she was doing, there was a crash from inside the apartment and a pair of SecurCorp officers burst through the doors at the far end of the balcony, their guns drawn. Beatrix screamed.

'Place your weapons on the ground immediately,' barked the taller of the two.

Sadiya lifted a hand to stop them. 'We're police officers engaged in the lawful execution of our duties,' she said.

'I said place your weapons on the ground!' said the guard. Findlay glanced at Sadiya and she gave him a small nod. Unclipping their guns they knelt down and placed them on the ground. As Findlay straightened a third SecurCorp officer appeared through the door to the home office and, grabbing him by the shirt, shoved him against the wall. Findlay raised his hands in the air but didn't resist. Lifting her hands higher, Sadiya stepped across herself before the officer could grab her. Lowering his own gun, the guard who had told them to drop their weapons approached the wife and the two daughters.

'Are you all okay?'

Sarah laughed bitterly. 'What do you think?' She took a breath, then shook her head. 'She's telling the truth. They're police officers.'

'We're trying to locate a missing child,' said Sadiya. 'You need to return our weapons and let us leave.'

'A resident is dead. We can't let you do that.'

'We're police officers,' said Findlay.

'Then you can explain that to your colleagues when they arrive.'

'You're making a mistake,' Sadiya said. 'We were here to arrest him. He jumped to avoid us.'

'That may well be true,' the first officer said. 'But we still can't let you leave until we're satisfied the situation is under control.'

'We don't have time for that!' Sadiya said.

At the sound of Sadiya's voice Beatrix began to wail. Sarah reached out and pulled the child to her. The guard turned to the man who was holding Findlay in place.

'Remove them from the apartment,' he said.

'No,' Sadiya said. 'You can't.'

But the guard holding Findlay had already grabbed his arm to wrench him around. Suddenly Ava stepped forward.

'Wait!' she said. 'It's true. He jumped.'

The first guard stared at her. 'I'm sorry?'

'What they said, it's true. They tried to question him and he jumped. He killed somebody. And stole money.'

'No!' said the wife. 'Ava, don't!'

'And they say he kidnapped a girl.'

'I'm afraid our procedures are clear. They have to be detained.'

Sarah held out a hand to restrain her, but Ava shrugged it off. 'Until when?'

'Until we can establish what happened here.'

'But if the storm hits that could be too late for the girl they're looking for.'

'She's right,' Sadiya said. 'We don't have time to waste.'

The guard turned to Sarah. 'Is what she's saying true? Did he jump?'

Sarah nodded, her manner stiff and defiant. For a second or two the guard didn't move. Then he turned to the officer who was holding Findlay against the wall.

'Pick up their weapons and escort them out of the complex.'

The third officer knelt down and picked up their guns.

'Wait,' said Sadiya, turning to Ava. 'The address?'

Ava reached into her pocket and pulled out her screen. A moment later an alert pinged in Sadiya's lenses. Then the officer who had pushed Findlay against the wall marched the two of them to the door.

In the street outside the heat had grown even more intense, the air glassy with it, and overhead great bands of cloud obscured the sun. Now and then a gust of wind moved uncertainly through the leaves of the trees in the gardens behind them. Findlay slumped against the car.

'Fuck, fuck, fuck,' he said. 'They're going to crucify us.'

'Our cams will show it was suicide.' She flicked the photo Ava had sent her to him. It was an image of a screen, a message open on it. An address as well.

'Smart kid,' Findlay said.

Sadiya looked at him. 'Did you see the way the mother reacted? She was afraid of him. They all were.'

Findlay didn't reply. Sadiya knew she didn't need to say the rest of it, make explicit what they both knew: that the lives of all three of them would never be the same, and he had known that by jumping he would deny them the reckoning they deserved.

*

Tasim was in the corner of the holding room when the fight broke out. It had been almost four hours since anybody had been to check on them, and one of the detainees who had been brought in the night before had been pounding on the door and shouting for the guards for most of that time.

'When do you think he will realise his bellowing will not make them come?' said the young man who had been in the van when Tasim was arrested the day before. Tasim looked over at him and then shook his head in resignation.

The young man moved closer to him. 'Do you think they are still out there?' he asked.

Tasim stared at the man pounding on the door. It was so hot and stuffy in the room he was having trouble thinking straight. 'Surely they wouldn't just leave us?'

The young man's face grew solemn. 'The storm is almost here. Perhaps they decided to go home, be safe. This building ...' He gestured to the roof far above. 'It is not strong.'

Tasim was about to reply when one of the other men stood up and grabbed the man by the door by the shoulder and, pulling him back, began to yell at him, the veins standing out in his head. Tasim and the young man stood up, ready to move away if the two of them headed in their direction. A third and a fourth man joined in, shoving and shouting, then a siren blared and the red light above the door began to flash. A moment later there was a clunk and six guards burst through the door, batons in hand. One pushed the first man up against the wall while the others dragged the other three out. As the last guard turned to go he noticed Tasim and stopped.

'You?' he said, approaching him. 'What's your name?'

Tasim shifted uneasily and told him.

'And how old are you?'

'Fifteen,' said Tasim.

The guard sighed in exasperation. 'And what are you doing in here?'

Tasim shrugged. 'I don't know. They put me here yesterday.'

The guard shook his head. 'Okay. Come with me. We can't leave you in here.'

Tasim looked at the young man he had been brought in with. He smiled. 'It's good. You go,' he said.

Tasim nodded and began to follow the guard towards the door. 'Be safe, my friend,' said the young man as the guard closed the door behind him.

The guard led him to a processing area. A row of plastic seats was bolted to one wall. Opposite them was a plexiglass screen, behind which a Border Force officer could be seen. Half-a-dozen people were already seated in the area.

'Wait here,' said the guard. 'Somebody will be with you soon.'

Tasim sat down next to a man at the end of the row. Behind the plexiglass screen the officer was arguing with somebody on the phone. Tasim watched him uneasily. Through the security door at the other end of the room he could hear somebody shouting, but the officer didn't seem to have noticed. Tasim leaned back, his heart beating fast. If he could just get through the security door perhaps he could get away, find the girl.

His neighbour let out a low moan and, lifting his hand to his head, tugged on his hair. Tasim angled his body away from him, wary of unsettling or provoking him in some way. The man moaned again, a low, desperate sound, and Tasim stiffened, suddenly reminded of Sigit and his growing distress on the journey south. The last time he had seen his friend he had been loaded onto a transport heading for one of the adult camps, his dark eyes blank and haunted. Where was he now? Was he even alive?

He took a breath, trying not to be dragged down by the feeling of failure that still weighed on him when he remembered those days after the wreck of the boat. On a screen above the plexiglass barrier reporters were talking about the storm, their mouths moving silently; he forced himself to focus on them, to try to make sense of what they were saying, but he could not. Closing his eyes he tried to concentrate on the girl instead, to make sense of what he had seen before they caught him. Was she in one of those buildings? Which one? And how could he tell?

His thoughts were interrupted by a shout and the sound of the security door beside him opening. He looked up as two Border Force officers dragged a man into the room. The man was tall and thin and his loose khaki pants weren't long enough, and he was shouting and gesticulating. The two guards pushed him towards the plexiglass and the officer behind it stood up.

'We don't have an ID on this one,' said one of the officers, but Tasim wasn't listening. Next to him, the security door had not closed properly. He shot a glance at the guard behind the plexiglass: he was leaning forward to talk to the two officers. In one swift movement he got to his feet and made for the door, pulling it open and bolting through before anybody could stop him. He found himself in a small lobby, at the end of which an automatic door led outside. He ran for the door and emerged into a parking area where two Border Force vans stood. It was hotter than it had been inside, and the light was spectral, diffuse. Certain that at any moment somebody would come after him, he took off towards the street and sprinted away, sweat pouring down his face in the heat.

*

It took forty minutes to reach the address in the photo, forty minutes crawling through roadblocks and obstructions. On the highway a truck had overturned, a sea of broken bottles spreading out from it, while police waved vehicles past, one by one; elsewhere people were still piling sandbags and nailing up sheets of tin or lashing tarpaulins to roofs.

When they were halfway there Nguyen called, but Sadiya muted it, then caught Findlay looking at her.

'Nguyen?'

'I'll deal with her later,' said Sadiya. She paused. When she spoke again her voice was gentler. 'You don't have to come with me. I've got nothing left to lose. You do.'

Findlay shook his head. 'We need to find her.'

They pulled up outside a building not far from the Floodline, an older block on a deserted street. Approaching the door Sadiya pulled out her ID and pressed on the intercom for one of the apartments on the ground floor. A woman's voice answered.

'We're police,' she said. 'We need access to the building.'

There was a moment or two's silence and then the lock released. Sadiya unclipped the gun on her belt, and Findlay did the same. They headed up the stairs.

In the corridor on the fourth floor, they approached the door and stopped on either side of it. Sadiya reached one arm out and bashed her fist against the door. 'Police!' she shouted.

There was no answer. She looked at Findlay and he nodded. Stepping forward he kicked the door just below the lock, once and then again and then finally a third time. On the third kick the doorframe cracked and the door swung inwards.

The apartment they stepped into was small and very hot. On the left just inside the door there was an open-plan kitchen, beyond which lay a small living area. At the far end of the living area stood a pair of sliding doors, both covered in black plastic. The glass of one had been staved in, and lay scattered on the floor in front of it.

Sadiya assessed the space. A corridor ran off on her right; directing Findlay to check the balcony she turned down the corridor, which led to a bathroom and bedroom, both unoccupied.

She turned back. Findlay was standing in the living area.

'Nothing?' she asked.

'Nothing,' he replied.

'No,' she said, staring around. 'No, no, no. Where is she?'

'What about the door? Could she have escaped?'

Sadiya glanced at the broken glass. 'No. That was somebody coming in.'

Findlay crossed to the balcony. 'But who? And how? We're three floors up.'

Sadiya pulled a pair of latex gloves out of her pocket and put them on. She turned to the benchtop, the scattered equipment. Two drones, tracking tiles, cameras.

'Jesus. No wonder Nina was frightened of him,' Findlay said.

Sadiya didn't reply. How did these men live like this? All this desire for power, for control. It made her sick with fury. She clenched her fists and took a breath, steadying herself.

'He has to have taken her somewhere,' she said.

'Unless he killed her.'

She looked at Findlay. 'Do you think he killed her?'

Findlay hesitated. 'No.'

'Why not?'

'It doesn't feel right.'

'He must have somewhere else.'

'But where?'

'I don't know. But maybe something here will tell us.'

They searched quickly, desperately, scratching through the equipment on the desks, opening drawers, looking in cupboards. As they worked Sadiya noticed cameras installed in several places, cameras that were no doubt filming them, uploading images of their search to the cloud, some encrypted server only Manning had access to.

Sadiya was looking under the bed in the bedroom when Findlay called out to her. Hurrying back through she found him standing with a woman.

'This is Bey. She lives in the apartment next door.'

Sadiya nodded a greeting.

'Have you met the person who rents this apartment?'

Bey shook her head. 'Never.'

'Have you noticed anything unusual in the past few days?'

Bey pointed at the torn plastic over the door, the broken glass on the floor. 'I saw the kid who broke in.'

'What?' Sadiya said.

The woman looked confused. 'Isn't that why you're here? The other day, the kid I saw in the corridor? I reported it.'

'Which day?' Findlay asked.

Bey thought for a moment. 'Wednesday. In the afternoon. I heard the window break, so I knocked on the door. He answered the door and then ran off.'

'What did he look like? Do you remember?'

Bey looked confused. 'Of course. I've got a video of him.'

'I'm sorry?' Sadiya said in surprise.

'I told the police when I reported it. I took a video. You never know what will happen.'

'Can we see it?'

Bey took out her screen and turned so they could see it.

'There,' said Sadiya. 'His face, zoom in on it.'

Bey did as she was asked and Sadiya fell still. 'This boy, he came out of the apartment?' she asked.

'That's right.'

'And he was alone?'

'Yes.'

'And you haven't seen anybody else? A girl, perhaps?'

'No.'

Sadiya smiled. 'Thank you, Bey, this is incredibly helpful.'

'Are you going to try to catch him?'

'We'll do our best.'

The moment she was outside Findlay turned to Sadiya. 'The kid, from the security footage. What's he doing here? Could he be involved with Manning in some way? Maybe as his accomplice?'

'Then why would he have run on the night of the killing? And why break in if they're working with each other?'

Findlay looked at the broken glass on the floor.

'Perhaps he's looking for Casey as well,' Sadiya said. She spoke quietly, almost to herself.

Findlay turned to her. 'What do you mean?'

'He was there the night Manning killed Nina. He saw him burn her body. But perhaps he saw Casey as well. Maybe he's trying to find her as well.'

'Why would he do that?'

Sadiya stopped, thinking. Then she noticed a digital keyfob on the bench in the kitchen. She picked it up and held it up.

'Oliver's car,' she said. 'It was a Lexus, right?'

'Yep.'

'And they've got face-recognition ignitions?'

'Of course.'

She held the key up. 'Then why's he got this?'

Findlay looked at it. 'He must have a second car. One not registered in his name.'

They ran to the stairs and raced down to the car park. A dozen cars were parked against the walls. Sadiya hurried out into the space and pressed the button on the keyfob. There was an electronic beep and the lights on a white van flashed.

'Bingo,' she said.

*

Arman stared around, tears on his face. In his hand he had a hammer: he gazed at it for a moment trying to remember what it was about it that had affected him so much, then dropped it. Overhead a huge bank of cloud filled half the sky. The light was unearthly and a restless wind shifted and sighed.

He was standing in a yard behind a house he didn't recognise. Frightened he might have made some kind of mistake, he walked down the side and out into the street. He was certain there was a problem, that he needed to tell somebody. Perhaps he should go home, he thought, except he couldn't remember where home was. Not Dhaka, that was gone, together with the city, but perhaps Botany? Or the house out west, where there was always smoke? He stopped, staring ahead. He could hear a siren, a whooping in the distance. A man and a woman went past, the woman carrying a child, its head pressed to her neck, the man a shopping bag full of food and a plastic container of water. Arman stopped, wanting to ask them where he was, but they walked past him without stopping.

Not sure what to do he headed on, panic rising in his chest. Wherever he should be it wasn't here, not now. He could smell the rain approaching, the salt smell of the storm. He closed his eyes, and suddenly he was back there. The first rainy season after the Melt began. All over the world the weather had gone haywire, the first heat storms, cyclones, fire and floods, tornados in places they had never been seen before. Along the coast the government had been building barriers, bulldozing earth and rubble into walls to protect villages and towns, but it wasn't enough. With each new moon the ocean rose higher, seeping up through the ground, poisoning wells and trees, mingling with sewage and other waste to lie in evil, reeking pools and lakes that gleamed in the sun.

Arman knew the tides would keep getting higher, and the land would continue to be eaten away, but leaving felt like an act of cowardice. He and Leah argued about it every day, throwing the arguments back and forth. Australia was already imposing stricter and stricter border controls, and she was frightened that if they waited any longer it would be too late, that his visa would be suspended and he and Lina and Sadiya wouldn't be allowed in.

'What will we do then?' she demanded, her face drawn and angry.

In the end, though, it wasn't the sea that made their decision for them, but the rain. As the monsoon arrived it brought an impossible deluge that fell and fell, filling the rivers and streams inland and flowing seawards. There had been floods before, of course, but that year they arrived with a ferocity nobody had ever seen, transforming the roads into fast-moving torrents in which cars and trucks were borne along like toys.

As the water began to rise around their apartment block, they did what they could to prepare, sandbagging doors and windows, offering neighbours the chance to shelter in their apartment. But as the first floor disappeared beneath the flood, Arman realised they had left it too late to get to safety. He and Leah discussed their options in the kitchen, standing close to each other and keeping their voices low. In the next room Lina and Sadiya had their screens. They were supposed to be watching them, but Arman could see Lina staring at the two of them, her dark eyes frightened.

'We can't stay here,' Leah said. 'We need to get to higher ground.'

'It's too dangerous,' said Arman.

'Then what?'

Arman looked up. 'The roof?' he said. Leah turned. Lina was standing in the doorway.

'What if the water keeps rising?'

Arman shook his head. 'We don't have another option.'

Leah closed her eyes, trying to calm herself. Arman knew she wanted to tell him again that they should have left. 'Okay,' she said at last. 'Let's go upstairs.'

By the time they got Lina and Sadiya out onto the landing the balcony was already awash. The water splashing around their ankles, they ran to the end of the balcony, where a pair of ladders had been set up against the wall and half a dozen of their neighbours were waiting as those ahead of them climbed to the roof. By the time their turn came the water on the balcony was already shin-deep. Arman held Lina and Leah held Sadiya while a middle-aged man he recognised from the courtyard helped haul an older woman upwards, her tiny frame frail in his arms.

When their turn came, he sent Leah and Sadiya up first, then waited while Lina climbed ahead of him. Up on the roof the rain was still falling, and a brown and filthy torrent surged past around the building, carrying trees and branches and an impossible assortment of garbage with it. While the rain sluiced down their faces and necks, Arman squatted down and hugged Lina to himself. Next to him Leah was holding Sadiya and staring around, her eyes wild and her hair plastered to her scalp; on the other side a man he didn't recognise clutched a bag to his chest, his thin face set in a look of disbelief.

Arman wasn't sure how long they sat huddled on the roof in the pouring rain. At any other time people would have been arguing or complaining, but although one woman was softly sobbing, for the most part they were silent, their eyes fixed on the water. The building next door was slightly lower than theirs, and the stream was already above its roofline. As the water crested the edge of their roof there was a murmur of panic and people began to shout and talk over each other. Next to him Leah began to cry, and Arman put an arm around her and pulled her and Sadiya close.

'What's happening?' said Sadiya, her eyes wide with fear.

'It'll be all right,' said Arman.

'I'm scared, Amma,' said Lina.

Leah pressed Lina to her chest. 'I know,' she said, then looked at Arman. 'What are we going to do?'

Arman didn't reply, frightened he wouldn't be able to disguise the terror in his voice. The water was knee-deep when somebody farther along the roof cried out and then began shouting and waving their arms. Arman turned. A boat was heading through the rain towards them. It was a wooden fishing boat, long and narrow, with a raised prow and an engine in the stern. A boy of twelve or thirteen sat with his hand on the engine while a thin man sat in the front, his red t-shirt plastered to his skinny frame by the rain.

Even before the boat was beside the roof people were already wading down towards it. Several grabbed the side and started trying to clamber in.

'Careful!' shouted the man in the red t-shirt as the boat yawed alarmingly to one side, the floodwater churning around it. Arman shoved his way through and lifted Sadiya into the boat, then turned to help Leah with Lina. But Lina was screaming and refusing to leave the roof. In the boat Sadiya was crying as well; Arman placed a hand on her, trying to calm her, and turned back to call to Leah and Lina. But the man by the tiller had engaged the engine. Arman took a couple of steps as the boat began to pull him forward, calling to Leah to take his hand. Somebody else was shouting in the boat, telling him to let go, that the boat was going to capsize. Behind him Leah lifted Lina up and waded after him. Arman called out to her, telling her to hurry, but Leah stumbled and fell, Lina slipping from her arms into the water. Leah splashed after Lina, but the current already had her. Arman cried out, and then the roof beneath him disappeared as the boat pulled him over the edge. He plunged down into the water, wrenching his shoulder as he disappeared beneath the surface. Frantically, he pulled himself up, one hand still clutching the side of the boat, and looked back to see Leah and Lina's heads moving away from him, Lina still screaming and Leah holding one hand up as the filthy water swept them away. He cried out again, screaming their names over and over until they disappeared beneath the surface.

*

'You take the back,' said Sadiya when they reached the van. 'I'll check the front.'

She pulled the door open and jumped in. The van was old – a decade, maybe two – but its interior was clean and well-maintained. She opened the glovebox, pulled out a black cloth mask, gloves, cord and tape. She took them out, but then Findlay called her name.

She found him staring into the van's rear compartment, where a crumpled blanket lay in one corner beside a box of plastic water bottles. Sadiya climbed in and grabbed the blanket and something fell to the ground. She looked down to see a plastic sheet of zip cuffs lying by her feet. She lifted them and waved them at Findlay.

'If he needed zip cuffs to restrain her, then she was alive. Or at least she was when he had her in here.'

She ran around to the front of the van and hit the ignition button. The interface in the dash came to life, and she jabbed at it to pull up the map. Flicking through the menu she searched recent trips, but it came up blank.

'Shit. He's turned off the trip history.'

'Perhaps we can get something from Traffic,' Findlay said.

'You do that. I'll check the registration – it wasn't in his name, but perhaps if we can find out who it is registered to that will throw up something.'

While Findlay tried to access traffic data, Sadiya entered the registration into the system. A moment later the details appeared. The van was registered to an Anita Manning. Manning's mother? His aunt? She choked down her revulsion. All these secret, squalid lies. She ran the name through the system, looking for anything that might be useful, but it seemed Anita Manning lived in the Southern Highlands.

She turned to Findlay. 'I've got nothing. You?'

He held his screen up. 'He's clearly careful to avoid places he might be picked up by cameras, but look.' Findlay pointed to a series of hits that showed the van had been scanned several times at a mini-mart farther south, closer to the Floodline.

'I know that place,' said Sadiya. 'It's near Sydenham station. Let's get over there. See if we can find anything.'

'It's not enough. Even if he was keeping her somewhere near there we can't check every building nearby.'

'It's better than nothing,' said Sadiya.

The sky was dark and the streets were eerily empty as they drove towards the mini-mart. Sadiya checked the latest reports on the storm. Modelling suggested the storm surge was likely to be ten metres or more, and winds of almost 400 kilometres an hour had been reported. She tried to visualise what this would do to the buildings in the Floodline and elsewhere, and gave up. Even compared to the other storms of recent years it was unthinkable. They pulled up beside the mini-mart and jumped out. The store was in darkness, its windows taped and sandbags across its door. Sadiya ran up to the glass and peered in, but there was nobody there. She turned and looked around. There was a small park opposite the mini-mart, a scrappy bit of ground with a child's swing inside a wire fence. Behind it rose old apartment blocks and other buildings. She knew they were looking for a needle in a haystack, that even if Casey was here somewhere they had no way to find her, but the notion they had come so far, and got so close only to lose her now was unbearable.

'You go that way,' she said to Findlay. 'Call me if you find anything.'

'What if we get separated?' Findlay said.

Sadiya looked at the buildings behind him. 'Find somewhere safe, bed down until the first wave passes.'

Findlay paused and placed a hand on her shoulder. 'Be safe,' he said.

Sadiya put her hand over his. 'And you.'

She raced away along the pavement, staring around herself and shouting Casey's name at the top of her voice. A gust of wind swept up the street, scattering dirt and leaves before it; somewhere in the distance thunder rumbled. Glancing to the east she saw the sky had turned a strange amber hue. These streets often flooded, and many of the buildings along them had fallen into disrepair, their façades covered in graffiti and rubbish piled outside them. Near the corner a row of old shops stood in a half-metre of water, their burned-out shells empty and stained, but on the higher side a pair of old semi-detached houses stood on elevated blocks, their windows obscured behind sheets of plywood. Sadiya bounded up the steps and pounded on the door of the first.

'Police!' she shouted.

After a second or two the door opened and a heavily pregnant woman peered out.

Sadiya held up a photo of Manning on her screen. 'Have you seen this man recently?'

The woman's brow tightened. Then she shook her head.

'Are you sure?' Sadiya said. 'It's important.'

'Sorry.'

'I'm looking for a girl he may have abducted. Have you heard or seen anything suspicious in the past week? Any sign a girl might be being held near here.'

The woman stared at her. 'A girl?' She glanced at the children behind her. 'No, nothing like that.'

'Is anybody next door?' she asked.

'They went south on Wednesday.'

'Okay,' she said, and raced back down to the street. She ignored the house next door and ran on. The two houses past it were burned out, their walls blackened and stained, and the two after that were dark. Thunder rumbled again, louder this time, and another gust of wind blew past. She turned. At the end of the street the face of the storm loomed, an immense wall of cloud. The light had gone green. On the opposite side of the street was the old library building, its heavy brick and columns festooned with graffiti. She raced towards it and banged on the heavy door. The door opened and a woman of about Sadiya's age looked out.

'Are you looking for shelter?' she asked.

A gust of wind whipped past with a rattle of grit and dirt. Sadiya held out her ID.

'No,' she said. 'I'm looking for a girl who I think is being held near here.' She produced the image of Manning again. 'Have you seen this man?'

The woman looked at it and shook her head. 'Is he dangerous?'

Sadiya slipped her badge back in her pocket. 'Not anymore.' She was about to put her screen away when a man appeared behind the woman. He was small but powerfully built.

'What's going on?' he asked, glancing at the photo and then at Sadiya.

'I'm looking for anybody who may have seen this man.'

The man examined the image again.

'Sure. I saw him.'

'What? Are you sure?'

He looked up at her. He had a square face with a direct, intelligent gaze. 'I run a noodle truck down by the station. He bought food a couple of times this week.'

'Was he alone?'

'I think so.'

'Do you remember anything else about him? Where he went afterwards? Anything he said?'

'I only remember him because he came back more than once.'

'When was the last time he came?'

The man thought for a moment. 'Yesterday. But I wasn't there this morning.'

'Do you think anybody else in here might have seen him?'

The man and the woman exchanged a look, then the man shrugged. 'Perhaps,' he said, and the two of them stepped aside so she could enter.

Inside it was dimly lit, the air thick with the smell of damp and bodies, the heat unthinkable. People were seated against the wall and spread across the floor on mattresses and bags.

'It's the strongest building we have around here,' the woman said. 'A lot of people had nowhere else to go; others thought they'd be safer here.'

Approaching the nearest group, Sadiya pulled out her screen, and began showing Manning's photo to people and asking whether anybody had seen him. She was almost done when a woman approached her.

'Let me see that,' she said.

Sadiya held the screen out.

'Yeah, I seen him,' she said.

'What? When?' said Sadiya.

'A few days ago. He was parked outside one of the buildings by the old container yard.'

'You're certain? Where exactly?'

The woman looked vague. 'I dunno. Talbot Street somewhere.'

'Over by the highway?' said Sadiya.

'That's right.'

'You're sure?'

The woman nodded. Sadiya turned and ran back towards the entrance. Back in the entry hall the man and the woman who had admitted her were waiting. The woman stepped out in front of her.

'You're not going back out there, are you?' she said.

Sadiya saw the way she kept her distance and understood how much it had taken her to question a detective.

'I don't have any choice.'

'You can stay here with us,' the man said.

'Thank you,' Sadiya said. 'But I have to go.'

'Call Findlay,' she said to her assistant as she descended the stairs back to the street, but her assistant didn't reply. Touching her lenses she repeated herself, then saw the pulsing signal that showed the system was offline.

'Shit,' she said. She stared down the street in the direction Findlay had gone, hoping to catch a glimpse of him, but there was no sign of anybody. A gust of wind struck her, and in the distance there was a crack of thunder. She hesitated for a second or two, then sprinted towards the car.

*

Tasim finally stopped running a kilometre or so from the processing centre, gasping and sweating in the heat. While he caught his breath, he stared up at the impossible mass of the storm rising above him. He could feel electricity in the air and the wind was beginning to gust. Wiping his face he began to jog onwards again. Part of him didn't understand why he was here. Why not just let this go? Yet another part knew he couldn't do that. He should have done more to help the girl the first time he saw her. He knew that wasn't rational, that this was about Dewi, his mother, all the people he had left behind and could never replace, but he didn't care.

When he finally reached the highway and the street from the day before he stopped. Overhead the thunderhead filled the sky, traceries of lightning moving in its innards. In the street the surface of the rising water gleamed like shifting mercury in the weird light. He took a breath and waded out, the smell of salt filling his nostrils. He felt a tightness in his chest and all at once he was back in the boat, but he clenched his fists and forced himself to keep moving forward.

A dead dog floated past him in the water, its belly swollen and its legs sticking up. For a moment its face surfaced, the lips twisted back from its teeth as if it were revolted by the way it found itself. Tasim stepped aside to let it go, then began to splash towards the nearest building, pushing against the rising water. Where it met the street broken glass doors opened into a ruined space that might once have been an office; Tasim waded across and opened a door to reveal a space that had perhaps once been a factory or a workshop, but which was now roofless, its walls framing the boiling thunderhead above, a shifting mass of metal and timber creaking in the water beneath it.

Struggling against the flow he shoved his way out again. The water was waist-deep now, and in the distance a sound like wires in the wind moved through the air, shifting amplitude, but rising. Tasim remembered listening to the sound of Jupiter's magnetic fields on headphones, the way Dewi had mocked him afterwards making him choke.

The building across the road was little more than a burned-out shell, its sides stained black by the flames, but the one beyond it was intact, a long structure of pale bricks and dark windows. Unlike the first it had no shopfront; instead, two green doors fronted the street. As he floundered towards them Tasim almost lost his footing several times, only just avoiding being borne away in the tide of refuse. When he reached the doors he pushed on them, but they didn't move. Running his hand down them he found a chain and padlock wound through a pair of metal handles. He pulled at it a couple of times, but to no effect; the doors were locked tight.

Farther along the street two more buildings were visible, their fronts covered in graffiti and peeling paint, but unlike this one they didn't look to be locked. He waded towards the first. At its far end there was an alley with a loading bay in it. Tasim splashed over to it and climbed the stairs. At the rear of the area a roller door was padlocked to the concrete floor, but the concrete around it was pitted and damaged, as if it had been forced at some point.

Grabbing the door, Tasim tried to lift it, but although the bracket on the floor shifted, it didn't give. He tried again, straining and heaving, ignoring the pain in his back and side, but it wouldn't budge. Down in the loading bay the water was still rising. In one corner of the platform lay a pile of old rubbish bags, their sides split and spilling; in the opposite corner a pair of pallets lay smashed and broken. Grabbing a piece of timber, he slipped it under the bracket and tried to lever it up, ignoring the splinters that pierced his skin, but the soft timber splintered and broke. With a cry of frustration he grabbed another piece and tried again, but it snapped as well. He stumbled back and noticed an old screwdriver protruding from a pile of rubbish near the wall. Scooping it up he shoved it under the bracket, pushing and flexing it, not caring when his hand slipped and the metal ripped the skin from his knuckles, or even when the plastic handle began to crack; instead, he wrenched and shoved until, all at once, the bracket twisted loose.

Leaping up he shoved the roller door up and slid underneath. Inside was a storage area, and beyond that a door into a wide corridor and a staircase. He ignored the staircase and hurried down the corridor, passing a series of metal doors. Finally, he came to another area, wire cages one after another. Outside, the sound he had heard before was growing louder, wilder, and through the windows high in the wall an otherworldly light filtered down. At the end of the corridor was a wire fence covered in plastic. He stopped. How had he come this far only to fail? But just as he turned away something made him stop, some sense he had seen this scene before. Turning, he remembered the plastic on the windows in the apartment. He raced over to the gate and pulled on it, but it was padlocked. Reaching up he grabbed the plastic and dragged it down, exposing the wire grille and the space behind it. It wasn't large – perhaps three metres wide and four or five deep. A row of boxes divided it in half, but on the far side of them, pressed against the wall, her arms behind her back and her eyes wide above a gag, was the girl.

*

It was dark as night by the time she reached Talbot Street, the clouds overhead coiling and twisting like a living thing. As she climbed out of the car her ears popped from the falling air pressure and the wind keened, spectral and inhuman. The storm surge had already reached the top of the street, but she splashed out into the filthy tide of plastic and other refuse, ignoring the weight of the water moving against her and staring up at the buildings. Most were abandoned, although others were still sometimes used by the homeless. But without knowing more it was impossible to know which one Oliver had been visiting.

When the water reached her chest she stopped. Ahead of her the light had turned yellow-green, trees thrashing and debris flying beneath the vast purple-black weight of cloud. Realising the full force of the storm was about to hit, she turned and began to wade back, but the water was moving faster now, a river flowing through the streets, and it was difficult to remain standing. As the torrent shoved her forward her foot caught on something, and she stumbled, slipping under. Choking, she scrambled back to her feet. The wind had grown even louder, a wild, banshee-like wail. Then all at once she heard an unnatural hissing, and turned to see a wall of rain bearing down on her.

She pushed on through the rising water, searching for somewhere to take refuge. Glimpsing a door through the rain she waded towards it and grabbed the handle but it wouldn't budge. She stumbled down again, splashing around a corner into an alley where an old delivery bay opened in the side of the building, and crawled up half-a-dozen stairs and through an open door into the building. Behind her the rain and wind hit with the force of an explosion, a wall of sound that wiped out everything else. The surge was already rising around her feet as she stumbled on and into a stairwell. Pushing the door closed behind her she made her way up to a landing and fell exhaustedly to the ground, her hands over her ears as she tried to drown out the roar of the storm.

*

Arman stopped in the middle of the street. He felt peculiar, unravelled, the sound around him somehow distant, almost muffled. The air shimmered. Somewhere in the distance thunder rumbled, and litter and leaves and grit skittered here and there as the wind eddied around him.

He wanted to go home, but he couldn't remember where home was. Couldn't remember, he realised with a dim, crawling terror, who he was, or how he had got here. He looked down at his hands, saw the hands of an old man, wondered whose they were, how he had stopped being a child, by the river, by the water?

A horn blared behind him, the sound explosive, and he lurched to one side just in time to avoid being hit by a car. He stared after it, confused, then a moment later another horn blared, and he stumbled back the other way. He knew he needed to not be on the road, but he didn't know how to get off.

Somebody grabbed his arm. He swung around, startled. It was a man: thin, dark-haired.

'What are you doing out here?' he asked.

Arman opened his mouth to speak, but couldn't find the words. And then all at once he began to cry. The man drew him closer and put his arm around him.

'It's okay,' he said. 'Come with me.'

*

Once Sadiya had caught her breath she stood up again and opened the door. The noise of the wind outside was deafening, overwhelming, its monstrous howl like the keening of some primeval animal. But the roar of the wind was only part of it. Around her the building was heaving and groaning, the sound of it shifting in the wind interspersed by terrifying crashes and detonations as flying objects collided with it. As she passed a window she glimpsed a sheet of tin go windmilling past, and branches and leaves. Then there was an explosion of sound and force, and the glass blew inwards, something huge crashing through and throwing her back. Crawling to her feet she staggered towards another door. Bracing her shoulder against it and pushing against the wind she forced it closed, then staggered further into the room. Unlike the last one, this one had been occupied at some point – in the greenish half-light she could see mattresses and old clothes scattered on the floor, together with old food packaging – but whoever had been here was gone. Something struck the building with a sound like a bomb going off and she started. Recovering herself she headed for the inside wall and dropped down and pressed herself against it. She could feel the entire building moving, its structure straining and shifting. Now and again a shiver of dust dropped to the floor, dislodged from the mortar; overhead the roof creaked and groaned.

The sound reverberated through her body. She closed her eyes and pressed her hands to her ears, trying to block it out, but almost at once there was a massive crash nearby. She took another breath. And then, in a brief lull, she thought she heard something else, a voice, or a cry, although as soon as it was there it was gone again, drowned out in the roar of the storm. Sitting up she tried to slow her breathing, to listen harder, and then she heard it again. A voice, barely audible over the din. Getting to her feet she staggered to the far side of the room. Opening the door she stepped back out into the corridor, the wind smashing into it, the floor awash with rain and debris. There was no chance of hearing anything here: even staying on her feet was a challenge. Shielding her eyes against the wind and the rain that sliced into her skin, she stumbled down the length of the corridor, until she came to another staircase. She took a step or two down. Water moved below, black and foul, its surface slick with scum. The sound from outside was deafening, but then she heard the voice again. Gripping the rail she began to descend the stairs, the water warm around her as she stepped into it. By the time she reached the bottom it was up to her armpits. She steadied herself, aware of the risk of going further. If she lost her footing or got stuck she would almost certainly drown; if she was struck by debris she would be dragged under or injured.

Shoving her concerns down, she pushed forward, through the door and into the area beyond. This building had clearly been a storage facility at one point, and wire cages stood on either side, a filthy tide flowing between them. Sadiya allowed herself to be pulled along, moving with the water past the storage areas, their interiors piled with abandoned junk, their doors swinging free. An esky bumped past her, followed by a plastic milk crate and bottles and other refuse. At the far end the corridor turned and terminated in a wire gate. A teenager in a yellow t-shirt was pressed against it, his face pushed into the wire, the water surging around him. Although she couldn't make out his words or hear his voice over the roar of the wind, she could see his mouth was open.

Stumbling closer she glimpsed something on the other side of the gate. At first Sadiya couldn't make out what it was, but then she saw a child's face pushed above the surface – her features stricken with terror and her mouth wide as she gasped for air – and she knew who it was.

Casey.

The teenager turned to her, wild-eyed, as she splashed towards him.

'Please!' he shouted, barely audible over the screaming of the storm. 'You have to help her!'

Sadiya grabbed the gate and yanked it. It rattled but didn't move. In the gloom she made out a padlock, already half-submerged.

She looked up. Casey was almost completely underwater, only her face protruding from the filthy water.

'She's tied up!' shouted the boy, pressing his face close to hers.

She stared at Casey, horror rising in her. It couldn't end like this. Next to her the boy was screaming something. He pointed to the far wall. She followed his gaze and saw a fire extinguisher sticking out of the water. Frantically she fought through the flood towards it and, pulling it off the wall, half-walked, half-swam back towards him.

'Stand back!' she shouted. Lifting the canister she brought its weight down on the padlock, the impact jarring her shoulders and arms, but the padlock didn't break. Raising it above her head she brought it down again, and then again, until all at once the padlock broke. Dropping the fire extinguisher she grabbed the gate and pulled it open. She pushed through the opening, the boy behind her, and splashed towards Casey, but she was gone, swallowed by the rising water. Screaming Casey's name she plunged forward, searching beneath the water. In the half-light it was difficult to make out what was happening, and there were too many boxes and other pieces of garbage moving in the water. Taking a breath she dove underneath, and collided with something soft. Closing her arms around it she felt Casey struggle, and tried to pull her to the surface, but something was holding her down. Taking another breath she dove down and groped beneath the child's bound form until her arm struck a cord, pulled tight. She surfaced again and screamed to the boy to hold Casey, then reached for the knife she kept in her belt and dove back down to saw at the cord. For a moment she thought she wouldn't be able to get a purchase, but then, after a few seconds, the cord gave, and the girl shot to the surface.

Sadiya surfaced and turned the girl's face so it was above the water. 'Casey!' she screamed. 'Casey!' But the girl didn't respond, her small face blank in the gloom.

Sadiya screamed her name again, and then again. Beside her the boy was sobbing. Grabbing the girl's head, Sadiya twisted it sideways, hoping to clear her airways, then, pinching her nose, she blew into her mouth and released, first once, and then a second and a third time. Casey's body moved limply with the water. Sadiya grabbed her nose and forced air in again, and again, but still nothing happened.

'No!' she said, 'no, no, no,' and taking her face again repeated the action. And then, without warning, Casey coughed, and retched and water flowed from her mouth.

'Yes!' shouted Sadiya. 'That's right. Good girl.' Next to her the boy was grinning, tears streaming down his face. She realised she was crying as well, but she didn't care. Instead she began to laugh, and pulled the two of them to her.

*

The man led Arman into a space behind one of the restaurants, a storeroom in which a dozen others sheltered.

'Here,' he said, settling him down and giving him a bottle of water. 'It'll be okay. You'll be safe here.'

Arman did as he was told. He thought he had been here before, or was he misremembering? So many rooms over so many years, so many places with people slumped against walls clutching bottles of water or children, or sleeping on cardboard. So many waystations to a present he no longer understood.

Somewhere in the distance there was a rattling, and then a rumble that shook the building. Next to him a woman closed her eyes and whimpered. The sound grew louder, and a moment later the lights went off, leaving them in darkness for a few seconds, until somebody lit a lamp, the glare of the LED white in the darkness. Another crash, followed by a groaning, as if the building were trying to tear itself apart.

Arman didn't know how long it went on; forever, it seemed, every moment an eternity. At some point somebody wet themselves, the smell of hot piss filling the space. And then finally, almost without warning, it was over.

Standing up in the darkness, Arman groped his way towards the door. He didn't care where he went, all he knew was that he had to get out of here, to escape. He found the handle and pulled on it, rattling the door in its frame, once, twice, and then all of a sudden it was open, and light spilled in. He stumbled through and on, until finally he emerged into the street. The sky was incongruously clear, the stars incredibly bright, so close you could almost touch them, their light picking out the devastation on every side. Around him other people were emerging as well.

'What happened?' said someone behind him. 'Is it over?'

'I think it's the eye,' said somebody else. Somewhere, someone was sobbing.

Arman took a few steps through the velvety dark. The road was covered in debris, sheets of tin and branches, unrecognisable rubble. Farther along the street a car had overturned. He was back in the night of his childhood, alone in the dark, except he wasn't a child anymore – or was he? Where was Leah? She would know. Except she wasn't here.

He heard water flowing and walked towards it. At the end of the street, where the ground dropped away, a river moved by between the buildings, the light from the stars shifting in its black surface. He stopped. It was here. This was what he had been looking for, the still point about which everything moved, the place he had lost his way, lost them. Water might be liquid, unreliable, always in motion, but it was also memory. It was older than the planet, part of us, part of everything, the end in the beginning.

Closing his eyes he listened to it, the rush of it, and for a brief second he understood that he was there again, that it had all been undone, unhappened. Taking a step forward he felt the water begin to rise around his legs, pulling at him as he waded deeper, until at last his feet slipped free beneath him and the water carried him away, bearing him on towards wherever Lina and Leah were waiting.

*

Sadiya, Casey and the boy huddled in a corner. The shriek of the wind and the crash of debris striking the building was so loud it drowned out speech, so instead Sadiya just hugged Casey to herself, one arm around her head to protect her from the sound. Only when the wind finally began to drop did they stand and walk slowly towards the window. Outside the water spread out as far as the eye could see, a sea that had swallowed the city, the stars above reflected in it, as if the sky had fallen into the water. Cars bobbed here and there, and bits of debris drifted by. For a long time none of them spoke; instead they just stood, their bodies close, grateful for the animal presence of each other. And then Sadiya drew the other two close, and said, 'It's okay. We're here. We're alive.'

ACKNOWLEDGEMENTS

This novel would not exist without the assistance of a great many people. I'm especially grateful to David Young for his advice on law enforcement matters and to Kate Hancock, Agus Purwanto and Adiba Rahman for their incredibly generous help with cultural questions. I'm similarly indebted to Lauren Chater, Jonty Claypole, Sophie Cunningham, David Farrier, Kate Morgan, Jane Rawson, Giula Sandler, Morgan Springett, Sean Williams and Malcolm Knox, all of whom read various drafts and offered invaluable advice and encouragement. I would also like to thank my indefatigable agent, Matthew Turner from RCW Literary Agency, Tallulah Lyons and the team at Hodder & Stoughton in the United Kingdom, as well as everybody at Penguin Random House Australia, and in particular my publisher, Meredith Curnow, and my editor, Rachel Scully, for their ongoing support and enthusiasm. I am also grateful to Creative Australia for its generosity in awarding me an Arts Project Grant in 2020, support that made it possible for me to write the book across that very strange year. And finally I would like to thank my children, Annabelle and Theo, and my partner, Mardi McConnochie: none of this would be possible without them.

RAISING READERS
Books Build Bright Futures

Dear Reader,

We'd love your attention for one more page to tell you about the crisis in children's reading, and what we can all do.

Studies have shown that reading for fun is the **single biggest predictor of a child's future life chances** – more than family circumstance, parents' educational background or income. It improves academic results, mental health, wealth, communication skills, ambition and happiness.[1]

The number of children reading for fun is in rapid decline. Young people have a lot of competition for their time. In 2024, 1 in 10 children and young people in the UK aged 5 to 18 did not own a single book at home.[2]

Hachette works extensively with schools, libraries and literacy charities, but here are some ways we can all raise more readers:

- Reading to children for just 10 minutes a day makes a difference
- Don't give up if children aren't regular readers – there will be books for them!
- Visit bookshops and libraries to get recommendations
- Encourage them to listen to audiobooks
- Support school libraries
- Give books as gifts

There's a lot more information about how to encourage children to read on our website: **www.RaisingReaders.co.uk**

Thank you for reading.

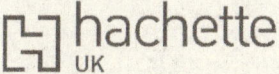

---

[1] OECD, '21st-Century Readers: Developing Literacy Skills in a Digital World', 2021, https://www.oecd.org/en/publications/21st-century-readers_a83d84cb-en.html

[2] National Literacy Trust, 'Book Ownership in 2024', November 2024, https://literacytrust.org.uk/research-services/research-reports/book-ownership-in-2024